The Wolfville stories are the first cowboy litera-ture, antedating Owen Wister's *The Virginian* but like it instrumental in capturing and fixing for-ever in the American imagination the legendary figure of the cowpoke. Alfred Henry Lewis (1858-1914) grew up in Ohio, became a lawyer, and then went west with his family where he became an itinerant cowboy and journalist. These years of wandering the Southwest provided the material for his greatest yarns, a broad sampling of which is presented here.

Wolfville was in reality Tombstone, Arizona, in its heydey a crossroads of western life more popu-lous than San Francisco. It was the town of the Earp Brothers, Doc Holliday, and a colorful flow of other cowboys, gamblers, adventurers, cavalry-men, Indians, miners, and entertainers. They emerge in Lewis' stories as a memorable cast of characters—Doc Peets, Faro Nell, Dave Tutt, Texas Thompson, the town marshall Jack Moore, and the old Wolfville chief, Old Man Enright. But his most memorable character was the Old Cattle-man who narrates most of the stories with an eye and ear as keen as a jackrabbit's and a wit as dry as the desert air.

Lewis' West is gone forever, drowned in ro-mance and commercialization. But his stories—the adventures, the tall tales, the human tragedies, the Indian stories—remain as an authentic record of the sounds, the sights, the very feel of the Southwest in its legendary years.

Professor Louis Filler, who first introduced Lewis in modern times as a muckraker in his *Crusaders for American Liberalism,* selected the stories in this collection and linked them together with commentary and a revealing introductory essay, "The West Belongs to All of Us."

The book also contains a generous selection of Frederic Remington's sketches of the West, some from the original editions of Lewis' works, others from Remington's vast sketchbooks, and includ-ing a frontispiece in color.

OLD WOLFVILLE

Chapters from the Fiction of Alfred Henry Lewis

Other Studies in Literature
by Louis Filler
BOOKS

Randolph Bourne (1943; new edition, 1965)
The Unknown Edwin Markham (1936)

EDITED WORKS

Mr. Dooley: Now and Forever, by Finley Peter Dunne (1954)
The World of Mr. Dooley (1962)
The Anxious Years (1963)
Wendell Phillips on Civil Rights and Freedom (1965)

INTRODUCTIONS

Chatterton, by Ernest Lacy (1952)
My Autobiography, by S. S. McClure (1962)
A Modern Symposium, by G. Lowes Dickinson (1963)

ALSO IN PUBLISHED VOLUMES

"A Tale of Two Authors: Theodore Dreiser and David Graham Phillips," i
   New Voices in American Studies (1966)

AMONG OTHER ARTICLES

"Susan Lenox: an American Odyssey," *Accent,* Fall, 1940
"Wolfville: the Fiction of A. H. Lewis," *New Mexico Qu.,* Spring, 1943
"Edward Bellamy and the Spirited Unrest," *Amer. Jour. of Econ. and Soc.*
   April, 1948
"Randolph Bourne: Reality and Myth," *Humanist,* Spring, 1951
"Harry Alan Potamkin," *Midwest Jour.,* Summer, 1951
"Arts and the Man," *Midwest Jour.,* Winter, 1951
"Why Historians Ignore Folklore," *Midwest Folklore,* Summer, 1954
"Post-Mortem on Political Literature," *Southwest Review,* Summer, 1954
"John Chamberlain and American Liberalism," *Colorado Qu.,* Fall, 1957
"The Question of Social Significance," *Union Review,* 1962

OLD WOLFVILLE

Chapters from the Fiction of
Alfred Henry Lewis

*Selected and edited
with an introduction and commentary
by Louis Filler*

Illustrations by Frederic Remington

THE ANTIOCH PRESS
1968

CONTENTS

1455713

Introduction: The West Belongs to All of Us, *by Louis Filler* vii

Some Cowboy Facts, *by Alfred Henry Lewis* 1

The Old Cattleman

Wolfville's First Funeral 11

Bill Hoskins's Coon 19

The Dismissal of Silver Phil 30

Johnny Florer's Axle Grease 47

Some Indian Tales

How the Raven Died 63

Moh-Kwa and the Three Gifts 74

How Strongarm Was an Elk 83

Wolfville, with a Difference, and Others

Cheyenne Bill 93

The Wiping Out of M'Candlas 101

The Great Stewart Campaign 108

Wagon Mound Sal 115

The Luck of Cold-Sober Simms 123

When the Capitol Was Moved 130

The Old Cattleman

The Treachery of Curly Ben 139

How Prince Hal Got Help 154

Death: and the Donna Anna 162

How Jack Rainey Quit 180

From *Old Man Enright's Love* 190

From *When the Stage Was Stopped* 202

Jaybird Horne 213

Top and Bottom 220

Long Ago on the Rio Grande 229

A Sort of Appendix

The Rescue of Cimarron Bill 247

Introduction

THE WEST BELONGS TO ALL OF US

There is no use asking the historians about Wolfville. They are busy with cattle drives, western migration, land grants, and other lordly matters. Such splendid work they do, too. Our history of the West is warm, detailed, fascinating, whether you take it for glamor or technical-scientific information. They have heard of Tombstone, Arizona—the town for which Wolfville was named—and they have enjoyed reading and writing of Doc Holliday, the Earps, Bat Masterson, and like characters. They remember that Tombstone was once more populous than San Francisco: a fact I, for one, find hard to keep firmly in mind. But they aren't strong on the difference between history and literature, and this is no place for a seminar on the subject.

Stand at the bar in the Crystal Palace Saloon in Tombstone, and order a drink. Look at the original bullet-hole in the big, antique mirror. Let your mind relax and blur until you hear the tramp of cowboy boots in and out of the big bar, the pounding of the piano, the mounting roar of conversation about silver mines, dance-hall girls, outlaws, round-ups, famous westerners and unknowns—listen to the flip of the cards, the clatter of horses' hooves outside, the routine sounds of what was once one of the main crossroads of cowboy country in the southwest.

Tombstone calls itself "the town that was too tough to die," and in a real sense this is true. There are in Tombstone, or were several years ago, people who go back fifty and more years, and their memories take them still further back to the glamorous years, when Virgil Earp was town marshal. They would like to see those days come back again, at least in terms of visitors interested in eating and drinking, staying over, and buying souvenirs. Their big hope is the O. K. Corral, which is more alive than ever. I'm afraid all that will ever come of this is another tourist trap to mess up the bare original, as it has Boot Hill in that historic shell of what was once Dodge City.

Well, you can't blame the good people of Tombstone for wanting to make money. And you can respect them on their own terms, just as you do people anywhere. But, like people everywhere, they confuse the physical with the real. It is hard for them to understand that an old hat is just an old hat, unless one can see past it to the old live time. And a very, very few of them have just barely heard of Alfred Henry Lewis, who walked among them and, as a working cowboy, felt and contributed to their vitality, and captured it in his immortal Wolfville tales.

The folk mind is a wonderful thing. It holds the raw materials of life, and molds them into songs and stories and memories. Everybody in Tombstone knows about the O. K. Corral, of course, and has opinions about the Earps and about the Clantons. A lady at the Bird Cage Opera House (as Lewis called it; Tombstone called it and calls it the Bird Cage Theatre) seemed to remember having heard something about the Wolfville versions of the town, and recalled an old lady who had once lived there, and who had liked them, or had copies of some of the books . . . or something like that. . . .

But there are no memories at all of the young cowboy Lewis who once drank and played cards and rode herd like other cowboys, but whose mind was different from theirs. He was a reader. Legends and poems swam in his mind. He lived for the moment, as they did, made money and spent it, and tried to make more. But he knew that life in the Great Plains region early in the 1880's was one of the most wonderful of moments—a swirl of heroes and adventurers—and his mind collected an eternity of impressions. They became more and more vivid and tender as the golden years slipped quickly away from him.

It was the depression of 1883 which did in Lewis' West: the West of the cattle country; he was somewhat less interested in the mines. The prices of cattle went down, never quite to recoup in the old way. The cowboy became another paid hand. So Lewis left: went into the real estate business in Dodge City, and also into newspaper work, editing the Mora County *Pioneer* and the

Las Vegas *Optic*. Journalism took him to Chicago and Washington and New York. He died in the East, from which, long before, he had come; he had been born in Cleveland, Ohio, and lived there until he was in his early twenties and a brilliant young lawyer.

There in the East he collected as varied and diverse a set of cronies as he had ever known. They included Bat Masterson, who ended up as a United States Marshal in New York, and a sports writer. He knew the muckraker Charles Edward Russell, and was himself wrongly identified as a muckraker. He knew the remarkable prizefighter Kid McCoy—"the real McCoy"—and the novelist David Graham Phillips. All these among many others. He was a friend of Theodore Roosevelt, T.R. himself, whom he had first met in 1893, and who urged him to collect his first Wolfville stories, and helped him with the manuscript. Gusty people: all talented, forceful, and above all, individual.

Americans have a thing about the West. It hypnotized them, and they don't quite know what to do with the feelings it stirs in them. There are the descendents of Ned Buntline, the scribbler, who are satisfied to ramble on and on, about the West, making up empty yarns about Indian fights, gold and silver strikes, heroic rescues, and all the rest. TV has created unbelievably new lows for the likes of these. It strikes them as fresh and amusing to marry off General Grant to Calamity Jane. They submerge their guilt-feelings about American Indian policy by creating Noble Redmen who bore us to death with lectures about the need for white brothers to join redskins in peace pact: a kind of frontier parody of the United Nations.

A second level of western fanciers emphasize the Truth of things. A story is no good, according to them, if it puts the Chisholm Trail a mile west, where another trail had been, or if it gets the year wrong when barbed wire was first used somewhere in the West. Such critics or storytellers are great on the pots and pans of western life. They can tell you how cowboys cooked their tomato soup. But they have too little feeling for the difference between a live cowboy and a dead cowboy. And though they know the hills and streams of cowboy-land, they cannot locate the country of the mind: how the cowboy thought about himself, how he lived, and what he lived for. They do not understand what makes fiction real or unreal, shoddy or memorable and great.

Actually, there is no true chasm between fiction and reality, and there have been fine works created in both areas. J. Frank Dobie wrote memorable prose; so did Andy Adams in his *The Log of a Cowboy* (1903). There are creative principles operating in writings by both of these westerners. But both differ from Eugene Manlove Rhodes, who was cowboy and storyteller, and set down things with a different essence from that of Dobie's history and Adams' recollections.

Alfred Henry Lewis was closer to Rhodes than to either of the others, but he was also very different from Rhodes. It is hard to write about writers without having some tangible comparative data about them in reasonable circulation, so I must do the best I can and leave it at that. Put simply, Rhodes and Lewis stemmed from different western impulses. Rhodes spoke for a free community which, as he saw it in his heart and mind, admired goodness and chivalry, and found ways and means to punish such cardinal sins as cowardice, greed, and lack of respect for women. I wouldn't for a moment denigrate Rhodes' world, and it met and crossed Lewis' world at many points. Only, Lewis had, more than Rhodes, the spirit of the journalist who saw too many untidy human details to be able to keep black and white as neatly separated as Rhodes did. Lewis had his sentimental side, as do so many journalists—as Bret Harte did, for example—and it damaged some of his perceptions. Also, he had strong, even unreasonable, admirations and hatreds. But when he kept them under control, he saw shadings of human effort, paradoxes of human behavior which illuminated life on the range and in the cattle towns and everywhere. Then he was great, and, in his own domain, inimitable.

I once wrote an essay intended to put Lewis in the tradition of American literature: its humor, its western character, its insights and limitations.[1] The essay was intended for literary folk, but I have since learned better. There are worthy books in the general area. The tragic Douglas Branch's *The Cowboy and His Interpreters* (1926). *The American Cowboy: the Myth and the Reality*

[1] "Wolfville," *New Mexico Quarterly*, Spring 1943.

(1955) by Joe B. Frantz and Julian Ernest Choate, Jr. And many more; see *Guide to Life and Literature of the Southwest,* by the aforementioned Dobie: a book charmingly *not* copyrighted in 1942, and again, revised and enlarged, *not* copyrighted in 1952. It is a burst of warm, fragrant wind in the face just to invoke these subjects and these treatments. But they do not bring us closer to Lewis. For one thing, they are not sufficiently literary for the situation. For another, they do not adequately communicate an experience—any experience—with Lewis, to enable us to get him between our own teeth, so that we can match the scholars' experience with experience. What I say of Lewis is true also of other creative topics in Americana—western, and otherwise— which are yet to be recast for modern appreciation.

Lewis will be remembered and refined by the people who read him without pretension and without prejudgments, and they are not likely to be official, certified critics. I have more faith in the readers of *Real West* or *True West* or *Frontier Times* than in all the Literature Departments from Cambridge to Los Angeles. For people read the magazines and remember their fathers and the soil that bore them. It would be instructive to review what the official litterateurs read, and how they think, but it suffices here that it is not because of them that Jack London's writings, for example, still live and breathe. They have not kept Frank Norris alive, or E. W. Howe, or John Reed, or Vachel Lindsay. And they won't do much, if anything, for A. H. Lewis.

I thought of this when I visited "Jack London's Rendezvous" in Oakland, California: a tiny, miserable drinking den with fly-speckled mementoes of London's early years. The people who crowded it—why were they there? Well, they were having a night out. How much of Jack London they had ever read or would read, we will never know. But they had enough of an idea of who he had been to make it worth their while to have a drink while being uncomfortable for a space in the den he had frequented; and to call this fun and an experience.

The people of Tombstone are less wise, at this stage, than the people of Oakland, but they, or someone else in Lewis' West, will get the point and teach it to the professors. And they will get it from the streams of visitors who pass over the plains and into the Rocky Mountain Empire, and who ask the old questions: Where have we been? Where are we going? And what is it all about?

It is these who have kept Lewis alive: who read his books, literally to pieces, so that copies of *Wolfville,* with its Remington illustrations, sell for five and fifteen dollars among antiquarian bookmen.

I shall let Lewis speak for himself, for the most part, but let me note how much there is yet to do before we have our heritage safe and useful in our hands. Lewis' generation was like ours. It poured out its days. It lived lavishly, and without thought for yesterday and tomorrow. Lewis himself wrote reams and mountains of stories, reminiscences, journalese, miscellaneous fact and fancy of every kind. Much of it was not worth preserving, and was not the most precious part of him. But all of it deserves its day in court.

And this is true not only of Lewis but of a score of others who have been diverted away from us by our changing intellectual fads. They feature such drab cliches as "disillusionment" and "social significance" and "explication." But the people know better and ask whether something is a good story, or sincere, or some other enduring word. The people will yet save some of the late Ernest Hemingway's writings from his idiotic idolaters, and make them part of a living literature. It will include, in its western phase, Bret Harte, too little actively appreciated, and Rhodes, among others. And it will include tales from Lewis' *Wolfville* saga. I give him the last word in his own behalf; he is speaking of the "Old Cattleman," his other self, the repository of his memories and affections, through whom he transmitted his vision of what the West had been and what it had meant:

> Let him go forth. Let him go forth; not to the critic but to the public. I distrust the critic as I distrust myself. A critic never buys a book and as often understands one. All that is good in literature has survived against the critics. A critic is a book-cook; he boils books and seldom tastes one. In the steams and vapors of his labors your critic's palate is dulled. He may no more get the flavor of a book than may a *chef* the flavor of a dinner. I do not quarrel with critics; I commiserate them as hopeless book-invalids. Then I turn to that public—the actual not the invented public of the critics—which does not make its reading its business, and whose taste runs true.

LOUIS FILLER

ALFRED HENRY LEWIS
(1858-1914)

SOME COWBOY FACTS

There are certain truths of a botanical character that are not generally known. Each year the trees in their occupation creep further west. There are regions in Missouri—not bottom lands—which sixty years ago were bald and bare of trees. Today they are heavy with timber. Westward, beyond the trees, lie the prairies, and beyond the prairies, the plains; the first are green with long grasses, the latter bare, brown and with a crisp, scorched, sparse vesture of vegetation scarce worth the name. As the trees march slowly westward in conquest of the prairies, so also do the prairies, in their verdant turn, become aggressors and push westward upon the plains. These last stretches, extending to the base of that bluff and sudden bulwark, the Rocky Mountains, can go no further. The Rockies hold the plains at bay and break, as it were, the teeth of the desert. As a result of this warfare of vegetations, the plains are to first disappear in favour of the prairies; and the prairies to give way before the trees. These mutations all wait on rain; and as the rain belt goes ever and ever westward, a strip of plains each year surrenders its aridity, and the prairies and then the trees press on and take new ground.

These facts should contain some virtue of interest; the more since with the changes chronicled, come also changes in the character of both the inhabitants and the employments of these regions. With a civilised people extending themselves over new lands, cattle form ever the advance guard. Then come the farms.

This is the procession of a civilised, peaceful invasion; thus is the column marshalled. First, the pastoral; next, the agricultural; third and last, the manufacturing;—and per consequence, the big cities, where the treasure chests of a race are kept. Blood and bone and muscle and heart are to the front; and the money that steadies and stays and protects and repays them and their efforts, to the rear.

Forty years ago about all that took place west of the Mississippi of a money-making character was born of cattle. The cattle were worked in huge herds and, like the buffalo supplanted by them, roamed in unnumbered thousands. In a pre-railroad period, cattle were killed for their hides and tallow, and smart Yankee coasters went constantly to such ports as Galveston for these cargoes. The beef was left to the coyotes.

Cattle find a natural theatre of existence on the plains. There, likewise, flourishes the pastoral man. But cattle herding, confined to the plains, gives way before the westward creep of agriculture. Each year beholds more western acres broken by the plough; each year witnesses a diminution of the cattle ranges and cattle herding. This need ring no bell of alarm concerning a future barren of a beef supply. More cattle are the product of the farm-regions than of the ranges. That ground, once range and now farm, raises more cattle now than then. Texas is a great cattle State. Ohio, Indiana, Illinois, Iowa, and Missouri are first States of agriculture. The area of Texas is about even with the collected area of the other five. Yet one finds double the number of cattle in Ohio, Indiana, Illinois, Iowa, and Missouri than in Texas, to say nothing of tenfold the sheep and hogs. No; one may be calm; one is not to fall a prey to any hunger of beef.

While the farms in their westward pushing do not diminish the cattle, they reduce the cattleman and pinch off much that is romantic and picturesque. Between the farm and the wire fence, the cowboy, as once he flourished, has been modified, subdued, and made partially to disappear. In the good old days of the Jones and Plummer trail there were no wire fences, and the sullen farmer had not yet arrived. Your cowboy at that time was a person of thrill and consequence. He wore a broad-brimmed Stetson hat, and all about it a rattlesnake skin by way of band, retaining head and rattles. This was to be potent against headaches—a malady, by the way, which swept down no cowboy save in hours emergent of a spree. In such case the snake cure didn't cure. The hat was retained in defiance of winds, by a leathern cord caught about the back of the head, not under the chin. This cord was beautiful with a garniture of three or four perforated poker chips, red, yellow, and blue.

There are sundry angles of costume where the dandyism of a cowboy of spirit and conceit may acquit itself; these are hatband, spurs, saddle, and leggins. I've seen hatbands made of braided gold and silver filigree; they were from Santa Fe, and always in the form of a rattlesnake, with rubies or emeralds or diamonds for eyes. Such gauds would cost from four hundred to two thousand dollars. Also, I've encountered a saddle which depleted its proud owner a round twenty-five hundred dollars. It was of finest Spanish leather, stamped and spattered with gold bosses. There was gold-capping on the saddle horn, and again on the circle of the cantle. It was a dream of a saddle, made at Paso del Norte; and the owner had it cinched upon a bronco dear at twenty dollars. One couldn't have sold the pony for a stack of white chips in any faro game of that neighbourhood (Las Vegas) and they were all crooked games at that.

Your cowboy dandy frequently wears wrought steel spurs, inlaid with silver and gold; price, anything you please. If he flourish a true Brummel of the plains his leggins will be fronted from instep to belt with the thick pelt, hair outside, of a Newfoundland dog. These "chapps," are meant to protect the cowboy from rain and cold, as well as plum bushes, wire fences and other obstacles inimical, and against which he may lunge while riding headlong in the dark. The hair of the Newfoundland, thick and long and laid the right way, defies the rains; and your cowboy loathes water.

Save in those four cardinals of vanity enumerated, your cowboy wears nothing from weakness; the rest of his outfit is legitimate. The long sharp heels of his boots are there to dig into the ground and hold fast to his mother earth while roping on foot. His gay pony when "roped" of a frosty morning would skate him all across and about the plains if it were not for these heels. The buckskin gloves tied in one of the saddle strings are used when roping, and to keep the half-inch manila lariat—or mayhap it's horsehair or rawhide pleated—from burning his hands. The red silken sash one was wont aforetime to see knotted about his waist, was used to hogtie and hold down the big cattle when roped and thrown. The sash—strong, soft and close—could be tied more tightly, quickly, surely than anything besides. In these days, with wire pastures and branding pens and the fine certainty of modern round-ups and a consequent paucity of mavericks, big cattle are seldom roped; wherefor the sash has been much cast aside.

The saddle-bags or "war-bags,"—also covered of dogskin to match the leggins, and worn behind, not forward of the rider— are the cowboy's official wardrobe wherein he carries his second suit of underclothes, and his other shirt. His handkerchief, red cotton, is loosely knotted about the cowboy's neck, knot to the rear. He wipes the sweat from his brow therewith on those hot Texas days when in a branding pen he "flanks" calves or feeds the fires or handles the irons or stands off the horned indignation of the cows, resentful because of burned and bawling offspring.

It would take two hundred thousand words to tell in half fashion the story of the cowboy. His religion of fatalism, his courage, his rides at full swing in midnight darkness to head and turn and hold a herd stampeded, when a slip on the storm-soaked grass by his unshod pony, or a misplaced prairie-dog hole, means a tumble, and a tumble means that a hundred and fifty thousand dollars worth of cattle, with hoofs like chopping knives, will run over him and make him look and feel and become as dead as a cancelled postage stamp; his troubles, his joys, his soberness in camp, his drunkenness in town, and his feuds and occasional "gun plays" are not to be disposed of in a preface. One cannot in such cramped space so much as hit the high places in a cowboy career.

At work on the range and about his camp—for, bar accidents, wherever you find a cowboy you will find a camp—the cowboy is a youth of sober quiet dignity. There is a deal of deep politeness and nothing of epithet, insult or horseplay where everybody wears a gun.

There are no folk inquisitive on the ranges. No one asks your name. If driven by stress of conversation to something akin to it the cowboy will say: "What may I call you, sir?" And he's as careful to add the "sir," as he is to expect it in return. You are at liberty to select what name you prefer. Where you hail from? where going? why? are queries never put. To look at the brand on your pony—you, a stranger—is a dangerous vulgarity to which no gentleman of the Panhandle or any other region of pure southwestern politeness would stoop. And if you wish to arouse an instant combination of hate, suspicion and contempt in the bosom of a cowboy you have but to stretch forth your artless Eastern hand and ask: "Let me look at your gun."

Cowboys on the range or in the town are excessively clannish. They never desert each other, but stay and fight and die and storm a jail and shoot a sheriff if needs press, to rescue a comrade made captive in their company. Also they care for each other when sick or injured, and set one another's bones when broken in the falls and tumbles of their craft. On the range the cowboy is quiet, just and peaceable. There are neither women nor cards nor rum about the cow camps. The ranches and the boys themselves banish the two latter; and the first won't come. Women, cards and whiskey, the three war causes of the West, are confined to the towns.

Those occasions when cattle are shipped and the beef-herds, per consequence, driven to the shipping point become the only times when the cowboy sees the town. In such hours he blooms and lives fully up to his opportunity. He has travelled perhaps two hundred miles and has been twenty days on the trail, for cattle may only be driven about ten miles a day; he has been up day and night and slept half the time in the saddle; he has made himself hoarse singing "Sam Bass" and "The Dying Ranger" to keep the cattle quiet and stave off stampedes; he has ridden ten ponies to shadows in his twenty days of driving, wherefore, and naturally, your cowboy feels like relaxing.

There would be as many as ten men with each beef-herd; and the herd would include about five thousand head. There would be six "riders," divided into three watches to stand night guard over the herd and drive it through the day; there would be two "hoss hustlers," to hold the eighty or ninety ponies, turn and turn about, and carry them along with the herd; there would be the cook, with four mules and the chuck wagon; and lastly there would be the herd-boss, a cow expert he, and at the head of the business.

Once the herd is off his hands and his mind at the end of the drive, the cowboy unbuckles and reposes himself from his labours. He becomes deeply and famously drunk. Hungering for the excitement of play he collides amiably with faro and monte and what other deadfalls are rife of the place. Never does he win; for the games aren't arranged that way. But he enjoys himself; and his losses do not prey on him.

Sated with faro bank and monte—they can't be called games of chance, the only games of chance occurring when cowboys engage with each other at billiards or pool—sated, I say, with faro and Mexican monte, and exuberant of rum, which last has regular quick renewal, our cowboy will stagger to his pony, swing into the saddle, and with gladsome whoops and an occasional outburst from his six shooter directed toward the heavens, charge up and down the street. This last amusement appeals mightily to cowboys too drunk to walk. For, be it known, a gentleman may ride long after he may not walk.

If a theatre be in action and mayhap a troop of "Red Stocking Blondes," elevating the drama therein, the cowboy is sure to attend. Also he will arrive with his lariat wound about his body under his coat; and his place will be the front row. At some engaging crisis, such as the "March of the Amazons," having first privily unwound and organised his lariat to that end, he will arise and "rope" an Amazon. This will produce bad language from the manager of the show, and compel the lady to sit upon the stage to the detriment of her wardrobe if no worse, and all to keep from being pulled across the footlights. Yet the exercise gives the cowboy deepest pleasure. Having thus distinguished the lady of his admiration, later he will meet her and escort her to the local dancehall. There, mingling with their frank companions, the two will drink, and loosen the boards of the floor with the strenuous dances of our frontier till daylight does appear.

For the matter of a week, or perchance two—it depends on how fast his money melts—in these fashions will our gentleman of cows engage his hours and expand himself. He will make a deal of noise, drink a deal of whiskey, acquire a deal of what he terms "action"; but he harms nobody, and, in a town toughened to his racket and which needs and gets his money, disturbs nobody.

"Let him whoop it up; he's paying for it, ain't he?" will be the prompt local retort to any inquiry as to why he is thus permitted to disport.

So long as the cowboy observes the etiquette of the town, he will not be molested or "called down" by marshal or sheriff or citizen. There are four things your cowboy must not do. He must not insult a woman; he must not shoot his pistol in a store or bar-room; he must not ride his pony into those places of resort; and as a last proposal he must not ride his pony on the sidewalks. Shooting or riding into bar-rooms is reckoned as dangerous; riding on the sidewalk comes more under the head of insult, and is popularly regarded as a taunting defiance of the town marshal. On such occasions the marshal never fails to respond, and the cowboy is called upon to surrender. If he complies, which to the credit of his horse-sense he commonly does, he is led into brief captivity to be made loose when cooled. Does he resist arrest, there is an explosive rattle of six shooters, a mad scattering of the careful citizenry out of lines of fire, and a cowboy or marshal is added to the host beyond. At the close of the festival, if the marshal still lives he is congratulated; if the cowboy survives he is lynched; if both fall, they are buried with the honours of frontier war; while whatever the event, the communal ripple is but slight and only of the moment, following which the currents of Western existence sweep easily and calmly onward as before.

ALFRED HENRY LEWIS

The Old Cattleman

A certain "Uncle Billy" Plaster was once identified as the "original" of Lewis' "Old Cattleman," and others from among Lewis' regular troup of characters were supposed to have been drawn from gamblers, bartenders, cowboys, and marshals he had known. Lewis' imagination may well have been stimulated by one or another of his acquaintances or friends. But it mistakes the quality of his art to take his tales too literally. We know enough about it—and can remark enough in the following pages— to realize that Lewis did indeed see his West and its people in personal, emotional terms. But though he was insatiable in his hunger for gossip and details, his mind sought meaning in them, and drew them together into patterns. The Old Cattleman was a pattern-weaver; he was Lewis himself, in no small measure—the inner Lewis, the Lewis who weathered life's problems and disappointments, who used drama and humor, fancies and photographic precision to give vividness and depth to reminiscences of his beloved West.

The Old Cattleman is a good companion, and it is not gracious or intelligent to hold him too closely to the facts. He was interested in the quality of life, not its computerized sum. He tells us much about the way his comrades saw the world. In the following, the first of his Wolfville tales, we are present at one of the crossroads of the region: its passage from frontier to civilization.

WOLFVILLE'S FIRST FUNERAL

"These yere obsequies which I'm about mentionin'," observed the Old Cattleman, "is the first real funeral Wolfville has."

The old fellow had lighted a cob pipe and tilted his chair back in a fashion which proclaimed a plan to be comfortable. He had begun to tolerate—even encourage—my society, although it was clear that as a tenderfoot he regarded me with a species of gentle disdain.

I had provoked the subject of funeral ceremonies by a recurrence to the affair of the Yellowhouse Man, and a query as to what would have been the programme of the public-spirited hamlet of Wolfville if that invalid had died instead of yielding to the nursing of Jack Moore and that tariff on draw-poker which the genius of Old Man Enright decreed.

It came in easy illustration, as answer to my question, for the Old Cattleman to recall the funeral of a former leading spirit of Southwestern society. The name of this worthy was Jack King; and with a brief exposition of his more salient traits, my grizzled *raconteur* led down to his burial with the remark before quoted.

"Of course," continued the Old Cattleman, "of course while thar's some like this Yallerhouse gent who survives; thar's others of the boys who is downed one time an' another, an' goes shoutin' home to heaven by various trails. But ontil the event I now recalls, the remainders has been freighted east or west every time, an' the camp gets left. It's hard luck, but at last it comes toward us; an' thar we be one day with a corpse all our'n, an' no partnership with nobody nor nothin'.

" 'It's the chance of our life,' says Doc Peets, 'an' we plays it. Thar's nothin' too rich for our blood, an' these obsequies is goin' to be spread-eagle, you bet! We'll show Red Dog an' sim'lar villages they ain't sign-camps compared with Wolfville.'

"So we begins to draw in our belts an' get a big ready. Jack King, as I says before, is corpse, eemergin' outen a game of poker as sech. Which prior tharto, Jack's been peevish, an' pesterin' an' pervadin' 'round for several days. The camp stands a heap o' trouble with him an' tries to smooth it along by givin' him his whiskey an' his way about as he wants 'em, hopin' for a change. But man is only human, an' when Jack starts in one night to make a flush beat a tray full for seven hundred dollars, he asks too much.

"Thar ain't no ondertakers, so we rounds up the outfit, an' knowin' he'd take a pride in it, an' do the slam-up thing, we puts in Doc Peets to deal the game unanimous.

" 'Gents,' he says, as we-alls turns into the Red Light to be refreshed, 'in assoomin' the present pressure I feels the compliments paid me in the seelection. I shall act for the credit of the camp, an' I needs your he'p. I desires that these rites be a howlin' vict'ry. I don't want people comin' 'round next week allowin' thar ain't been no funeral, an' I don't reckon much that they will. We've got the corpse, an' if we gets bucked off now it's our fault.'

"So he app'ints Old Monte an' Dan Boggs to go for a box for Jack, an' details a couple of niggers from the corral to dig a tomb.

" 'An' mind you-alls,' says Peets, 'I wants that hole at least a mile from camp. In order to make a funeral a success, you needs distance. That's where deceased gets action. It gives the procession a chance to spread an' show up. You can't make no funeral imposin' except you're plumb liberal on distances.'

"It all goes smooth right off the reel. We gets a box an' grave

ready, an' Peets sticks up a notice on the stage-station door, settin' the excitement for third-drink time next day. Prompt at the
drop of the hat the camp lets go all holds an' turns loose in a
body to put Jack through right. He's laid out in splendid shape
in the New York Store, with nothin' to complain of if he's asked
to make the kick himse'f. He has a new silk necktie, blue shirt
an' pearl buttons, trousers, an' boots. Some one—Benson Annie,
I reckons—has pasted some co't plaster over the hole on his
cheek-bone where the bullet gets in, an' all 'round Jack looks
better than I ever sees him.

" 'Let the congregation remove its hats,' says Peets, a-settin'
down on a box up at Jack's head, 'an' as many as can will please
get somethin' to camp on. Now, my friends,' he continues, 'thar
ain't no need of my puttin' on any frills or gettin' in any scroll
work. The objects of this convention is plain an' straight. Mister
King, here present, is dead. Deceased is a very headstrong person,
an' persists yesterday in entertainin' views touchin' a club flush,
queen at the head, which results in life everlastin'. Now, gents,
this is a racket full of solemnity. We wants nothin' but good
words. Don't mind about the trooth; which the same ain't in play
at a funeral, nohow. We all knows Jack; we knows his record.
Our information is ample that a-way; how he steals a hoss at
Tucson; how he robs a gent last fall at Tombstone; how he
downs a party at Cruces; how that scar on his neck he gets from
Wells-Fargo's people when he stands up the stage over on the
Lordsburg trail. But we lays it all aside to-day. We don't copper
nary bet. Yesterday mornin', accompanied by the report of a
Colt's forty-five, Mister King, who lies yere so cool an' easy,
leaves us to enter in behind the great white shinin' gates of pearl
an' gold, which swings inward to glory eternal. It's a great set
back at this time thar ain't no sky-pilot in the camp. This deefi-
ciency in sky-pilots is a hoss onto us, but we does our best. At a
time like this I hears that singin' is a good, safe break, an' I tharfore calls on that little girl from Flagstaff to give us "The Dyin'
Ranger." ' "

"So the little Flagstaff girl cl'ars her valves with a drink, an'
gives us the song; an' when the entire congregation draws kyards
on the last verse it does everybody good.

" 'Far away from his dear old Texas,
    We laid him down to rest;
    With his saddle for a pillow,
    And his gun across his breast.'

"Then Peets gets out the Scriptures. 'I'm goin' to read a chapter outen these yere Testaments,' he says. 'I ain't makin' no
claim for it, except it's part of the game an' accordin' to Hoyle.
If thar's a preacher yere he'd do it, but bein' thar's no sech brand
on this range I makes it as a forced play myse'f.'

"So he reads us a chapter about the sepulcher, an' Mary Mag-
dalene, an' the resurrection; an' everybody takes it in profound
as prairie-dogs, for that's the lead to make, an' we knows it.

"Then Peets allows he'd like to hear from any gent onder the
head of 'good of the order.'

" 'Mister Ondertaker an' Chairman,' says Jim Hamilton, 'I
yields to an inward impulse to say that this yere play weighs on
me plumb heavy. As keeper of the dance-hall I sees a heap of the
corpse an' knows him well. Mister King is my friend, an' while
his moods is variable an' oncertain; an' it's cl'arly worth while to
wear your gun while he's hoverin' near, I loves him. He has his
weaknesses, as do we all. A disp'sition to make new rooles as he
plays along for sech games of chance as enjoys his notice is perhaps his greatest failin'. His givin' way to this habit is primar'ly
the cause of his bein' garnered in. I hopes he'll get along thar,
an' offers a side bet, even money, up to five hundred dollars, he
will. He may alter his system an' stand way up with the angels
an' seraphs, an' if words from me could fix it, I'd shorely stack
'em in. I would say further that after consultin' with Billy Burns,
who keeps the Red Light, we has, in honor of the dead an' to
mark the occasion of his cashin' in, agreed upon a business departure of interest to all. This departure Mister Burns will state.
I mournfully gives way to him for said purpose.'

" 'Mister Peets, an' ladies an' gents,' says Burns, 'like Mister Hamilton, who I'm proud to meet yere as gent, citizen, an' friend, I knows deceased. He's a good man, an' a dead-game sport from 'way back. A protracted wrastle with the remorseless drinks of the frontier had begun to tell on him, an' for a year or so he's been liable to have spells. Referrin' to the remarks of Mister Hamilton, I states that by agreement between us an' in honor to departed, the quotations on whiskey in this yere camp, from now on, will be two drinks for two bits, instead of one as previous. We don't want to onsettle trade, an' we don't believe this will. We makes it as a ray of light in the darkness an' gloom of the hour.'

"After this yere utterance, which is well received, we forms the procession. Doc Peets, with two buglers from the Fort, takes the lead, with Jack an' his box in one of the stage coaches comin' next. Enright, Tutt, Boggs, Short Creek Dave, Texas Thompson, an' me, bein' the six pallbearers, is on hosses next in line; an' Jack Moore commandin' of the rest of the outfit, lines out permiscus.

" 'This is a great day for Wolfville,' says Peets, as he rides up an' down the line. 'Thar ain't no camp this side of St. Looey could turn this trick. Which I only wishes Jack could see it himse'f. It's more calculated to bring this outfit into fav'rable notice than a lynchin'.'

"At the grave we turns in an' gives three cheers for King, an' three for Doc Peets; an' last we gives three more an' a tiger for the camp. The buglers cuts loose everythin' they knows, from the 'water-call' to the 'retreat,' an' while the niggers is a-shovelin' in the sand we bangs away with our six-shooters for general results delightful. You can gamble thar ain't been no funeral like it before or since.

"At the last Peets hauls outen the stage we uses for Jack, a headboard. When it's set up it looks like if Jack ain't satisfied, he's shorely hard to suit. On it in big letters is:

```
┌─────────────────────────────────┐
│          JaCK KInG              │
│          LIfE AiN'T             │
│               IN                │
│      HOLDING A GOOD HAND        │
│              BUT                │
│     In plAyinG a PoRE HANd      │
│             WELL.               │
└─────────────────────────────────┘
```

" 'You sees, we has to work in a little sentiment,' says Doc Peets.

"Then we details the niggers to stand watch-an'-watch every night till further orders. No; we ain't afraid Jack'll get out none, but the coyotes is shore due to come an' dig for him, so the niggers has to stand gyard. We don't allow to find spec'mens of Jack spread 'round loose after all the trouble we takes."

The Old Cattleman's yarns about animals serve many purposes. They are pleasant ways of passing long nights on the range. They help the narrator take the measure of his auditor. They communicate feelings and attitudes. To my mind, they need not be quaint and regional. Those of us from the East and from the city also have time which can be passed profitably or otherwise. We also need to project our views of human nature, broaden our understanding of the curious ideas and stratagems of which people are capable. Lewis' anecdotes are imaginative in the better sense of the word. When we have more fully put gags, wisecracks, and "yakking" in their proper place, and restored human communication, we will grasp the uses of such tales as the following better.

BILL HOSKINS'S COON

"Now I thoroughly saveys," remarked the Old Cattleman reflectively, at a crisis in our conversation when the talk turned on men of small and cowardly measure, "I thoroughly saveys that taste for battle that lurks in the deefiles of folk's nacher like a wolf in the hills. Which I reckons now that I, myse'f, is one of the peacefullest people as ever belts on a weepon; but in my instincts—while I never jestifies or follows his example—I cl'arly apprehends the emotions of a gent who convenes with another gent all sim'lar, an' expresses his views with his gun. Sech is human nacher onrestrained, an' the same, while deplorable, is not s'prisin'.

"But this yere Olson I has in my mem'ry don't have no sech manly feelin's as goes with a gun play. Olson is that cowardly he's even furtive; an' for a low-flung measly game let me tell you-all what Olson does. It's shorely ornery.

"It all arises years ago, back in Tennessee, an' gets its first start out of a hawg which is owned by Olson an' is downed by a gent named Hoskins—Bill Hoskins. It's this a-way.

"Back in Tennessee in my dream-wreathed yooth, when livestock goes projectin' about permiscus, a party has to build his fences 'bull strong, hawg tight, an' hoss high,' or he takes results. Which Hoskins don't make his fences to conform to this yere rool none; leastwise they ain't hawg tight as is shown by one of Olson's hawgs.

"The hawg comes pirootin' about Hoskins's fence, an' he goes through easy; an' the way that invadin' animal turns Bill's potatoes bottom up don't hinder him a bit. He shorely loots Bill's lot; that's whatever.

"But Bill, perceivin' of Olson's hawg layin' waste his crop, reaches down a 8-squar' rifle, 30 to the pound, an' stretches the hawg. Which this is where Bill falls into error. Layin' aside them deeficiencies in Bill's fence, it's cl'ar at a glance a hawg can't be held responsible. Hawgs is ignorant an' tharfore innocent; an' while hawgs can be what Doc Peets calls a 'casus belli,' they can't be regarded as a foe legitimate.

"Now what Bill oughter done, if he feels like this yere hawg's done put it all over him, is to go an' lay for Olson. Sech action by Bill would have been some excessive,—some high so to speak; but it would have been a line shot. Whereas killin' the hawg is 'way to one side of the mark; an' onder.

"However, as I states, Bill bein' hasty that a-way, an' oncapable of perhaps refined reasonin', downs the pig, an' stands pat, waitin' for Olson to fill his hand, if he feels so moved.

"It's at this pinch where the cowardly nacher of this yere Olson begins to shine. He's ugly as a wolf about Bill copperin' his hawg that a-way, but he don't pack the nerve to go after Bill an' make a round-up of them grievances. An' he ain't allowin' to pass it up none onrevenged neither. Now yere's what Olson does; he 'sassinates Bill's pet raccoon.

"That's right, son, jest massacres a pore, confidin' raccoon, who don't no more stand in on that hawg-killin' of Bill's, than me an' you,—don't even advise it.

"Which I shorely allows you saveys all thar is to know about a raccoon. No? Well, a raccoon's like this: In the first place he's plumb easy, an' ain't lookin' for no gent to hold out kyards or ring a cold deck on him. That's straight; a raccoon is simpleminded that a-way; an' his impressive trait is, he's meditative. Besides bein' nacherally thoughtful, a raccoon is a heap melancholy,—he jest sets thar an' absorbs melancholy from merely bein' alive.

"But if a raccoon is melancholy or gets wropped in thought that a-way, it's after all his own play. It's to his credit that once when he's tamed, he's got mountainous confidence in men, an' will curl up to sleep where you be an' shet both eyes. He's plumb trustful; an' moreover, no matter how mournful a raccoon feels, or how plumb melancholy he gets, he don't pester you with no yarns.

"I reckons I converses with this yere identical raccoon of Bill's plenty frequent; when he feels blue, an' ag'in when he's at his gailiest, an' he never remarks nothin' to me except p'lite general'ties.

"If this yere Olson was a dead game party who regards himse'f wronged, he'd searched out a gun, or a knife, or mebby a club, an' pranced over an' rectified Bill a whole lot. But he's too timid an' too cowardly, an' afraid of Bill. So to play even, he lines out to bushwhack this he'pless, oninstructed raccoon. Olson figgers to take advantage of what's cl'arly a loop-hole in a raccoon's constitootion.

"Mebby you never notices it about a raccoon, but once he gets interested in a pursoot, he's rigged so he can't quit none ontil the project's a success. Thar's herds an' bands of folks an' animals who's fixed sim'lar. They can start, an' they can't let up. Thar's bull-dogs: They begins a war too easy; but the c'pacity to quit is left out of bull-dogs entire. Same about nose-paint with gents I knows. They capers up to whiskey at the beginnin' like a kitten to warm milk; an' they never does cease no more. An' that's how the kyards falls to raccoons.

"Knowin' these yere deefects in raccoons, this Olson plots to take advantage tharof; an' by playin' it low on Bill's raccoon, get even with Bill about that dead hawg. Which Bill wouldn't have took a drove of hawgs; no indeed! not the whole Fall round-up of hawgs in all of West Tennessee, an' lose that raccoon.

"It's when Bill's over to Pine Knot layin' in tobacker, an' nose-paint an' corn meal, an' sech necessaries, when Olson stands in to down Bill's pet. He goes injunnin' over to Bill's an' finds the camp all deserted, except the raccoon's thar, settin', battin' his eyes mournful an' lonesome on the doorstep. This Olson camps down by the door an' fondles the raccoon an' strokes his coat, an' lets him search his pockets with his black hands ontil he gets that friendly an' confident about Olson he'd told him anythin'. It's then this yere miscreant, Olson, springs his game.

"He's got a couple of crawfish which he's fresh caught at the Branch. Now raccoons regards crawfish as onusual good eatin'. For myse'f, I can't say I deems none high of crawfish as viands, but raccoons is different; an' the way they looks at it, crawfish is pie.

"This Olson brings out his two crawfish an' fetchin' a jar of water from the spring, he drops in a crawfish an' incites an' aggravates Zekiel—that's the name of Bill's raccoon—to feel in an' get him a whole lot.

"Zekiel ain't none shy on the play. He knows crawfish like a gambler does a red chip; so turnin' his eyes up to the sky, like a raccoon does who's wropped in pleasant anticipations that a-way, he plunges in his paw an' gets it.

"Once Zekiel acquires him, the pore crawfish don't last as long as two-bits at faro-bank. When Zekiel has him plumb devoured he turns his eyes on Olson, sorter thankful, an' 'waits developments.

"Olson puts in the second crawfish, an' Zekiel takes him into camp same as t'other. It's now that Olson onfurls his plot on Zekiel. Olson drops a dozen buckshot into the jar of water. Nacherally, Zekiel, who's got his mind all framed up touchin' crawfish, goes after the buckshot with his fore foot. But it's different with buckshot; Zekiel can't pick 'em up. He tries an' tries with his honest, simple face turned up to heaven, but he can't make it. All Zekiel can do is feel 'em with his foot, an' roll 'em about on the bottom of the jar.

"Now as I remarks prior, when a raccoon gets embarked that a-way, he can't quit. He ain't arranged so he can cease. Olson, who's plumb aware tharof, no sooner gets Zekiel started on them buckshot, than knowin' that nacher can be relied on to play her hand out, he sa'nters off to his wickeyup, leavin' Zekiel to his fate. Bill won't be home till Monday, an' Olson knows that before then, onless Zekiel is interrupted, he'll be even for that hawg Bill drops. As Olson comes to a place in the trail where he's goin' to lose sight of Bill's camp, he turns an' looks back. The picture is all his revenge can ask. Thar sets Zekiel on the doorstep, with his happy countenance turned up to the dome above, an' his right paw elbow deep in the jar, still rollin' an' feelin' them buckshot 'round, an' allowin' he's due to ketch a crawfish every moment.

"Which it works out exactly as the wretched Olson figgers. The sun goes down, an' the Sunday sun comes up an' sets ag'in; an' still pore Zekiel is planted by the jar, with his hopeful eyes on high, still feelin' of them buckshot. He can't quit no more'n if he's loser in a poker game; Zekiel can't. When Bill rides up to his door about second-drink time Monday afternoon, Olson is shorely even on that hawg. Thar lays Zekiel, dead. He's jest set thar with them buckshot an' felt himse'f to death.

"But speakin' of the sapiency of Bill Hoskins's Zekiel," continued the old gentleman as we lighted pipes and lapsed into desultory puffing, "while Zekiel for a raccoon is sóme deep, after all you-all is jest amazed at Zekiel 'cause I calls your attention to him a whole lot. If you was to go into camp with 'em, an' set down an' watch 'em, you'd shorely be s'prised to note how level-headed all animals be.

"Now if thar's anythin' in Arizona for whose jedgement I don't have respect nacheral, it's birds. Arizona for sech folks as you an' me, an' coyotes an' jack-rabbits, is a good range. Sech as we-alls sorter fits into the general play an' gets action for our stacks. But whatever a bird can find entrancin' in some of them Southwestern deserts is allers too many for me.

"As I su'gests, I former holds fowls, who of free choice continues a residence in Arizona, as imbeciles. Yet now an' then I observes things that makes me oncertain if I'm onto a bird's system; an' if after all Arizona is sech a dead kyard for birds. It's possible a gent might be 'way off on birds an' the views they holds of life. He might watch the play an' esteem 'em loser, when from a bird's p'int of view they's makin' a killin', an' even callin' the turn every deal.

"What he'ps to open my eyes a lot on birds is two Road Runners Doc Peets an' me meets up with one afternoon comin' down from Lordsburg. These yere Road Runners is a lanky kind of prop'sition, jest a shade off from spring chickens for size. Which their arrangements as to neck an' laigs is onrestricted an' liberal, an' their long suit is runnin' up an' down the sun-baked trails of Arizona with no object. Where he's partic'lar strong, this yere Road Runner, is in waitin' ontil some gent comes along, same as Doc Peets an' me that time, an' then attachin' of himse'f to said cavalcade an' racin' along ahead. A Road Runner keeps up this exercise for miles, an' be about the length of a lariat ahead of your pony's nose all the time. When you-all lets out a link or two an' stiffens your pony with the spur, the Road Runner onbuckles sim'lar an' exults tharat. You ain't goin' to run up on him while he can wave a laig, you can gamble your last chip, an' you confers favors on him by sendin' your pony at him. Thar he stays, rackin' along ahead of you ontil satiated. Usual thar's two Road Runners, an' they clips it along side by side as if thar's somethin' in it for 'em; an' I reckons, rightly saveyed, thar is. However, the profits to Road Runners of them excursions ain't obvious, none whatever; so I won't try to set 'em forth. Them journeys they makes up an' down the trail shorely seems aimless to me.

"But about Doc Peets an' me pullin' out from Lordsburg for Wolfville that evenin': Our ponies is puttin' the landscape behind 'em at a good road-gait when we notes a brace of them Road Runners with wings half lifted, pacin' to match our speed along the trail in front. As Road Runners is frequent with us, our minds don't bother with 'em none. Now an' then Doc an' me can see they converses as they goes speedin' along a level or down a slope. It's as if one says to t'other, somethin' like this yere:

" 'How's your wind, Bill? Is it comin' easy?'

" 'Shore,' it would seem like Bill answers. 'Valves never is in sech shape. I'm on velvet; how's your laigs standin' the pace, Jim?'

" 'Laigs is workin' like they's new oiled,' Jim replies back; 'it's a plumb easy game. I reckons, Bill, me an' you could keep ahead of them mavericks a year if we-alls feels like it.'

" 'Bet a blue stack on it,' Bill answers. 'I deems these yere gents soft. Before I'd ride sech ponies as them, I'd go projectin' 'round some night an' steal one.'

" 'Them ponies is shorely a heap slothful,' Jim answers.

"At this mebby them Road Runners ruffles their feathers an' runs on swifter, jest to show what a slow racket keepin' ahead of me an' Peets is. An' these yere locoed birds keeps up sech conversations for hours.

"Mind I ain't sayin' that what I tells you is what them Road Runners really remarks; but I turns it over to you-all the way it strikes me an' Doc at the time. What I aims to relate, however, is an incident as sheds light on how wise an' foxy Road Runners be.

"Doc Peets an' me, as I states, ain't lavishin' no onreasonable notice on these yere birds, an' they've been scatterin' along the trail for mebby it's an hour, when one of 'em comes to a plumb halt, sharp. The other stops likewise an' rounds up ag'inst his mate; an' bein' cur'ous to note what's pesterin' 'em, Peets an' me curbs to a stand-still. The Road Runner who stops first—the same bein' Bill—is lookin' sharp an' interested-like over across the plains.

" 'Rattlesnake,' he imparts to his side partner.

" 'Where's he at?' says the side partner, which is Jim, 'where's this yere snake at, Bill? I don't note no rattlesnake.'

" 'Come round yere by me,' Bill says. 'Now on a line with the top of yonder mesa an' a leetle to the left of that soap-weed; don't you-all see him quiled up thar asleep?'

" 'Which I shorely does,' says Jim, locatin' the rattlesnake with his beady eye, 'an' he's some sunk in slumber. Bill, that serpent is our meat.'

" 'Move your moccasins easy,' says Bill, 'so's not to turn him out. Let's rustle up some flat cactuses an' corral him.'

"Tharupon these yere Road Runners turns in mighty diligent; an' not makin' no more noise than shadows, they goes pokin' out on the plains ontil they finds a flat cactus which is dead; so they can tear off the leaves with their bills. Doc Peets an' me sets in our saddles surveyin' their play; an' the way them Road Runners goes about the labors of their snake killin' impresses us it ain't the first bootchery of the kind they appears in. They shorely don't need no soopervisin'.

"One after the other, Jim an' Bill teeters up, all silent, with a flat cactus leaf in their beaks, an' starts to fence in the rattle-snake with 'em. They builds a corral of cactus all about him, which the same is mebby six-foot across. Them engineerin' feats takes Jim an' Bill twenty minutes. But they completes 'em; an' thar's the rattlesnake, plumb surrounded.

"These yere cactuses, as you most likely saveys, is thorny no limit; an' the spikes is that sharp, needles is futile to 'em. Jim an' Bill knows the rattlesnake can't cross this thorny corral.

"He don't look it none, but from the way he plays his hand, I takes it a rattlesnake is sensitive an' easy hurt onder the chin.

"An' it's plain to me an' Peets them Road Runners is aware of said weaknesses of rattlesnakes, an' is bankin' their play tharon. We-alls figgers, lookin' on, that Jim an' Bill aims to put the rattle-snake in prison; leave him captive that a-way in a cactus cala-boose. But we don't size up Jim an' Bill accurate at all. Them two fowls is shorely profound.

"No sooner is the corral made, than Jim an' Bill, without a word of warnin', opens up a war-jig 'round the outside; flappin' their pinions an' screechin' like squaws. Nacherally the rattle-snake wakes up. The sight of them two Road Runners, Jim an' Bill, cussin' an' swearin' at him, an' carryin' on that a-way scares him.

"It's trooth to say Bill an' Jim certainly conducts themse'fs scand'lous. The epithets they heaps on that pore ignorant rattle-snake, the taunts they flings at him, would have done Apaches proud.

"The rattlesnake buzzes an' quils up, an' onsheaths his fangs, an' makes bluffs to strike Bill an' Jim, but they only hops an' dances about, thinkin' up more ornery things to say. Every time the rattlesnake goes to crawl away—which he does frequent—he strikes the cactus thorns an' pulls back. By an' by he sees he's elected, an' he gets that enraged he swells up till he's big as two snakes; Bill an' Jim maintainin' their sass. Them Road Runners is abreast of the play every minute, you can see that.

"At last comes the finish, an' matters gets dealt down to the turn. The rattlesnake suddenly crooks his neck, he's so plumb locoed with rage an' fear, an' socks his fangs into himse'f. That's the fact; bites himse'f, an' never lets up till he's dead.

"It don't seem to astound Jim an' Bill none when the rattlesnake 'sassinates himse'f that a-way, an' I reckons they has this yere sooicide in view. They keeps pesterin' an' projectin' about ontil the rattlesnake is plumb defunct, an' then they emits a whirlwind of new whoops, an' goes over to one side an' pulls off a skelp dance. Jim an' Bill is shorely cel'bratin' a vic'try.

"After the skelp dance is over, Bill an' Jim tiptoes over mighty quiet an' sedate, an' Jim takes their prey by the tail an' yanks it. After the rattlesnake's drug out straight, him an' Bill runs their eyes along him like they's sizin' him up. With this yere last, however, it's cl'ar the Road Runners regards the deal as closed. They sa'nters off down the trail, arm in arm like, conversin' in low tones so Peets an' me never does hear what they says. When they's in what they takes to be the c'rrect p'sition, they stops an' looks back at me an' Peets. Bill turns to Jim like he's sayin':

" 'Thar's them two short-horns ag'in. I wonders if they ever aims to pull their freight, or do they reckon they'll pitch camp right yere?' "

As I say, it does not help enjoyment of Lewis' art to take him too literally. He used materials, rather than transcribed them. Nor can one always predict when they will turn out carefully molded and memorable. For instance, Lewis wrote several times of the great O. K. Corral fight, but not satisfactorily enough, in my view, to repay reprint here. The reason was, I think, that Lewis (like many others) was so completely, so sentimentally partisan to the Earps that he could not give a strong, individual account of that immortal moment. The O. K. Corral murders—for want of a better word—will always, apparently, be either the famous legend, or else the hard, uncomfortable tale which Frank Waters unearthed in his The Earp Brothers of Tombstone: the Story of

Mrs. Virgil Earp *(1960)*. *Lewis cannot bring himself to cope with the troublesome details.*

His account of Billy the Kid, on the other hand, is more inventive, and gets a proper bead on him as the wretched delinquent he was. Some inhabitants of Lincoln County, New Mexico, persist, today, in treating the boy from New York and points west as kind-hearted, a great man with the gun, and so forth, and are positively surly about Sheriff Pat Garrett. There is nothing any of us can do about this except, if we must, go on reading such books as William A. Keleher's Violence in Lincoln County, 1869-1881 *(1959)*. . . . *Lewis' account puts the matter in a larger context.*

THE DISMISSAL OF SILVER PHIL

"His name, complete, is 'Silver City Philip.' In them social observances of the Southwest wherein haste is a feacher an' brev'ty the bull's eye aimed at, said cognomen gets shortened to 'Silver Phil.' "

The Old Cattleman looked thoughtfully into his glass, as if by that method he collected the scattered elements of a story. There was a pause; then he lifted the glass to his lips as one who being now evenly equipped of information, proposed that it arrive. hand in hand with the inspiration which should build a tale from it.

"Shore, this Silver Phil is dead now; an' I never yet crosses up with the gent who's that sooperfluous as to express regrets. It's Dan Boggs who dismisses Silver Phil; Dan does it in efforts he puts forth to faithfully represent the right.

"Doc Peets allers allows this Silver Phil is a 'degen'rate;' leastwise that's the word Peets uses. An' while I freely concedes I ain't none too cl'ar as to jest what a degen'rate is, I stands ready to back Peets' deescription to win. Peets is, bar Colonel William Greene Sterett, the best eddicated sharp in Arizona; also the wariest as to expressin' views. Tharfore when Peets puts it up, onflinchin', that this yere Silver Phil's a degen'rate, you-all can spread your blankets an' go to sleep on it that a degen'rate he is.

"Silver Phil is a little, dark, ignorant, tousled-ha'red party, none too neat in costume. He's as black an' small an' evil-seemin'

as a Mexican; still, you sees at a glance he ain't no Greaser neither. An' with all this yere surface wickedness, Silver Phil has a
quick, hyster'cal way like a woman or a bird; an' thar's ever a
grin on his face. You can smell 'bad' off Silver Phil, like smoke
in a house, an' folks who's on the level—an' most folks is—con-
ceives a notion ag'in him the moment he an' they meets up.

"The first time I observes Silver Phil, he's walkin' down the
licker room of the Red Light. As he goes by the bar, Black
Jack—who's rearrangin' the nosepaint on the shelf so it shows to
advantage—gets careless an' drops a bottle.

" 'Crash!' it goes onto the floor.

"With the sound, an' the onexpected suddenness of it stampedin' his nerves, that a-way, Silver Phil leaps into the air like a
cat; an' when he 'lights, he's frontin' Black Jack an' a gun in each
hand.

" 'Which I won't be took!' says Silver Phil, all flustered.

"His eyes is gleamin' an' his face is palin' an' his ugly grin gets
even uglier than before. But like a flash, he sees thar's nothin' to
go in the air about—nothin' that means him; an' he puts up his
hardware an' composes himse'f.

" 'You-all conducts yourse'f like a sport who has something on
his mind,' says Texas Thompson, who's thar present at the time,
an' can't refrain from commentin' on the start that bottle-smash-
in' gives Silver Phil.

"This Silver Phil makes no response, but sort o' grins plenty
ghastly, while his breath comes quick.

"Still, while you-all notes easy that this person's scared, it's
plain he's a killer jest the same. It's frequent that a-way. I'm
never much afraid of one of your cold game gents like Cherokee
Hall; you can gamble the limit they'll never put a six-shooter in
play till it's shorely come their turn. But timid, feverish, locoed
people, whose jedgment is bad an' who's prone to feel themse'fs
in peril; they're the kind who kills. For myse'f I shuns all sech. I
won't say them erratic, quick-to-kill sports don't have courage;
only it strikes me—an' I've rode up on a heap of 'em—it's more
like a fear-bit f'rocity than sand.

"Take Enright or Peets or Cherokee or Tutt or Jack Moore or Boggs or Texas Thompson; you're plumb safe with sech gents— all or any. An' yet thar ain't the first glimmer of bein' gun-shy about one of 'em; they're as clean strain as the eternal granite, an' no more likely to hide out from danger than a hill. An' while they differs from each other, yet they're all different from sech folks as Silver Phil. Boggs, goin' to war, is full of good-humoured grandeur, gala and confident, ready to start or stop like a good hoss. Cherokee Hall is quiet an' wordless; he gets pale, but sharp an' deadly; an' his notion is to fight for a finish. Peets is haughty an' sooperior on the few o'casions when he onbends in battle, an' comports himse'f like a gent who fights downhill; the same, ondoubted, bein' doo to them book advantages of Peets which elevates him an' lifts him above the common herd a whole lot. Enright who's oldest is of course slowest to embark in blood, an' pulls his weepons—when he does pull 'em—with sorrowful resignation.

" 'Which I'm shorely saddest when I shoots,' says Enright to me, as he reloads his gun one time.

"These yere humane sentiments, however, don't deter him from shootin' soon an' aimin' low, which latter habits makes Wolfville's honoured chief a highly desp'rate game to get ag'inst.

"Jack Moore, bein' as I explains former, the execyootive of the Stranglers, an' responsible for law an' order, has a heap of shootin' shoved onto him from time to time. Jack allers transacts these fireworks with a ca'm, offishul front, the same bein' devoid, equal, of anger or regrets. Tutt, partic'lar after he weds Tucson Jennie, an' more partic'lar still when he reaps new honours as the originator of that blessed infant Enright Peets Tutt, carries on what shootin' comes his way in a manner a lot dignified an' lofty; while Texas Thompson—who's mebby morbid about his wife down in Laredo demandin' she be divorced that time— although he picks up his hand in a fracas, ready an' irritable an' with no delays, after all is that well-balanced he's bound to be each time plumb right.

"Which, you observes, son, from these yere settin's forth, that thar's a mighty sight of difference between gents like them pards of mine an' degen'rates of the tribe of Silver Phil. It's the difference between right an' wrong; one works from a impulse of pure jestice, the other is moved of a sperit of crime; an' thar you be.

"Silver Phil, we learns later—an' it shore jestifies Peets in his theeries about him bein' a degen'rate—has been in plenty of blood. But allers like a cat; savage, gore-thirsty, yet shy, prideless, an' ready to fly. It seems he begins to be homicidal in a humble way by downin' a trooper over near Fort Cummings. That's four years before he visits us. He's been blazin' away intermittent ever since, and allers crooel, crafty an' safe. It's got to be a shore thing or Silver Phil quits an' goes into the water like a mink.

"This yere ondersized miscreant ain't ha'nted about Wolfville more'n four days before he shows how onnecessary he is to our success. Which he works a ha'r copper on Cherokee Hall. What's a ha'r copper? I'll onfold, short and terse, what Silver Phil does, an' then you saveys. Cherokee's dealin' his game—farobank she is; an' if all them national banks conducts themse'fs as squar' as that enterprise of Cherokee's, the fields of finance would be as safely honest as a church. Cherokee's turnin' his game one evenin'; Faro Nell on the lookout stool where she belongs. Silver Phil drifts up to the lay-out, an' camps over back of the king-end. He gets chips, an' goes to takin' chances alternate on the king, queen, jack, ten; all side an' side they be. Cherokee bein' squar' himse'f ain't over prone to expect a devious play in others. He don't notice this Silver Phil none speshul, an' shoves the kyards.

"Silver Phil wins three or four bets; it's Nell that catches on to his racket, an' signs up to Cherokee onder the table with her little foot. One glance an' Cherokee is loaded with information. This Silver Phil, it seems, in a sperit of avarice, equips himse'f with a copper—little wooden checker, is what this copper is—one he's done filched from Cherokee the day prior. He's fastened a long black hoss-ha'r to it, an' he ties the other end of the hoss-ha'r to his belt in front. This ha'r is long enough as he's planted at the table that a-way, so it reaches nice to them four nearest kyards,—the king, queen, jack, ten. An' said ha'r is plumb invisible except to eyes as sharp as Faro Nell's. The deceitful Silver Phil will have a stack on one of 'em, coppered with this yere ha'r copper. He watches the box. As the turns is made, if the kyards come his way, well an' good. Silver Phil does nothin' but garners in results. When the kyards start to show ag'in him, however, that's different. In sech events Silver Phil draws in his breath, sort o' takin' in on the hoss-ha'r, an' the copper comes off the bet. When the turn is made, thar's Silver Phil's bet—by virchoo of said fraud—open an' triumphant an' waitin' to be paid.

"Cherokee gets posted quick an' with a look. As sharp as winkin' Cherokee has a nine-inch bowie in his hand an' with one slash cuts the hoss-ha'r clost up by Silver Phil's belt.

" 'That's a yoonique invention!' observes Cherokee, an' he's sarcastic while he menaces with the knife at Silver Phil; 'that contraption is shorely plenty sagacious! But it don't go here. Shove in your chips.' Silver Phil obeys: an' he shows furtive, ugly, an' alarmed, an' all of 'em at once. He don't say a word. 'Now pull your freight,' concloods Cherokee. 'If you ever drifts within ten foot of a game of mine ag'in I'll throw this knife plumb through you—through an' through.' An' Cherokee, by way of 'lustration lets fly the knife across the bar-room. It comes like a flash.

" 'Chuck!'

"Thar's a picture paper pasted onto the wooden wall of the Red Light, displayin' the liniaments of some party. That bowie pierces the picture—a shot in the cross it is—an' all with sech fervour that the p'int of the blade shows a inch an' a half on the other side of that individyool board.

" 'The next time I throws a knife in your presence,' remarks Cherokee to Silver Phil, an' Cherokee's as cold an' p'isonous as a rattlesnake, 'it'll be la'nched at you.'

"Silver Phil don't say nothin' in retort. He's aware by the lib'ral way Cherokee sep'rates himse'f from the bowie that said weepon

1455713

can't constitoote Cherokee's entire armament. An' as Silver Phil don't pack the sperit to face no sech flashlight warrior, he acts on Cherokee's hint to *vamos,* an' fades into the street. Shore, Cherokee don't cash the felon's chips none; he confiscates 'em. Cherokee ain't quite so tenderly romantic as to make good to a detected robber. Moreover, he lets this Silver Phil go onharmed when by every roole his skelp is forfeit. It turns out good for the camp, however, as this yere experience proves so depressin' to Silver Phil he removes his blankets to Red Dog. Thar among them purblind tarrapins, its inhabitants, it's likely he gets prosperous an' ondetected action on that little old ha'r copper of his.

"It's not only my beliefs, but likewise the opinions of sech joodicial sports as Enright, Peets, an' Colonel Sterett, that this maverick, Silver Phil, is all sorts of a crim'nal. An' I wouldn't wonder if he's a pure rustler that a-way; as ready to stand up a stage as snake a play at farobank. This idee settles down on the Wolfville intell'gence on the heels of a vicissitoode wherein Dan Boggs performs, an' which gets pulled off over in the Bird Cage Op'ry House. Jack Moore ain't thar none that time. Usual, Jack is a constant deevotee of the dramy. Jack's not only a first-nighter, he comes mighty clost to bein' a every-nighter. But this partic'lar evenin' when Boggs performs, Jack's rummagin' about some'ers else.

"If Jack's thar, it's even money he'd a-had that second shot instead of Boggs; in which event, the results might have been something graver than this yere minoote wound which Boggs confers. I'm confident Jack would have cut in with the second shot for sech is his offishul system. Jack more'n once proclaims his position.

" 'By every roole of law,' says Jack at epocks when he declar's himse'f, 'an' on all o'casions, I, as kettle-tender to the Stranglers, is entitled to the first shot. When I uses the term "o'casion," I would be onderstood as alloodin' to affairs of a simply social kind, an' not to robberies, hold-ups, hoss-larcenies, an' other an' sim'lar transactions in spec'latif crime when every gent defends his own. Speakin' social, however, I reasserts that by every roole of guidance, I'm entitled to the first shot. Which a doo regyard for these plain rights of mine would go far to freein' Wolfville upper circles of the bullets which occurs from time to time, an' which even the most onconventional admits is shore a drawback. All I can add as a closer,' concloods Jack, 'is that I'll make haste to open on any sport who transgresses these fiats an' goes to shootin' first. Moreover, it's likely that said offender finds that when I'm started once, what I misses in the orig'nal deal I'll make up in the draw, an' I tharfore trusts that none will prove so sooicidal as to put me to the test.'

"This Bird Cage Op'ry House evenin', however, Jack is absent a heap. Dan Boggs is present, an' is leanin' back appreciatin' the show an' the Valley Tan plenty impartial. Dan likes both an' is doin' 'em even jestice. Over opp'site to Dan is a drunken passel of sports from Red Dog, said wretched hamlet bein' behind Wolfville in that as in all things else an' not ownin' no op'ry house.

"As the evenin' proceeds—it's about sixth drink time—a casyooal gun goes off over among the Red Dog outfit, an' the lead tharfrom bores a hole in the wall clost to Dan's y'ear. Nacherally Dan don't like it. The show sort o' comes to a balk, an' takin' advantages of the lull Dan arises in a listless way an' addresses the Red Dogs.

" 'I merely desires to inquire,' says Dan 'whether that shot is inadvertent; or is it a mark of innocent joobilation an' approval of the show; or is it meant personal to me?'

" 'You can bet your moccasins!' shouts one of the Red Dog delegation, 'thar's no good fellowship with that gun-play. That shot's formal an' serious an' goes as it lays.'

" 'My mind bein' now cl'ar on the subject of motive,' says Dan; 'the proper course is plain.'

"With this retort Dan slams away gen'ral—shoots into the flock like—at the picnickers from Red Dog, an' a party who's plenty drunk an' has his feet piled up on a table goes shy his off big toe.

"As I remarks yeretofore it's as well Jack Moore ain't thar. Jack would have corralled something more momentous than a toe. Which Jack would have been shootin' in his capac'ty as mar-

shal, an' couldn't onder sech circumstances have stooped to
toes. But it's different with Dan. He is present private an' only
idlin' 'round; an' he ain't driven to take high ground. More partic'lar since Dan's playin' a return game in the nacher of reproofs
an' merely to resent the onlicensed liberties which Red Dog takes
with him, Dan, as I says, is free to accept toes if he so decides.

"When Dan busts this yere inebriate, the victim lams loose a
yell ag'inst which a coyote would protest. That sot thinks he's
shore killed. What with the scare an' the pain an' the nosepaint,
an' regyardin' of himse'f as right then flutterin' about the rim of
eternity, he gets seized with remorse an' allows he's out to confess his sins before he quits. As thar's no sky pilot to confide in,
this drunkard figgers that Peets 'll do, an' with that he onloads
on Peets how, bein' as he is a stage book-keep over in Red Dog,
he's in cahoots with a outfit of route agents an' gives 'em the
word when its worth while to stand-up the stage. An' among
other crim'nal pards of his this terrified person names that outlaw
Silver Phil. Shore, when he rounds to an' learns it ain't nothin'
but a toe, this party's chagrined to death.

"This yere confidin' sport's arrested an' taken some'ers—Prescott mebby—to be tried in a shore-enough co't for the robberies;
the Red Dog Stranglers not bein' game to butt in an' hang him a
lot themse'fs. They surrenders him to the marshal who rides over
for him; an' they would have turned out Silver Phil, too, only
that small black outcast don't wait, but goes squanderin' off to
onknown climes the moment he hears the news. He's vamoosed
Red Dog before this penitent bookkeep ceases yelpin' an' sobbin'
over his absent toe.

"It ain't no time, however, before we hears further of Silver
Phil; that is, by way of roomer. It looks like a couple of big cow
outfits some'ers in the San Simon country—they're the 'Three-
D' an' the 'K-in-a-box' brands—takes first to stealin' each other's
cattle, an', final, goes to war. Each side retains bands of murder-
ers an' proceeds buoyantly to lay for one another. Which Silver
Phil enlists with the 'Three-D' an' sneaks an' prowls an' bush-
whacks an' shoots himse'f into more or less bloody an' ignoble

prom'nence. At last the main war-chiefs of the Territory declar's themse'fs in on the riot an' chases both sides into the hills; an' among other excellent deeds they makes captive Silver Phil.

"It's a great error they don't string this Silver Phil instanter. But no; after the procrastinatin' fashion of real law, they permits the villain—who's no more use on the surface of Arizona that a-way than one of them hydrophoby polecats whose bite is death—to get a law sharp to plead an' call for a show-down before a jedge an' jury. It takes days to try Silver Phil, an' marshals an' sheriff gents is two weeks squanderin' about gettin' witnesses; an' all to as much trouble an' loss of time an' *dinero* as would suffice to round-up the cattle of Cochise county. Enright an' the Stranglers would have turned the trick in twenty minutes an' never left the New York Store ontil with Silver Phil an' a lariat they reepairs to the windmill to put the finishin' touches on their lucoobrations.

"Still, dooms slow an' shiftless as they shore be, at the wind-up Silver Phil's found guilty, an' is put in nom'nation by the presidin' alcade to be hanged; the time bein' set in a crazy-hoss fashion for a month away. As Silver Phil—which he's that bad an' hard he comes mighty clost to bein' game—is leavin' the co't-room with the marshal who's ridin' herd on him, he says:

" 'I ain't payin' much attention at the time,'—Silver Phil's talkin' to that marshal gent,—'bein' I'm thinkin' of something else, but do I onderstand that old grey sport on the bench to say you-all is to hang me next month?'

" 'That's whatever!' assents this marshal gent, 'an' you can gamble a bloo stack that hangin' you is a bet we ain't none likely to overlook. Which we're out to put our whole grateful souls into the dooty.'

" 'Now I thinks of it,' observes Silver Phil, 'I'm some averse to bein' hanged. I reckons, speakin' free an' free as between fellow sports, that in order for that execootion to be a blindin' success I'll have to be thar personal?'

" 'It's one of the mighty few o'casions,' responds the marshal, 'when your absence would shorely dash an' damp the gen'ral joy.

As you says, you'll have to be thar a heap personal when said hangin' occurs.'

" 'I'm mighty sorry,' says Silver Phil, 'that you-all lays out your game in a fashion that so much depends on me. The more so, since the longer I considers this racket, the less likely it is I'll be thar. It's almost a cinch, with the plans I has, that I'll shore be some'ers else.'

"They corrals Silver Phil in the one big upper room of a two-story 'doby, an' counts off a couple of dep'ty marshals to gyard him. These gyards, comin' squar' down to cases, ain't no improvement, moral, on Silver Phil himse'f; an' since they're twice his age—Silver Phil not bein' more'n twenty—it's safe as a play to say that both of 'em oughter have been hanged a heap before ever Silver Phil is born. These two hold-ups, however, turns dep'ty marshals in their old age, an' is put in to stand watch an' watch an' see that Silver Phil don't work loose from his hobbles an' go pirootin' off ag'in into parts onknown. Silver Phil is loaded with fetters,—handcuffs an' laig-locks both—an' these hold-up sentries is armed to the limit.

"It's the idee of Doc Peets later, when he hears the details, that if the gyards that time treats Silver Phil with kindness, the little felon most likely would have remained to be hanged. But they don't: they abooses Silver Phil; cussin' him out an' herdin' him about like he's cattle. They're a evil-tempered couple, them dep'ties, an' they don't give Silver Phil no sort o' peace.

" 'As I su'gests yeretofore,' says Doc Peets, when he considers the case, 'this Silver Phil is a degen'rate. He's like a anamile. He don't entertain no reg'lar scheme to work free when he waxes sardonic with the marshal; that's only a bluff. Later, when them gyards takes to maltreatin' him an' battin' him about, it wakes up the venom in him, an' his cunnin' gets aroused along with his appetite for revenge.'

"This Silver Phil, who's lean an' slim like I explains at the jump, has hands no bigger than a cat's paws. It ain't no time when he discovers that by cuttin' himse'f a bit on the irons, he can shuck the handcuffs whenever he's disposed. Even then, he don't outline no campaign for liberty; jest sort o' roominates an' waits.

"It's one partic'lar mornin', some two weeks after Silver Phil's sentenced that a-way. The marshal gent himse'f ain't about, bein' on some dooty over to Tucson. Silver Phil is upsta'rs on the top floor of the 'doby with his gyards. Which he's hotter than a wild-cat; the gyards an' him has been havin' a cussin' match, an' as Silver Phil outplays 'em talkin', one of 'em's done whacked him over the skelp with his gun. The blood's tricklin' down Silver Phil's fore'erd as he sits glowerin'.

"One of the gyards is loadin' a ten-gauge Greener—a whole mouthful of buckshot in each shell. He's grinnin' at Silver Phil as he shoves the shells in the gun an' slams her shet.

" 'Which I'm loadin' that weepon for you,' says the gyard, con-templatin' Silver Phil derisive.

" 'You be, be you!' replies Silver Phil, his eyes burnin' with rage. 'Which you better look out a whole lot; you-all may get it yourse'f.'

"The gyard laughs ugly an' exasperatin' an' puts the ten-gauge in a locker along with two or three Winchesters. Then he turns the key on the firearms an' goes caperin' off to his feed.

"The other gyard, his *compadre,* is settin' on a stool lookin' out a window. Mebby he's considerin' of his sins. It would be more in his hand at this time if he thinks of Silver Phil.

"Silver Phil, who's full of wrath at the taunts of the departed gyard, slips his hands free of the irons. Most of the hide on his wrists comes with 'em, but Silver Phil don't care. The gyard's back is to him as that gent sits gazin' out an' off along the dusty trail where it winds gray an' hot toward Tucson. Silver Phil or-ganises, stealthy an' cat-cautious; he's out for the gyard's gun as it hangs from his belt, the butt all temptin' an' su'gestive.

"As Silver Phil makes his first move the laig-locks clanks. It ain't louder than the jingle of a brace of copper *centouse* knock-in' together. It's enough, however; it strikes on the y'ear of that thoughtful gyard like the roar of a '44. He emerges from his reverie with a start; the play comes cl'ar as noonday to him in a moment.

"The gyard leaps, without even lookin' 'round, to free himse'f from the clutch of Silver Phil. Which he's the splinter of a second too late. Silver Phil makes a spring like a mountain lion, laig-locks an' all, an' grabs the gun. As the gyard goes clatterin' down sta'rs, Silver Phil pumps two loads into him an' curls him up at the foot. Then Silver Phil hurls the six-shooter at him with a volley of mal'dictions.

"Without pausin' a moment, Silver Phil grabs the stool an' smashes to flinders the locker that holds the 10-gauge Greener. He ain't forgot none; an' he's fair locoed to get that partic'lar weepon for the other gyard. He rips it from the rack an' shows at the window as his prey comes runnin' to the rescoo of his pard:

" 'Oh, you! Virg Sanders!' yells Silver Phil.

"The second gyard looks up; an' as he does, Silver Phil gives him both bar'ls. Forty-two buckshot; an' that gyard's so clost he stops 'em all! As he lays dead, Silver Phil breaks the Greener in two, an' throws, one after the other, stock an' bar'l at him.

" 'Which I'll show you-all what happens when folks loads a gun for me!' says Silver Phil.

"Nacherally, this artillery practice turns out the entire plaza. The folks is standin' about the 'doby which confines Silver Phil, wonderin' whatever that enthoosiast's goin' to do next. No, they don't come after him, an' I'il tell you why. Shore, thar's twenty gents lookin' on, any one of whom, so far as personal apprehensions is involved, would trail Silver Phil single-handed into a wolf's den. Which he'd feel plumb confident he gets away with Silver Phil an' the wolves thrown in to even up the odds. Still, no one stretches forth to capture Silver Phil on this yere voylent o'casion. An' these is the reasons. Thar's no reg'lar offishul present whose dooty it is to rope up this Silver Phil. If sech had chanced to be thar, you can put down a stack he'd come a-runnin', an' him or Silver Phil would have caught up with the two gyards on their

journey into the beyond. But when it gets down to private people volunteerin' for dooty as marshals, folks in the Southwest
goes some slothful to work. Thar's the friends of the accoosed—
an' as a roole he ain't none friendless—who would mighty likely
resent sech zeal. Also, in the case of Silver Phil, his captivity
grows out of a cattle war. One third the public so far as it stands
about the 'doby where Silver Phil is hived that time is 'Three-D'
adherents, mebby another third is 'K-in-a-box' folks, while the
last third is mighty likely nootral. Whichever way it breaks, however, thar's a tacit stand-off, an' never a sport of 'em lifts a finger
or voice to head off Silver Phil.

" 'Which she's the inalien'ble right of Americans onder the
constitootion to escape with every chance they gets,' says one.

" 'That's whatever!' coincides his pard; 'an' moreover this ain't
our round-up nohow.'

"It's in that fashion these private citizens adjusts their dooty
to the state while pausin' to look on, in a sperit of cur'osity
while Silver Phil makes his next play.

"They don't wait long. Silver Phil comes out on the roof of a
stoop in front. He's got a Winchester by now, an' promptly throws
the muzzle tharof on a leadin' citizen. Silver Phil allows he'll
plug this dignitary if they don't send up a sport with a file to cut
loose the laig-locks. Tharupon the pop'lace, full of a warm interest by this time, does better. They gropes about in the war-bags
of the Virg Sanders sharp who stops the buckshot an' gets his
keys; a moment after, Silver Phil is free.

"Still, this ontirin' hold-up goes on menacin' the leadin' citizen
as former. Which now Silver Phil demands a bronco, bridled an'
saddled. He gives the public ten minutes; if the bronco is absent
at the end of ten minutes Silver Phil allows he'll introdooce
about a pound of lead into where that village father does his
cogitatin'. The bronco appears with six minutes to spar'. As it
arrives, the vivacious Silver Phil jumps off the roof of the stoop—
the same bein' low—an' is in the saddle an' out o' sight while as
practised a hand as Huggins is pourin' out a drink. Where the
trail bends 'round a *mesa* Silver Phil pulls up.

" 'Whoop! whoop! whoopee! for Silver Phil,' he shouts.

"Then he waves the Winchester, an' as he spurs 'round the corner of the hill it's the last that spellbound outfit ever sees of Silver Phil.

"Nacherally now," remarked my old friend, as he refreshed himself with a mouthful of scotch, "you-all is waitin' an' tryin' to guess wherever does Dan Boggs get in on this yere deal. An' it won't take no time to post you; the same bein' a comfort.

"Not one word do we-all wolves of Wolfville hear of the divertin' adventures of Silver Phil—shootin' up his gyards an' fetchin' himse'f free—ontil days after. No one in camp has got Silver Phil on his mind at all; at least if he has he deems him safe an' shore in hock, a-waitin' to be stretched. Considerin' what follows, I never experiences trouble in adoptin' Doc Peets' argyments that the eepisodes wherein this 'onhappy Silver Phil figgers sort o' aggravates his intellects ontil he's locoed.

" 'Bein' this Silver Phil's a degen'rate,' declar's Peets, explanatory, 'he's easy an' soon to loco. His mind as well as his moral nacher is onbalanced congenital. Any triflin' jolt, much less than what that Silver Phil runs up on, an' his fretful wits is shore to leave the saddle.'

"Now that Silver Phil's free, but loonatic like Peets says, an' doubly vicious by them tantalisin' gyards, it looks like he thinks of nothin' but wreckin' reprisals on all who's crossed his trail. An' so with vengeance eatin' at his crim'nal heart he p'ints that bronco's muzzle straight as a bird flies for Wolfville. Whoever do you-all reckon now he wants? Cherokee Hall? Son, you've followed off the wrong waggon track. Silver Phil—imagine the turpitoode of sech a ornery wretch!—is out for the lovely skelp of Faro Nell who detects him in his ha'r-copper frauds that time.

"Which the first intimations we has of Silver Phil after that escape, is one evenin' about fifth drink time—or as you-all says 'four o'clock.' The sun's still hot an' high over in the west. Thar's no game goin'; but bein' it's as convenient thar as elsewhere an' some cooler, Cherokee's settin' back of his layout with Faro Nell as usual on her lookout perch. Dan Boggs is across the street in the dancehall door, an' his pet best bronco is waitin' saddled in front. Hot an' drowsy; the street save for these is deserted.

"It all takes place in a moment. Thar's a clattering rush; an' then, pony a-muck with sweat an' alkali dust, Silver Phil shows in the portals of the Red Light. Thar's a flash an' a spit of white smoke as he fires his six-shooter straight at Faro Nell.

"Silver Phil is quick, but Cherokee is quicker. Cherokee sweeps Faro Nell from her stool with one motion of his arm an' the bullet that's searchin' for her lifts Cherokee's ha'r a trifle where he 'most gets his head in its way.

"Ondoubted, this Silver Phil allows he c'llects on Faro Nell as planned. He don't shoot twice, an' he don't tarry none, but wheels his wearied pony, gives a yell, an' goes surgin' off.

"But Silver Phil's got down to the turn of that evil deal of his existence. He ain't two hundred yards when Dan Boggs is in the saddle an' ridin' hard. Dan's bronco runs three foot for every one of the pony of Silver Phil's; which that beaten an' broken cayouse is eighty miles from his last mouthful of grass.

"As Dan begins to crowd him, Silver Phil turns in the saddle an' shoots. The lead goes 'way off yonder—wild. Dan, grim an' silent, rides on without returnin' the fire.

" 'Which I wouldn't dishonour them guns of mine,' says Dan, explainin' later the pheenomenon of him not shootin' none, 'which I wouldn't dishonour them guns by usin' 'em on varmints like this yere Silver Phil.'

"As Silver Phil reorganises for a second shot his bronco stumbles. Silver Phil pitches from the saddle an' strikes the grass to one side. As he half rises, Dan lowers on him like the swoop of a hawk. It's as though Dan's goin' to snatch a handkerchief from the ground.

"As Dan flashes by, he swings low from the saddle an' his right hand takes a troo full grip on that outlaw's shoulder. Dan has the thews an' muscles of a cinnamon b'ar, an' Silver Phil is only a scrap of a man. As Dan straightens up in the stirrups, he heaves this Silver Phil on high to the length of his long arm; an' then he dashes him ag'inst the flint-hard earth; which the manoover—we-all witnesses it from mebby a quarter of a mile—which the man-oover that a-way is shore remorseless! This Silver Phil is nothin' but shattered bones an' bleedin' pulp. He strikes the plains like he's come from the clouds an' is dead without a quiver.

" 'Bury him? No!' says Old Man Enright to Dave Tutt who asks the question. 'Let him find his bed where he falls.'

"While Enright speaks, an' as Dan rides up to us at the Red Light, a prompt raven drops down over where this Silver Phil is layin'. Then another raven an' another—black an' wide of wing—comes floatin' down. A coyote yells—first with the short, sharp yelp, an' then with that multiplied patter of laughter like forty wolves at once. That daylight howl of the coyote allers tells of a death. Shore, raven an' wolf is gatherin'. As Enright says: 'This yere Silver Phil ain't likely to be lonesome none to-night.'

" 'Did you kill him, Dan?' asks Faro Nell.

" 'Why, no, Nellie,' replies Dan, as he steps outen the stirrups an' beams on Faro Nell. She's still a bit onstrung, bein' only a little girl when all is said. 'Why, no, Nellie; I don't kill him spee-cific as Wolfville onderstands the word; but I dismisses him so effectual the kyard shore falls the same for Silver Phil.' "

Lewis' narrative often seems to ramble, and I have generally sought tales which were manifestly tight and purposeful. This does omit stories which can doubtless give pleasure to Lewis fanciers, either because they are less demanding on the score of trim narrative, or because they perceive method in his apparent randomness. In any event, his finest stories clearly balance cause and effect. His stories-within-stories, for example, balance tragedy with comedy, cowboy lore with eastern expectations, or, in the following case, Indian ways with white.

Lewis was, at least on one level, no friend of the Indian, let alone an admirer. The prissy and dogmatic and virtuous among us will simper that he was "prejudiced," and that in this enlightened day and age we must be intolerant of prejudice. The wise among us will be more patient—will read and think, and ponder the meaning of literary writings, and their uses.

And then they will read the section which follows "Johnny Florer's Axle Grease," and ask themselves whether the prissy and dogmatic and virtuous among us could have written those tales, or anything remotely comparable to them.

JOHNNY FLORER'S AXLE GREASE

It was the afternoon—cool and beautiful. I had been nursing my indolence with a cigar and one of the large arm-chairs which the veranda of the great hotel afforded. Now and then I considered within myself as to the whereabouts of my Old Cattleman, and was in a half humor to hunt him up. Just as my thoughts were hardening into decision in that behalf, a high, wavering note, evidently meant for song, came floating around the corner of the house, from the veranda on the end. The singer was out of range of eye, but I knew him for my aged friend. Thus he gave forth:

> "Dogville, Dogville!
> A tavern an' a still,
> That's all thar is in all Dog-ville."

"How do you feel today?" I asked as I took a chair near the venerable musician. "Happy and healthy, I trust?"

"Never feels better in my life," responded the Old Cattleman. "If I was to feel any better, I'd shorely go an' see a doctor."

"You are a singer, I observe."

"I'm melodious nacheral, but I'm gettin' so I sort o' stumbles in my notes. Shoutin' an' singin' 'round a passel of cattle to keep 'em from stampedin' on bad nights has sp'iled my voice, that a-way. Thar's nothin' so weakenin', vocal, as them efforts in the open air an' in the midst of the storms an' the elements. What for a song is that I'm renderin'? Son, I learns that ballad

long ago, back when I'm a boy in old Tennessee. It's writ, word
and music, by little Mollie Hines, who lives with her pap, old
Homer Hines, over on the 'Possum Trot. Mollie Hines is shore a
poet, an' has a mighty sight of fame, local. She's what you-all
might call a jo-darter of a poet, Mollie is; an' let anythin' touchin' or romantic happen anywhere along the 'Possum Trot, so as
to give her a subjeck, an' Mollie would be down on it, instanter,
like a fallin' star. She shorely is a verse maker, an' is known in
the Cumberland country as 'The Nightingale of Big Bone Lick.'
I remembers when a Shylock over to the Dudleytown bank fore-
closes a mortgage on old Homer Hines, an' offers his settlements
at public vandue that a-way, how Mollie prances out an' pours a
poem into the miscreant. Thar's a hundred an' 'leven verses into
it, an' each one like a bullet outen a Winchester. It goes like this:

> "Thar's a word to be uttered to the rich man in his pride.
> (Which a gent is frequent richest when it's jest before he died!)
> Thar's a word to be uttered to the hawg a-eatin' truck.
> (Which a hawg is frequent fattest when it's jest before he's stuck!)

"Mighty sperited epick, that! You recalls that English preacher
sharp that comes squanderin' 'round the tavern yere for his
health about a month ago? Shore! I knows you couldn't have
overlooked no bet like that divine. Well, that night in them par-
lors, when he reads some rhymes in a book,—whatever is that
piece he reads? Locksley Hall; right you be, son! As I was sayin',
when he's through renderin' said Locksley Hall, he comes buttin'
into a talk with me where I'm camped in a corner all cosy as a
toad onder a cabbage leaf, reecoverin' myse'f with licker from
them recitals of his, an' he says to me, this parson party does:

" 'Which it's shorely a set-back America has no poets,' says he.

" 'It's evident,' I says, 'that you never hears of Mollie Hines.'

" 'No, never once,' he replies; 'is this yere Miss Hines a poet?'

" 'Is Mollie Hines a poet!' I repeats, for my scorn at the mere
idee kind o' stiffens its knees an' takes to buckin' some. 'Mollie
Hines could make that Locksley Hall gent you was readin' from,
or even the party who writes Watt's Hymns, go to the diskyard.'

An' then I repeats some forty of them stanzas, whereof that one I jest now recites is a speciment.

"What does this pulpit gent say? He see I has him cinched, an' he's plumb mute. He confines himse'f to turnin' up his nose in disgust like Bill Storey does when his father-in-law horsewhips him."

Following this, the Old Cattleman and I wrapped ourselves in thoughtful smoke, for the space of five minutes, as ones who pondered the genius of "The Nightingale of Big Bone Lick"— Mollie Hines on the banks of the 'Possom Trot. At last my friend broke forth with a question.

"Whoever is them far-off folks you-all was tellin' me is related to Injuns?"

"The Japanese," I replied. "Undoubtedly the Indians and the Japanese are of the same stock."

"Which I'm foaled like a mule," said the old gentleman, "a complete prey to inborn notions ag'in Injuns. I wouldn't have one pesterin' 'round me more'n I'd eat offen the same plate with a snake. I shore has aversions to 'em a whole lot. Of course, I never sees them Japs, but I saveys Injuns from feathers to moccasins, an' comparin' Japs to Injuns, I feels about 'em like old Bill Rawlins says about his brother Jim's wife."

"And how was that?" I asked.

The afternoon was lazy and good, and I in a mood to listen to my rambling grey comrade talk of anybody or anything.

"It's this a-way," he began. "This yere Bill an' Jim Rawlins is brothers an' abides in Roanoke, Virginny. They splits up in their yooth, an' Jim goes p'intin' out for the West. Which he shore gets thar, an' nothin' is heard of him for forty years.

"Bill Rawlins, back in Roanoke, waxes a heap rich, an' at last cleans up his game an' resolves he takes a rest. Also he concloods to travel; an' as long as he's goin' to travel, he allows he'll sort o' go projectin' 'round an' see if he can't locate Jim.

"He gets a old an' musty tip about Jim, this Bill Rawlins does, an' it works out all right. Bill cuts Jim's trail 'way out yonder on the Slope at a meetropolis called Los Angeles. But this yere Jim ain't thar none. The folks tells Bill they reckons Jim is over to Virginny City.

"It's a month later, an' Bill is romancin' along on one of them Nevada mountain-meadow trails, when he happens upon a low, squatty dugout, the same bein' a camp rather than a house, an' belongs with a hay ranche. In the door is standin' a most ornery seemin' gent, with long, tangled ha'r an' beard, an' his clothes looks like he's shorely witnessed times. The hands of this ha'ry gent is in his pockets, an' he exhibits a mighty sooupercilious air. Bill pulls up his cayouse for a powwow.

" 'How far is it to a place where I can camp down for the night?' asks Bill.

" 'It's about twenty miles to the next wickeyup,' says the sooupercilious gent.

" 'Which I can't make it none to-night, then,' says Bill.

" 'Not on that hoss,' says the sooupercilious gent, for Bill's pony that a-way is plenty played.

" 'Mebby, then,' says Bill, 'I'd better bunk in yere.'

" 'You can gamble you-all don't sleep yere,' says the sooupercilious gent; 'none whatever!'

" 'An' why not?' asks Bill.

" 'Because I won't let you,' says the sooupercilious gent, a-bitin' off a piece of tobacco. 'This is my camp, an' force'ble invasions by casooal hold-ups like you, don't preevail with me a little bit. I resents the introosion on my privacy.'

" 'But I'll have to sleep on these yere plains,' says Bill a heap plaintif.

" 'Thar's better sports than you-all slept on them plains,' says the sooupercilious gent.

"Meanwhile, thar's a move or two, speshully the way he bats his eyes, about this sooupercilious gent that sets Bill to rummagin' 'round in his mem'ry. At last he asks:

" 'Is your name Rawlins?'

" 'Yes, sir, my name's Rawlins,' says the sooupercilious gent.

" 'Jim Rawlins of Roanoke?'

" 'Jim Rawlins of Roanoke;' an' the soopercilious gent reaches inside the door of the dugout, searches forth a rifle an' pumps a cartridge into the bar'l.

" 'Stan' your hand, Jim!' says Bill, at the same time slidin' to the ground with the hoss between him an' his relatif; 'don't get impetyoous. I'm your brother Bill.'

" 'What!' says the soopercilious gent, abandonin' them hostile measures, an' joy settlin' over his face. 'What!' he says; 'you my brother Bill? Well, don't that beat grizzly b'ars amazin'! Come in, Bill, an' rest your hat. Which it's simply the tenderness of hell I don't miss you.'

"Whereupon Bill an' Jim tracks along inside an' goes to canvassin' up an' down as to what ensooes doorin' them forty years they've been parted. Jim wants to know all about Roanoke an' how things stacks up in old Virginny, an' he's chuckin' in his questions plenty rapid.

"While Bill's replyin', his eye is caught by a frightful-lookin' female who goes slyin' in an' out, a-organizin' of some grub. She's the color of a saddle, an' Bill can't make out whether she's a white, a Mexican, a Digger Injun or a nigger. An' she's that hideous, this female is, she comes mighty near givin' Bill heart failure. Son, you-all can't have no idee how turrible this person looks. She's so ugly the flies won't light on her. Yes, sir! ugly enough to bring sickness into a fam'ly. Bill can feel all sorts o' horrors stampedin' about in his frame as he gazes on her. Her eyes looks like two bullet holes in a board, an' the rest of her feachers is tetotaciously indeescrib'ble. Bill's intellects at the awful sight of this yere person almost loses their formation, as army gents would say. At last Bill gets in a question on his rapid-fire relatif, who's shootin' him up with queries touchin' Roanoke to beat a royal flush.

" 'Jim,' says Bill, sort o' scared like, 'whoever is this yere lady who's roamin' the scene?'

" 'Well, thar now!' says Jim, like he's plumb disgusted, 'I hope my gun may hang fire, if I don't forget to introdooce you! Bill, that's my wife.'

"Then Jim goes surgin' off all spraddled out about the noomerous an' manifest excellencies of this female, an' holds forth alarmin' of an' concernin' her virchoos an' loveliness of face an' form, an' all to sech a scand'lous degree, Bill has to step outdoors to blush.

" 'An', Bill,' goes on Jim, an' he's plumb rapturous, that a-way, 'may I never hold three of a kind ag'in, if she ain't got a sister who's as much like her as two poker chips. I'm co'tin' both of 'em mighty near four years before ever I can make up my mind whichever of 'em I needs. They're both so absolootely sim'lar for beauty, an' both that aloorin' to the heart, I simply can't tell how to set my stack down. At last, after four years, I ups an' cuts the kyards for it, an' wins out this one.'

" 'Well, Jim,' says Bill, who's been settin' thar shudderin' through them rhapsodies, an' now an' then gettin' a glimpse of this yere female with the tail of his eye: 'Well, Jim, far be it from me, an' me your brother, to go avouchin' views to make you feel doobious of your choice. But candor's got the drop on me an' compels me to speak my thoughts. I never sees this sister of your wife, Jim, but jest the same, I'd a heap sight rather have her.'

"An' as I observes previous," concluded the old gentleman, "I feels about Japs an' Injuns like Bill does about Jim's wife that time. I never sees no Japs, but I'd a mighty sight rather have 'em."

There was another pause after this, and cigars were produced. For a time the smoke curled in silence. Then my friend again took up discussion.

"Thar comes few Injuns investigatin' into Wolfville. Doorin' them emutes of Cochise, an' Geronimo, an' Nana, the Apaches goes No'th an' South clost in by that camp of ours, but you bet! they're never that locoed as to rope once at Wolfville. We-all would shorely have admired to entertain them hostiles; but as I su'gests, they're a heap too enlightened to give us a chance.

"Savages never finds much encouragement to come ha'ntin' about Wolfville. About the first visitin' Injun meets with a contreetemps; though this is inadvertent a heap an' not designed.

This buck, a Navajo, I takes it, from his feathers, has been pirootin' about for a day or two. At last I reckons he allows he'll eelope off into the foothills ag'in. As carryin' out them roode plans which he forms, he starts to scramble onto the Tucson stage jest as Old Monte's c'llectin' up his reins. But it don't go; Injuns is barred. The gyard, who's perched up in front next to Old Monte, pokes this yere aborigine in the middle of his face with the muzzle of his rifle; an' as the Injun goes tumblin', the stage starts, an' both wheels passes over him the longest way. That Injun gives a groan like twenty sinners, an' his lamp is out.

"Old Monte sets the brake an' climbs down an' sizes up the remainder. Then he gets back on the box, picks up his six hosses an' is gettin' out.

" 'Yere, you!' says French, who's the Wells-Fargo agent, a-callin' after Old Monte, 'come back an' either plant your game or pack it with you. I'm too busy a gent to let you or any other blinded drunkard go leavin' a fooneral at my door. Thar's enough to do here as it is, an' I don't want no dead Injuns on my hands.'

" 'Don't put him up thar an' go sp'ilin' them mail-bags,' howls Old Monte, as French an' a hoss-hustler from inside the corral lays hold of the Navajo to throw him on with the baggage.

" 'Then come down yere an' ride herd on the play yourse'f, you murderin' sot!' says French.

"An' with that, he shore cuts loose an' cusses Old Monte frightful; cusses till a cottonwood tree in front of the station sheds all its leaves, an' he deadens the grass for a hundred yards about.

" 'Promotin' a sepulcher in this rock-ribbed landscape,' says French, as Jack Moore comes up, kind o' apol'gisin' for his profane voylence at Old Monte; 'framin' up a tomb, I say, in this yere rock-ribbed landscape ain't no child's play, an' I'm not allowin' none for that homicide Monte to put no sech tasks on me. He knows the Wolfville roole. Every gent skins his own polecats an' plants his own prey.'

" 'That's whatever!' says Jack Moore, 'an' onless Old Monte is thirstin' for trouble in elab'rate forms, he acquiesces tharin.'

"With that Old Monte hitches the Navajo to the hind axle with

a lariat which French brings out, an' then the stage, with the
savage coastin' along behind, goes rackin' off to the No'th. Later,
Monte an' the passengers hangs this yere remainder up in a pine
tree, at an Injun crossin' in the hills, as a warnin'. Whether it's a
warnin' or no, we never learns; all that's shore is that the remainder an' the lariat is gone next day; but whatever idees the other
Injuns entertains of the play is, as I once hears a lecture sharp
promulgate, 'concealed with the customary stoicism of the American savage.'

"Most likely them antipathies of mine ag'in Injuns is a heap
enhanced by what I experiences back on the old Jones an' Plummer trail, when they was wont to stampede our herds as we goes
drivin' through the Injun Territory. Any little old dark night one
of them savages is liable to come skulkin' up on the wind'ard
side of the herd, flap a blanket, cut loose a yell, an' the next
second thar's a hundred an' twenty thousand dollars' worth of
property skally-hootin' off into space on frenzied hoofs. Next
day, them same ontootered children of the woods an' fields
would demand four bits for every head they he'ps round up an'
return to the bunch. It's a source of savage revenoo, troo; but
plumb irritatin'. Them Injuns corrals sometimes as much as a
hundred dollars by sech treacheries. An' then we-all has to rest
over one day to win it back at poker.

"Will Injuns gamble? Shore! an' to the limit at that! Of course,
bein', as you saveys, a benighted people that a-way, they're some
easy, havin' no more jedgment as to the valyoo of a hand than
Steve Stevenson, an' Steve would take a pa'r of nines an' bet
'em higher than a cat's back. We allers recovers our *dinero,* but
thar's time an' sleep we lose an' don't get back.

"Yes, indeed, son, Injuns common is as ornery as soapweed.
The only good you-all can say of 'em is, they're nacheral-born
longhorns, is oncomplainin', an' saveys the West like my black
boy saveys licker. One time—this yere is 'way back in my Texas
days—one time I'm camped for long over on the Upper Hawg-
thief. It's rained a heap, an' bein' as I'm on low ground anyhow,
it gets that soft an' swampy where I be it would bog a butterfly.

For once I'm took sick; has a fever, that a-way. An' lose flesh! shorely you should have seen me! I falls off like persimmons after a frost, an' gets as ga'nt an' thin as a cow in April. So I allows I'll take a lay-off for a couple of months an' reecooperate some.

"Cossettin' an' pettin' of my health, as I states, I saddles up an' goes cavortin' over into the Osage nation to visit an old *compadre* of mine who's a trader thar by the name of Johnny Florer. This yere Florer is an old-timer with the Osages; been with 'em it's mighty likely twenty year at that time, an' is with 'em yet for all the notice I ever receives.

"On the o'casion of this ambassy of mine, I has a chance to study them savages, an' get a line on their char'cters a whole lot. This time I'm with Johnny, what you-all might call Osage upper circles is a heap torn by the ontoward rivalries of a brace of eminent bucks who's each strugglin' to lead the fashion for the tribe an' raise the other out.

"Them Osages, while blanket Injuns, is plumb opulent. Thar's sixteen hundred of 'em, an' they has to themse'fs 1,500,000 acres of as good land as ever comes slippin' from the palm of the Infinite. Also, the gov'ment is weak-minded enough to confer on every one of 'em, each buck drawin' the *dinero* for his family, a hundred an' forty big iron dollars anyooally. Wherefore, as I observes, them Osages is plenty strong, financial.

"There yere two high-rollin' bucks I speaks of, who's strugglin' for the social soopremacy, is in the midst of them strifes while I'm visitin' Florer. It's some two moons prior when one of 'em, which we'll call him the 'Astor Injun,' takes a heavy fall out of the opp'sition by goin' over to Cherryvale an' buyin' a sooperannuated two-seat Rockaway buggy. To this he hooks up a span of ponies, loads in his squaws, an' p'rades 'round from Pawhusky to Greyhoss—the same bein' a couple of Osage camps—an' tharby redooces the enemy—what we'll name the 'Vanderbilt Injuns'—to desp'ration. The Astor savage shorely has the call with that Rockaway.

"But the Vanderbilt Osage is a heap hard to down. He takes one look at the Astor Injun's Rockaway with all its blindin' splendors, an' then goes streakin' it for Cherryvale, like a drunkard to a barbecue. An' he sees the Rockaway an' goes it several better. What do you-all reckon now that savage equips himse'f with? He wins out a hearse, a good big black roomy hearse, with ploomes onto it an' glass winders in the sides.

"As soon as ever this Vanderbilt Injun stiffens his hand with the hearse, he comes troopin' back to camp with it, himse'f on the box drivin', an' puttin' on enough of lordly dog to make a pack of hounds. Which he shorely squelches the Astors; they jest simply lay down an' wept at sech grandeur. Their Rockaway ain't one, two, three,—ain't in the money.

"An' every day the Vanderbilt Injun would load his squaws an' papooses inside the hearse, an' thar, wropped in their blankets an' squattin' on the floor of the hearse for seats, they would be lookin' out o' the winders at common savages who ain't in it an' don't have no hearse. Meanwhiles, the buck Vanderbilt is drivin' the outfit all over an' 'round the cantonments, the entire bunch as sassy an' as flippant as a coop o' catbirds. It's all the Astors can do to keep from goin' plumb locoed. The Vanderbilts win.

"One mornin', when Florer an' me has jest run our brands onto the fourth drink, an old buck comes trailin' into the store. His blanket is pulled over his head, an' he's pantin' an' givin' it out he's powerful ill.

" 'How is my father?' says Johnny in Osage.

" 'Oh, my son,' says the Injun, placin' one hand on his stomach, an' all mighty tender, 'your father is plenty sick. Your father gets up this mornin', an' his heart is very bad. You must give him medicine or your father will die.'

"Johnny passes the invalid a cinnamon stick an' exhorts him to chew on that, which he does prompt an' satisfactory, like cattle on their cud. This cinnamon keeps him steady for 'most five minutes.

" 'Whatever is the matter with this savage?' I asks of Johnny.

" 'Nothin' partic'lar,' says Johnny. 'Last night he comes pushin' in yere an' buys a bottle of Worcestershire sauce; an' then he gets gaudy an' quaffs it all up on a theery she's a new-fangled fire water. He gets away with the entire bottle. It's now he realizes them errors, an' takes to groanin' an' allowin' it gives him a bad heart. Which I should shorely admit as much!'

" 'Your father is worse,' says the Osage, as he comes cuttin' in on Johnny ag'in. 'Must have stronger medicine. That medicine,' holdin' up some of the cinnamon, 'that not bad enough.'

"At this, Johnny passes his 'father' over a double handful of black pepper before it's ground.

" 'Let my father get away with that,' says Johnny, 'an' he'll feel like a bird. It will make him gay an' full of p'isen, like a rattlesnake in August.'

"Out to the r'ar of Johnny's store is piled up onder a shed more'n two thousand boxes of axle grease. It was sent into the nation consigned to Johnny by some ill-advised sports in New York, who figgers that because the Osages as a tribe abounds in wagons, thar must shorely be a market for axle grease. That's where them New York persons misses the ford a lot. Them savages has wagons, troo; but they no more thinks of greasin' them axles than paintin' the runnin' gear. They never goes ag'inst that axle grease game for so much as a single box; said ointment is a drug. When he don't dispose of it none, Johnny stores it out onder a shed some twenty rods away, an' regyards it as a total loss.

" 'Axle grease,' says Johnny, 'makes a p'int in civilization to which the savage has not yet clambered, an' them optimists, East, who sends it on yere, should have never made no sech break.'

"Mebby it's because this axle grease grows sullen an' feels neglected that a-way; mebby it's the heats of two summers an' the frosts of two winters which sp'iles its disp'sition; shore it is at any rate that at the time I'm thar, that onguent seems fretted to the core, an' is givin' forth a protestin' fragrance that has stood off a coyote an' made him quit at a distance of two hundred yards. You might even say it has caused Nacher herse'f to pause an' catch her breath.

"It's when the ailin' Osage, whose malady is too deep-seated to be reached by cinnamon or pimento, comes frontin' up for a third preescription, that the axle grease idee seizes Johnny.

" 'Father,' says Johnny, 'come with me. Your son will now saw off some big medicine on you; a medicine meant for full-blown gents like you an' me. Come, father, come with your son, an' you shall be cured in half the time it takes to run a loop on a lariat.'

"Johnny breaks open one of the axle grease boxes, arms the savage with a chip for a spoon, an' exhorts him to cut in on it a whole lot.

"Son, the odors of them wares is awful; Kansas butter is violets to it; but it never flutters that Osage. He takes Johnny's chip an' goes to work, spadin' that axle grease into his mouth, like he ain't got a minute to live. When he's got away with half the box, he tucks the balance onder his blanket an' retires to his teepee with a look of gratitoode on his face. His heart has ceased to be bad, an' them illnesses, which aforetime has him on the go, sur-renders to the powers of this yere new medicine like willows to the wind. With this, he goes caperin' out for his camp, idly hum-min' a war song, sech is his relief.

"An' here's where Johnny gets action on that axle grease. It shorely teaches, also, the excellence of them maxims, 'Cast your bread upon the waters an' you'll be on velvet before many days.' Within two hours a couple of this sick buck's squaws comes sidlin' up to Johnny an' desires axle grease. It's quoted at four bits a box, an' the squaws changes in five pesos an' beats a retreat, carryin' away ten boxes. Then the fame of this big, new medicine spreads; that axle grease becomes plenty pop'lar. Other bucks an' other squaws shows up, changes in their money, an' is made happy with axle grease. They never has sech a time, them Osages don't, since the battle of the Hoss-shoe. Son, they packs it off in blankets, freights it away in wagons. They turns loose on a reg'lar axle grease spree. In a week every box is sold, an' thar's orders stacked up on Florer's desk for two kyar-loads more, which is bein' hurried on from the East. Even the Injuns' agent gets wrought up about it, an' begins to bellow an' paw 'round by way of compliments to Johnny. He makes Johnny a speech.

" 'Which I've made your excellent discovery, Mr. Florer,' says this agent, 'the basis of a report to the gov'ment at Washin'ton. I sets forth the mad passion of these yere Osages for axle grease as a condiment, a beverage, an' a cure. I explains the tribal leanin' that exists for that speshul axle grease which is crowned with years, an' owns a strength which comes only as the cor'lary of hard experience. Axle grease is like music an' sooths the savage breast. It is oil on the troubled waters of aboriginal existence. Its feet is the feet of peace. At the touch of axle grease the hostile abandons the war path an' surrenders himse'f. He washes off his paint an' becometh with axle grease as the lamb that bleateth. The greatest possible uprisin' could be quelled with a consignment of axle grease. Mr. Florer, I congratulate you. From a humble storekeep, sellin' soap, herrin' an' salt hoss, you takes your stand from now with the ph'lanthropists an' leaders among men. You have conjoined Injuns an' axle grease. For centuries the savage has been a problem which has defied gov'ment. He will do so no more. Mr. Florer, you have solved the savage with axle grease.' "

Some Indian Tales

HOW THE RAVEN DIED

"Which if you-all is out to hear of Injuns, son," observed the Old Cattleman, doubtfully, "the best I can do is shet my eyes an' push along regyardless, like a cayouse in a storm of snow. But I don't guarantee no facts; none whatever! I never does bend myse'f to severe study of savages an' what notions I packs concernin' 'em is the casual frootes of what I accidental hears an' what I sees. It's only now an' then, as I observes former, that Injuns invades Wolfville; an' when they does, we-all scowls 'em outen camp—sort o' makes a sour front, so as to break 'em early of habits of visitin' us. We shore don't hone none to have 'em hankerin' 'round.

"Nacherally, I makes no doubt that if you goes clost to Injuns an' studies their little game you finds some of 'em good an' some bad, some gaudy an' some sedate, some cu'rous an' some indifferent, same as you finds among shore-enough folks. It's so with mules an' broncos; wherefore, then, may not these differences exist among Injuns? Come squar' to the turn, you-all finds white folks separated the same. Some gents follows off one waggon track an' some another; some even makes a new trail.

"Speakin' of what's opposite in folks, I one time an' ag'in sees two white chiefs of scouts who frequent comes pirootin' into Wolfville from the Fort. Each has mebby a score of Injuns at his

heels who pertains to him personal. One of these scout chiefs is
all buck-skins, fringes, beads an' feathers from y'ears to hocks,
while t'other goes garbed in a stiff hat with a little jim crow rim—
one of them kind you deenom'nates as a darby—an' a diag'nal
overcoat; one chief looks like a dime novel on a spree an' t'other
as much like the far East as he saveys how. An' yet, son, this
voylent person in buckskins is a Second Lootenent—a mere boy,
he is—from West P'int; while that outcast in the reedic'lous hat
is foaled on the plains an' never does go that clost to the risin'
sun as to glimpse the old Missouri. The last form of maverick
bursts frequent into Western bloom; it's their ambition, that a-
way, to deloode you into deemin' 'em as fresh from the States
as one of them tomatter airtights.

"Thar's old gent Jeffords; he's that sort. Old Jeffords lives for
long with the Apaches; he's found among 'em when Gen'ral
Crook—the old 'Grey Fox'—an' civilisation and gatlin' guns
comes into Arizona arm in arm. I used to note old Jeffords hiber-
natin' about the Oriental over in Tucson. I shore reckons he's
procrastinatin' about thar yet, if the Great Sperit ain't done
called him in. As I says, old Jeffords is that long among the
Apaches back in Cochise's time that the mem'ry of man don't
run none to the contrary. An' yet no gent ever sees old Jeffords
wearin' anything more savage than a long-tail black surtoot an'
one of them stove pipe hats. Is Jeffords dangerous? No, you-all
couldn't call him a distinct peril; still, folks who goes devotin'
themse'fs to stirrin' Jeffords up jest to see if he's alive gets disas-
terous action. He has long grey ha'r an' a tangled white beard
half-way down his front; an' with that old plug hat an' black
coat he's a sight to frighten children or sour milk! Still, Jeffords
is all right. As long as towerists an' other inquisitive people don't
go pesterin' Jeffords, he shore lets 'em alone. Otherwise, you
might as well be up the same saplin' with a cinnamon b'ar;
which you'd most likely hear something drop a lot!

"For myse'f, I likes old Jeffords, an' considers him a pleasin'
conundrum. About tenth drink time he'd take a cha'r an' go
camp by himse'f in a far corner, an' thar he'd warble hymns.

Many a time as I files away my nosepaint in the Oriental have I been regaled with,

> Jesus, Lover of my soul,
> Let me to Thy bosom fly,
> While the nearer waters roll,
> While the tempest still is high,

as emanatin' from Jeffords where he's r'ared back conductin' some personal services. Folks never goes buttin' in interferin' with these concerts; which it's cheaper to let him sing.

"Speakin' of Injuns, as I su'gests, I never does see over-much of 'em in Wolfville. An' my earlier experiences ain't thronged with 'em neither, though while I'm workin' cattle along the Red River I does carom on Injuns more or less. Thar's one old hostile I recalls speshul; he's a fool Injun called Black Feather;—Choctaw, he is. This Black Feather's weakness is fire-water; he thinks more of it than some folks does of children.

"Black Feather used to cross over to where Dick Stocton maintains a store an' licker house on the Upper Hawgthief. Of course, no gent sells these Injuns licker. It's ag'in the law; an' onless you-all is onusual eager to make a trip to Fort Smith with a marshal ridin' herd on you doorin' said visit, impartin' of nosepaint to aborigines is a good thing not to do. But Black Feather, he'd come over to Dick Stocton's an' linger 'round the bar'ls of Valley Tan, an' take a chance on stealin' a snifter or two while Stocton's busy.

"At last Stocton gets tired an' allows he'll lay for Black Feather. This yere Stocton is a mighty reckless sport; he ain't carin' much whatever he does do; he hates Injuns an' shot guns, an' loves licker, seven-up, an' sin in any form; them's Stocton's prime characteristics. An' he gets mighty weary of the whiskey-thievin' Black Feather, an' lays for him.

"One evenin' this aggravatin' Black Feather crosses over an' takes to ha'ntin' about Dick Stocton's licker room as is his wont. It looks like Black Feather has already been buyin' whiskey of one of them boot-laig parties who takes every chance an' goes among the Injuns an' sells 'em nosepaint on the sly. 'Fore ever

he shows up on the Upper Hawgthief that time, this Black Feather
gets nosepaint some'ers an' puts a whole quart of it away in the
shade; an' he shore exhibits symptoms. Which for one thing he
feels about four stories tall!

"Stocton sets a trap for Black Feather. He fills up the tin cup
into which he draws that Valley Tan with coal-oil—karoseen
you-all calls it—an' leaves it, temptin' like, settin' on top a whiskey
bar'l. Shore! it's the first thing Black Feather notes. He sees his
chance an' grabs an' downs the karoseen; an' Stocton sort o'
startin' for him, this Black Feather gulps her down plump swift.
The next second he cuts loose the yell of that year, burns up
about ten acres of land, and starts for Red River. No, I don't
know whether the karoseen hurts him none or not; but he
certainly goes squatterin' across the old Red River like a wounded
wild-duck, an' he never does come back no more.

"But, son, as you sees, I don't know nothin' speshul or much
touchin' Injuns, an' if I'm to dodge the disgrace of ramblin'
along in this desultory way, I might better shift to a tale I hears
Sioux Sam relate to Doc Peets one time in the Red Light. This
Sam is a Sioux, an a mighty decent buck, considerin' he's Injun;
Sam is servin' the Great Father as a scout with the diag'nal-coat,
darby-hat sharp I mentions. Peets gives this saddle-tinted longhorn a 4-bit piece, an' he tells this yarn. It sounds plenty childish; but you oughter b'ar in mind that savages, mental, ain't no
bigger nor older than ten year old young-ones among the pale-
faces.

" 'This is the story my mother tells me,' says Sioux Sam, 'to
show me the evils of cur'osity. "The Great Sperit allows to every
one the right to ask only so many questions," says my mother,
"an' when they ask one more than is their right, they die."

" 'This is the story of the fate of Kaw-kaw-chee, the Raven, a
Sioux Chief who died long ago exackly as my mother told me.
The Raven died because he asked too many questions an' was
too cur'ous. It began when Sublette, who was a trader, came up
the Mitchi-zoor-rah, the Big-Muddy, an' was robbed by the Ra-

ven's people. Sublette was mad at this, an' said next time he would bring the Sioux a present so they would not rob him. So he brought a little cask of fire-water an' left it on the bank of the Big-Muddy. Then Sublette went away, an' twenty of the Raven's young men found the little cask. An' they were greedy an' did not tell the camp; they drank the fire-water where it was found.

" 'The Raven missed his twenty young men an' when he went to spy for them, behold! they were dead with their teeth locked tight an' their faces an' bodies writhen an' twisted as the whirl-wind twists the cottonwoods. Then the Raven thought an' thought; an' he got very cur'ous to know why his young men died so writhen an' twisted. The fire-water had a whirlwind in it, an' the Raven was eager to hear. So he sent for Sublette.

" 'Then the Raven an' Sublette had a big talk. They agreed not to hurt each other; an' Sublette was to come an' go an' trade with the Sioux; an' they would never rob him.

" 'At this, Sublette gave the Raven some of the whirlwind that so killed an' twisted the twenty young men. It was a powder, white; an' it had no smell. Sublette said its taste was bitter; but the Raven must not taste it or it would lock up his teeth an' twist an' kill him. For to swallow the white powder loosed the whirlwind on the man's heart an' it bent him an' twisted him like the storms among the willows.

" 'But the Raven could give the powder to others. So the Raven gave it in some deer's meat to his two squaws; an' they were twisted till they died; an' when they would speak they couldn't, for their teeth were held tight together an' no words came out of their mouths,—only a great foam. Then the Raven gave it to others that he did not love; they were twisted an' died. At last there was no more of the powder of the whirlwind; the Raven must wait till Sublette came up the Big-Muddy again an' brought him more.

" 'There was a man, the Gray Elk, who was of the Raven's people. The Gray Elk was a Choo-ayk-eed, a great prophet. And the Gray Elk had a wife; she was wise an' beautiful, an' her name was Squaw-who-has-dreams. But Gray Elk called her Kee-nee-moo-sha, the Sweetheart.

" 'While the Raven waited for Sublette to bring him more powder of the whirlwind, a star with a long tail came into the sky. This star with the tail made the Raven heap cur'ous. He asked Gray Elk to tell him about it, for he was a prophet. The Raven asked many questions; they fell from him like leaves from a tree in the month of the first ice. So the Gray Elk called Chee-bee, the Spirit; an' the Spirit told the Gray Elk. Then the Gray Elk told the Raven.'

" 'It was not a tail, it was blood—star blood; an' the star had been bit an' was wounded, but would get well. The Sun was the father of the stars, an' the Moon was their mother. The Sun, Gheezis, tried ever to pursue an' capture an' eat his children, the stars. So the stars all ran an' hid when the Sun was about. But the stars loved their mother who was good an' never hurt them; an' when the Sun went to sleep at night an' Coush-ee-wan, the Darkness, shut his eyes, the Moon an' her children came together to see each other. But the star that bled had been caught by the Sun; it got out of his mouth but was wounded. Now it was frightened, so it always kept its face to where the Sun was sleeping over in the west. The bleeding star, Sch-coo-dah, would get well an' its wound would heal.

" 'Then the Raven wanted to know how the Gray Elk knew all this. An' the Gray Elk had the Raven into the medicine lodge that night; an' the Raven heard the spirits come about an' heard their voices; but he could not understand. Also, the Raven saw a wolf all fire, with wings like the eagle which flew overhead. Also he heard the Thunder, Boom-wa-wa, talking with the Gray Elk; but the Raven couldn't understand. The Gray Elk told the Raven to draw his knife an' stab with it in the air outside the medicine lodge. An' when he did, the Raven's blade an' hand came back covered with blood. Still, the Raven was cur'ous an' kept askin' to be told how the Gray Elk knew these things. An' the Gray Elk at last took the Raven to the Great Bachelor Syca-

more that lived alone, an' asked the Raven if the Bachelor Syca-
more was growing. An' the Raven said it was. Then Gray Elk
asked him how he knew it was growing. An' the Raven said he
didn't know. Then Gray Elk said he did not know how he knew
about Sch-coo-dah, the star that was bit. This made the Raven
angry, for he was very cur'ous; an' he thought the Gray Elk had
two tongues.

" 'Then it came the month of the first young grass an' Sublette
was back for furs. Also he brought many goods; an' he gave to
the Raven more of the powder of the whirlwind in a little box.
At once the Raven made a feast of ducks for the Gray Elk; an'
he gave him of the whirlwind powder; an' at once his teeth came
together an' the Gray Elk was twisted till he died.

" 'Now no one knew that the Raven had the powder of the
whirlwind, so they could not tell why all these people were
twisted and went to the Great Spirit. But the Squaw-who-has-
dreams saw that it was the Raven who killed her husband, the
Gray Elk, in a vision. Then the Squaw-who-has-dreams went into
the mountains four days an' talked with Moh-kwa, the Bear who
is the wisest of the beasts. The Bear said it was the Raven who
killed the Gray Elk an' told the Squaw-who-has-dreams of the
powder of the whirlwind.

" 'Then the Bear an' the Squaw-who-has-dreams made a fire
an' smoked an' laid a plot. The Bear did not know where to find
the powder of the whirlwind which the Raven kept always in a
secret place. But the Bear told the Squaw-who-has-dreams that
she should marry the Raven an' watch until she found where the
powder of the whirlwind was kept in its secret place; an' then
she was to give some to the Raven, an' he, too, would be twisted
an' die. There was a great danger, though; the Raven would, after
the one day when they were wedded, want to kill the Squaw-
who-has-dreams. So to protect her, the Bear told her she must
begin to tell the Raven the moment she was married to him the
Story-that-never-ends. Then, because the Raven was more cur'ous
than even he was cruel, he would put off an' put off giving the
powder of the whirlwind to the Squaw-who-has-dreams, hoping

to hear the end of the Story-that-never-ends. Meanwhile the Squaw-who-has-dreams was to watch the Raven until she found the powder of the whirlwind in its secret place.

" 'Then the wise Bear gave the Squaw-who-has-dreams a bowlful of words as seed, so she might plant them an' raise a crop of talk to tell the Story-that-never-ends. An' the Squaw-who-has-dreams planted the seed-words, an' they grew an' grew an' she gathered sixteen bundles of talk an' brought them to her wigwam. After that she put beads in her hair, an' dyed her lips red, an' rubbed red on her cheeks, an' put on a new blanket; an' when the Raven saw her, he asked her to marry him. So they were wedded; an' the Squaw-who-has-dreams went to the teepee of the Raven an' was his wife.

" 'But the Raven was old an' cunning like Yah-mee-kee, the Beaver, an' he said, "He is not wise who keeps a squaw too long!" An' with that he thought he would kill the Squaw-who-has-dreams the next day with the powder of the whirlwind. But the Squaw-who-has-dreams first told the Raven that she hated When-dee-goo, the Giant; an' that she should not love the Raven until he had killed When-dee-goo. She knew the Giant was too big an' strong for the Raven to kill with his lance, an' that he must get his powder of the whirlwind; she would watch him an' learn its secret place. The Raven said he would kill the Giant as the sun went down next day.

" 'Then the Squaw-who-has-dreams told the Raven the first of the Story-that-never-ends an' used up one bundle of talk; an' when the story ended for that night, the Squaw-who-has-dreams was saying: "An' so, out of the lake that was red as the sun came a great fish that was green, with yellow wings, an' it walked also with feet, an' it came up to me an' said:" But then she would tell no more that night; nor could the Raven, who was crazy with cur'osity, prevail on her. "I must now sleep an' dream what the green fish with the yellow wings said," was the reply of the Squaw-who-has-dreams, an' she pretended to slumber. So the Raven, because he was cur'ous, put off her death.

" 'All night she watched, but the Raven did not go to the

secret place where he had hidden the powder of the whirlwind.
Nor the next day, when the sun went down, did the Raven kill
the Giant. But the Squaw-who-has-dreams took up again the
Story-that-never-ends an' told what the green fish with the yellow
wings said; an' she used up the second bundle of talk. When she
ceased for that time, the Squaw-who-has-dreams was saying:
"An' as night fell, Moh-kwa, the Bear, called to me from his
canyon, an' said for me to come an' he would show me where
the great treasure of fire-water was buried for you who are the
Raven. So I went into the canyon, an' Moh-kwa, the Bear, took
me by the hand an' led me to the treasure of fire-water which
was greater an' richer than was ever seen by any Sioux."

" 'Then the Squaw-who-has-dreams would tell no more that
night, while the Raven eat his fingers with cur'osity. But he
made up a new plan not to twist the Squaw-who-has-dreams until she showed him the treasure of fire-water an' told him the
end of the Story-that-never-ends. On her part, however, the
Squaw-who-has-dreams, as she went to sleep, wept an' tore the
beads from her hair an' said the Raven did not love her; for he
had not killed the Giant as he promised. She said she would tell
no more of the Story-that-never-ends until the Giant was dead;
nor would she show to a husband who did not love her the great
treasure of fire-water which Moh-kwa, the Bear, had found. At
this, the Raven who was hot to have the treasure of fire-water
an' whose ears rang with cur'osity to hear the end of the Story-
that-never-ends saw that he must kill the Giant. Therefore, when
the Squaw-who-has-dreams had ceased to sob and revile him, an'
was gone as he thought asleep, the Raven went to his secret place
where he kept the powder of the whirlwind an' took a little an'
wrapped it in a leaf an' hid the leaf in the braids of his long hair.
Then the Raven went to sleep.

" 'When the Raven was asleep the Squaw-who-has-dreams went
also herself to the secret place an' got also a little of the powder
of the whirlwind. An' the next morning she arose early an' gave
the powder of the whirlwind to the Raven on the roast buffalo,
the Pez-hee-kee, which was his food.

" 'When the Raven had eaten, the Squaw-who-has-dreams went out of the teepee among the people an' called all the Sioux to come an' see the Raven die. So the Sioux came gladly, and the Raven was twisted an' writhen with the power of the whirlwind wrenching at his heart; an' his teeth were tight like a trap; an' no words, but only foam, came from his mouth; an' at last the Spirit, the Chee-bee, was twisted out of the Raven; an' the Squaw-who-has-dreams was revenged for the death of the Gray Elk whom she loved an' who always called her Kee-nee-moo-sha, the Sweetheart, because it made her laugh.

" 'When the Raven was dead, the Squaw-who-has-dreams went to the secret place an' threw the powder of the whirlwind into the Big-Muddy; an' after that she distributed her fourteen bundles of talk that were left among all the Sioux so that everybody could tell how glad he felt because the Raven was twisted and died. An' for a week there was nothing but happiness an' big talk among the Sioux; an' Moh-kwa, the Bear, came laughing out of his canyon with the wonder of listening to it; while the Squaw-who-has-dreams now, when her revenge was done, went with When-dee-goo, the Giant, to his teepee and became his squaw. So now everything was ended save the Story-that-never-ends.'

"When Sioux Sam gets this far," concluded the Old Cattleman, "he says, 'an' my mother's words at the end were: "An' boys who ask too many questions will die, as did the Raven whose cur'osity was even greater than his cruelty." ' "

"How the Raven Died" appeared in one of the Wolfville volumes: Wolfville Nights *(1902). But Lewis treasured Sioux Sam, who was one of his narrators in a volume,* The Black Lion Inn *(1903)—a kind of Mermaid Tavern set-up, which he peopled with a number of storytellers, including the Old Cattleman. Sioux Sam also told the following tale:*

MOH - KWA AND THE THREE GIFTS

This is in the long time ago when the sun is younger an' not so big an' hot as now, an' Kwa-Sind, the Strong Man, is a chief of the Upper Yellowstone Sioux. It is on a day in the Moon-of-the-first-frost an' Moh-Kwa, the Wise Bear, is gathering black-berries an' filling his mouth. As Moh-Kwa pulls the bush towards him, he pierces his paw with a great thorn so that it makes him howl an' shout, for much is his rage an' pain. Moh-Kwa cannot get the great thorn out; because Moh-Kwa's claws while sharp an' strong are not fingers to pull out a thorn; an' the more Moh-Kwa bites his paw to get at the thorn, the further he pushes it in. At last Moh-Kwa sits growling an' looking at the thorn an' wondering what he is to do.

While Moh-Kwa is wondering an' growling, there comes walking Shaw-shaw, the Swallow, who is a young man of the Sioux. The Swallow has a good heart; but his spirit is light an' his nature as easily blown about on each new wind as a dead leaf. So the Sioux have no respect for the Swallow but laugh when he comes among them, an' some even call him Shau-goh-dah-wah, the Coward, for they do not look close, an' mistake lightness for fear.

When the Swallow came near, Moh-Kwa, still growling, held forth his paw an' showed the Swallow how the thorn was buried in the big pad so that he could not bite it out an' only made it go deeper. An' with that the Swallow, who had a good heart, took Moh-Kwa's big paw between his knees an' pulled out the great thorn; for the Swallow had fingers an' not claws like Moh-Kwa, an' the Swallow's fingers were deft an' nimble to do any desired deed.

When Moh-Kwa felt the relief of that great thorn out of his paw, he was grateful to the Swallow an' thought to do him a favor.

"You are laughed at," said Moh-Kwa to the Swallow, "because your spirit is light as dead leaves an' too much blown about like a tumbleweed wasting its seeds in foolish travelings to go no-where for no purpose so that only it goes. Your heart is good, but your work is of no consequence, an' your name will win no respect; an' with years you will be hated since you will do no great deeds. Already men call you Shau-goh-dah-wah, the Cow-ard. I am Moh-Kwa, the Wise Bear of the Yellowstone, an' I would do you a favor for taking my paw an' the thorn apart. But I cannot change your nature; only Pau-guk, the Death, can do that; an' no man may touch Pau-guk an' live. Yet for a favor I will give you three gifts, which if you keep safe will make you rich an' strong an' happy; an' all men will love you an' no longer think to call you Shau-goh-dah-wah, the Coward."

Moh-Kwa when he had ended this long talk, licked his paw where had been the great thorn, an' now that the smart was gone an' he could put his foot to the ground an' not howl, he took the Swallow an' carried him to his house in the rocks. An' Moh-Kwa gave the Swallow a knife, a necklace of bear-claws, an' a buffalo robe.

"While you carry the knife," said Moh-Kwa, "all men will re-spect an' fear you an' the squaws will cherish you in their hearts. While you wear the bear-claws, you will be brave an' strong, an' whatever you want you will get. As for the skin of the buffalo, it is big medicine, an' if you sit upon it an' wish, it will carry you wherever you ask to go."

Besides the knife, the bear-claws an' the big medicine robe, Moh-Kwa gave the Swallow the thorn he had pulled from his foot, telling him to sew it in his moccasin, an' when he was in trouble it would bring Moh-Kwa to him to be a help. Also, Moh-Kwa warned the Swallow to beware of a cunning squaw.

"For," said Moh-Kwa, "your nature is light like dead leaves, an' such as you seek ever to be a fool about a cunning squaw."

When the Swallow came again among the Sioux he wore the knife an' the bear-claws that Moh-Kwa had given him; an' in his lodge he spread the big medicine robe. An' because of the knife an' the bear-claws, the warriors respected an' feared him, an' the squaws loved him in their hearts an' followed where he went with their eyes. Also, when he wanted anything, the Swallow ever got it; an' as he was swift an' ready to want things, the Swallow grew quickly rich among the Sioux, an' his lodge was full of robes an' furs an' weapons an' new dresses of skins an' feathers, while more than fifty ponies ate the grass about it.

Now, this made Kwa-Sind, the Strong Man, angry in his soul's soul; for Kwa-Sind was a mighty Sioux, an' had killed a Pawnee for each of his fingers, an' a Blackfoot an' a Crow for each of his toes, an' it made his breast sore to see the Swallow, who had been also called Shau-goh-dah-wah, the Coward, thought higher among the Sioux an' be a richer man than himself. Yet Kwa-Sind was afraid to kill the Swallow lest the Sioux who now sung the Swallow's praises should rise against him for revenge.

Kwa-Sind told his hate to Wah-bee-noh, who was a medicine man an' juggler, an' agreed that he would give Wah-bee-noh twenty ponies to make the Swallow again as he was so that the Sioux would laugh at him an' call him Shau-goh-dah-wah, the Coward.

Wah-bee-noh, the medicine man, was glad to hear the offer of Kwa-Sind, for he was a miser an' thought only how he might add another pony to his herd. Wah-bee-noh told Kwa-Sind he would surely do as he asked, an' that the Swallow within three moons would be despised among all the Sioux.

Wah-bee-noh went to his lodge an' made his strongest medicine an' called Jee-bi, the Spirit. An' Jee-bi, the Spirit, told Wah-bee-noh of the Swallow's knife an' bear-claws an' the medicine robe.

An' now Wah-bee-noh made a plan an' gave it to his daughter who was called Oh-pee-chee, the Robin, to carry out; for the

Robin was full of craft an' cunning, an' moreover, beautiful among the young girls of the Sioux.

The Robin dressed herself until she was like the red bird; an' then she walked up an' down in front of the lodge of the Swallow. An' when the Swallow saw her, his nature which was light as dead leaves at once became drawn to the Robin, an' the Swallow laughed an' made a place by his side for the Robin to sit down. With that the Robin came an' sat by his side; an' after a little she sang to him Ewah-yeah, the Sleep-song, an' the Swallow was overcome; his eyes closed an' slumber settled down upon him like a nightfog.

Then the Robin stole the knife from its sheath an' the bear-claws from about the neck of the Swallow; but the medicine robe the Robin could not get because the Swallow was asleep upon it, an' if she pulled it from beneath him he would wake up.

The Robin took the knife an' the bear-claws an' carried them to Wah-bee-noh, her father, who got twelve ponies from Kwa-Sind for them an' added the ponies to his herd. An' the heart of Wah-bee-noh danced the miser's dance of gain in his bosom from mere gladness; an' because he would have eight more ponies from Kwa-Sind, he sent the Robin back to steal the medicine robe when the Swallow should wake up.

The Robin went back, an' finding the Swallow still asleep on the medicine robe, lay down by his side; an' soon she too fell asleep, for the Robin was a very tired squaw since to be cunning an' full of craft is hard work an' soon wearies one.

When the Swallow woke up he missed his knife an' bear-claws. Also, he remembered that Moh-Kwa had warned him for the lightness of his spirit to beware of a cunning squaw. When these thoughts came to the Swallow, an' seeing the Robin still sleeping by his side, he knew well that she had stolen his knife an' bear-claws.

Now, the Swallow fell into a great anger an' thought an' thought what he should do to make the Robin return the knife an' bear-claws she had stolen. Without them the Sioux would laugh at him an' despise him as before, an' many would again call him Shau-goh-dah-wah, the Coward, an' the name bit into the Swallow's heart like a rattlesnake an' poisoned it with much grief.

While the Swallow thought an' the Robin still lay sleeping, a plan came to him; an' with that, the Swallow seeing he was with the Robin lying on the medicine robe, sat up an' wished that both himself an' the Robin were in a far land of rocks an' sand where a great pack of wolves lived.

Like the flash an' the flight of an arrow, the Swallow with the Robin still asleep by his side, an' with the medicine robe still beneath them on the ground, found himself in a desolate land of rocks an' sands, an' all about him came a band of wolves who yelped an' showed their teeth with the hunger that gnawed their flanks.

Because the wolves yelped, the Robin waked up; an' when she saw their white teeth shining with hunger she fell down from a big fear an' cried an' twisted one hand with the other, thinking Pau-guk, the Death, was on his way to get her. The Robin wept an' turned to the Swallow an' begged him to put her back before the lodge of Wah-bee-noh, her father.

But the Swallow, with the anger of him who is robbed, spoke hard words out of his mouth.

"Give me back the knife an' the bear-claws you have stolen. You are a bad squaw, full of cunning an' very crafty; but here I shall keep you an' feed you—legs an' arms an' head an' body—to my wolf-friends who yelp an' show their teeth out yonder, unless I have my knife an' bear-claws again."

This brought more fear on the Robin, an' she felt that the Swallow's words were as a shout for Pau-guk, the Death, to make haste an' claim her; yet her cunning was not stampeded but stood firm in her heart.

The Robin said that the Swallow must give her time to grow calm an' then she would find the knife an' bear-claws for him. While the Swallow waited, the Robin still wept an' sobbed for fear of the white teeth of the wolves who stood in a circle about them. But little by little, the crafty Robin turned her sobs softly

into Ewah-yeah, the Sleep-song; an' soon slumber again tied the
hands an' feet an' stole the eyes of the Swallow.

Now the Robin did not hesitate. She tore the big medicine
robe from beneath the Swallow; throwing herself into its folds,
the Robin wished herself again before Wah-bee-noh's lodge, an'
with that the robe rushed with her away across the skies like the
swoop of a hawk. The Swallow was only awake in time to see the
Robin go out of sight like a bee hunting its hive.

Now the Swallow was so cast down with shame that he thought
he would call Pau-guk, the Death, an' give himself to the wolves
who sat watching with their hungry eyes. But soon his heart
came back, an' his spirit which was light as dead leaves, stirred
about hopefully in his bosom.

While he considered what he should now do, helpless an'
hungry, in this desolate stretch of rocks an' sand an' no water,
the thorn which had been in Moh-Kwa's paw pricked his foot
where it lay sewed in his moccasin. With that the Swallow wished
he might only see the Wise Bear to tell him his troubles.

As the Swallow made this wish, an' as if to answer it, he saw
Moh-Kwa coming across the rocks an' the sand. When the wolves
saw Moh-Kwa, they gave a last howl an' ran for their hiding
places.

Moh-Kwa himself said nothing when he came up, an' the
Swallow spoke not for shame but lay quiet while Moh-Kwa took
him by the belt which was about his middle an' throwing him
over his shoulder as if the Swallow were a dead deer, galloped off
like the wind for his own house.

When Moh-Kwa had reached his house, he gave the Swallow a
piece of buffalo meat to eat. Then Moh-Kwa said:

"Because you would be a fool over a beautiful squaw who
was cunning, you have lost my three gifts that were your fortune
an' good fame. Still, because you were only a fool, I will get
them back for you. You must stay here, for you cannot help
since your spirit is as light as dead leaves, an' would not be steady
for so long a trail an' one which calls for so much care to follow."

Then Moh-Kwa went to the door of his house an' called his

three friends, Sug-gee-mah, the Mosquito, Sub-bee-kah-shee, the Spider, an' Wah-wah-tah-see, the Firefly; an' to these he said:

"Because you are great warriors an' fear nothing in your hearts I have called you."

An' at that, Wah-wah-tah-see, an' Sub-bee-kah-shee, an' Sug-gee-mah stood very straight an' high, for being little men it made them proud because so big a bear as Moh-Kwa had called them to be his help.

"To you, Sub-bee-kah-shee," said Moh-Kwa, turning to the Spider, "I leave Kwa-Sind; to you, Wah-wah-tah-see, the Firefly, falls the honor of slaying Wah-bee-noh, the bad medicine man; while unto you, Sug-gee-mah descends the hardest task, for you must fight a great battle with Nee-pah-win, the Sleep."

Moh-Kwa gave his orders to his three friends; an' with that Sub-bee-kah-shee, crept to the side of Kwa-Sind where he slept an' bit him on the cheek; an' Kwa-Sind turned first gray an' then black with the spider's venom, an' then died in the hands of Pau-guk, the Death, who had followed the Spider to Kwa-Sind's lodge.

While this was going forward, Wah-wah-tah-see, the Firefly, came as swift as wing could carry to the lodge where Wah-bee-noh was asleep rolled up in a bear-skin. Wah-bee-noh was happy, for with the big medicine robe which the Robin had brought him, he already had bought the eight further ponies from Kwa-Sind an' they then grazed in Wah-bee-noh's herd. As Wah-bee-noh laughed in his sleep because he dreamed of the twenty ponies he had earned from Kwa-Sind, the Firefly stooped an' stung him inside his mouth. An' so perished Wah-bee-noh in a flame of fever, for the poison of Wah-wah-tah-see, the Firefly, burns one to death like live coals.

Sug-gee-mah, the Mosquito, found Nee-pah-win, the Sleep, holding the Robin fast. But Sug-gee-mah was stout, an' he stooped an' stung the Sleep so hard he let go of the Robin an' stood up to fight.

All night an' all day an' all night, an' yet many days an' nights, did Sug-gee-mah, the bold Mosquito, an' Nee-pah-win, the Sleep, fight for the Robin. An' whenever Nee-pah-win, the Sleep, would take the Robin in his arms, Sug-gee-mah, the Mosquito, would strike him with his little lance. For many days an' nights did Sug-gee-mah, the Mosquito, hold Nee-pah-win, the Sleep, at bay; an' in the end the Robin turned wild an' crazy, for unless Nee-pah-win, the Sleep, takes each man an' woman in his arms when the sun goes down it is as if they were bitten by the evil pole-cats who are rabid; an' the men an' women who are not held in the arms of Nee-pah-win go mad an' rave like starved wolves till they die. An' thus it was with the Robin. After many days an' nights, Pau-guk, the Death, came for her also, an' those three who had done evil to the Swallow were punished.

Moh-Kwa, collecting the knife, the bear-claws an' the big medicine robe from the lodge of Kwa-Sind, gave them to the Swallow again. This time the Swallow stood better guard, an' no squaw, however cunning, might make a fool of him—though many tried—so he kept his knife, the bear-claws, an' the big med-icine robe these many years while he lived.

As for Sub-bee-kah-shee, the Spider, an' Wah-wah-tah-see, the Firefly, an' Sug-gee-mah, the brave Mosquito, Moh-Kwa, the Wise Bear, for a reward gave them an' their countless squaws an' pa-pooses forever that fine swamp where Apuk-wah, the Bulrush, grows thick an' green, an' makes a best hunting grounds for the three little warriors who killed Kwa-Sind, Wah-bee-noh, an' the Robin on that day when Moh-Kwa called them his enemies. An' now when every man was at peace an' happy, Moh-Kwa brought the Sioux together an' re-named the Swallow "Thorn-Puller;" an' by that name was he known till he died.

"How many are there of these Sioux folk-lore tales?" asks the Jolly Doctor of Sioux Sam.

"How many leaves in June?" asks Sioux Sam. Later he contributes the following:

HOW STRONGARM WAS AN ELK

Moh-Kwa was the wisest of all the beasts along the Upper Yellowstone; an' yet Moh-Kwa could not catch a fish. This made
Moh-Kwa have a bad heart, for next to honey he liked fish. What
made it worse was that in Moh-Kwa's cavern where he lived,
there lay a deep pool which was the camp of many fish; an'
Moh-Kwa would sit an' look at them an' long for them, while
the fish came close to the edge an' laughed at Moh-Kwa, for
they knew beneath their scales that he could not catch them; an'
the laughter of the fish made a noise like swift water running
among rocks. Sometimes Moh-Kwa struck at a fish with his big
paw, but the fish never failed to dive out of reach; an' this made
the other fish laugh at Moh-Kwa more than before. Once Moh-
Kwa got so angry he plunged into the pool to hunt the fish; but
it only made him seem foolish, for the fish swam about him in
flashing circles, an' dived under him an' jumped over him, laughing all the time, making a play an' a sport of Moh-Kwa. At last
he gave up an' swam ashore; an' then he had to sit by his fire an'
comb his fur all day to dry himself so that he might feel like the
same bear again.

One morning down by the Yellowstone, Moh-Kwa met Strongarm, the young Sioux, an' Strongarm had a buffalo fish which
he had speared in the river. An' because Moh-Kwa looked at the
fish hungrily an' with water in his mouth, Strongarm gave him
the buffalo fish. Also he asked Moh-Kwa why he did not catch

fish since he liked them so well an' the pool in his cavern was the camp of many fish. An' Moh-Kwa said it was because the fish were cowards an' would not stay an' fight with him, but ran away.

"They are not so brave as the bees," said Moh-Kwa, "for when I find a bee-tree, they make me fight for the honey. The bees have big hearts though little knives, but the fish have no hearts an' run like water down hill if they but see Moh-Kwa's shadow from his fire fall across the pool."

Strongarm said he would catch the fish for Moh-Kwa; an' with that he went to the Wise Bear's house an' with his spear took many fish, being plenty to feed Moh-Kwa two days. Moh-Kwa was very thankful, an' because Strongarm liked the Wise Bear, he came four times each moon an' speared fish for Moh-Kwa who was never so well fed with fish before.

Strongarm was a mighty hunter among the Sioux an' killed more elk than did the ten best hunters of his village. So many elk did Strongarm slay that his squaw, the Blossom, made for their little son, Feather-foot, a buckskin coat on which was sewed the eye-teeth of elk, two for each elk, until there were so many elk-teeth on Feather-foot's buckskin coat it was like counting the leaves on a cottonwood to find how many there were. An' the Blossom was proud of Feather-foot's coat, for none among the Sioux had so beautiful a garment an' the eye-teeth of the elk told how big a hunter was Strongarm.

While the Sioux wondered an' admired at the elk-tooth coat, it made the Big Medicine Elk, who was chief of the Elk people, hot an' angry, an' turned his heart black against Strongarm. The Big Medicine Elk said he would have revenge.

Thus it happened one day that when Strongarm stepped from his lodge, he saw standing in front a great Elk who had antlers like the branches of a tree. An' the great Elk stamped his foot an' snorted at Strongarm. Then Strongarm took his bow an' his lance an' his knife an' hunted the great Elk to kill him; but the great Elk ran always a little ahead just out of reach.

At last the great Elk ran into the Pouch canyon an' then

Strongarm took hope into his heart like a man takes air into his mouth, for the sides of the Pouch canyon were high an' steep an' it ended with a high wall, an' nothing save a bird might get out again once it went in; for the Pouch canyon was a trap which the Great Spirit had set when the world was new.

Strongarm was happy in his breast as he followed the great Elk into the Pouch canyon for now he was sure. An' he thought how the big eye-teeth of so great an Elk would look on the collar of Feather-foot's buckskin coat.

When Strongarm came to the upper end of the Pouch canyon, there the great Elk stood waiting.

"Hold!" said the great Elk, when Strongarm put an arrow on his bowstring.

But Strongarm shot the arrow which bounded off the great Elk's hide an' made no wound. Then Strongarm ran against the great Elk with his lance, but the lance was broken as though the great Elk was a rock. Then Strongarm drew his knife, but when he went close to the great Elk, the beast threw him down with his antlers an' put his forefoot on Strongarm an' held him on the ground.

"Listen," said the great Elk, an' Strongarm listened because he couldn't help it. "You have hunted my people far an' near; an' you can never get enough of their blood or their eye-teeth. I am the Big Medicine Elk an' chief of the Elk people; an' now for a vengeance against you, I shall change you from the hunter to the hunted, an' you shall know how good it is to have fear an' be an elk."

As the great Elk said this, Strongarm felt his head turn heavy with antlers, while his nose grew long an' his mouth wide, an' hair grew out of his skin like grass in the moon of new grass, an' his hands an' feet split into hoofs; an' then Strongarm stood on his four new hoofs an' saw by his picture in the stream that he was an elk. Also the elk-fear curled up in his heart to keep him ever in alarm; an' he snuffed the air an' walked about timidly where before he was Strongarm and feared nothing.

Strongarm crept home to his lodge, but the Blossom did not

know her husband; an' Feather-foot, his little son, shot arrows
at him; an' as he ran from them, the hunters of his village came
forth an' chased him until Strongarm ran into the darkness of
the next night as it came trailing up from the East, an' the darkness was kind an' covered him like a blanket an' Strongarm was
hid by it an' saved.

When Strongarm did not come with the next sun to spear fish
for Moh-Kwa, the Wise Bear went to Strongarm's lodge to seek
him for he thought that he was sick. An' Moh-Kwa asked the
Blossom where was Strongarm? An' the Blossom said she did not
know; that Strongarm chased the great Elk into the Pouch canyon an' never came out again; an' now a big Doubt had spread
its blankets in her heart an' would not leave, but was making a
long camp, saying she was a widow. Then the Blossom wept; but
Moh-Kwa told her to wait an' he would see, because he, Moh-
Kwa, owed Strongarm for many fish an' would now pay him.

Moh-Kwa went to the Big Medicine Elk.

"Where is the Strongarm?" said Moh-Kwa.

"He runs in the hills an' is an elk," said the Big Medicine Elk.
"He killed my people for their teeth, an' a great fright was on all
my people because of the Strongarm. The mothers dare not go
down to the river's edge to drink, an' their children had no time
to grow fat for they were ever looking to meet the Strongarm.
Now he is an elk an' my people will have peace; the mothers will
drink an' their babies be fat an' big, being no more chased by the
Strongarm."

Then Moh-Kwa thought an' thought, an' at last he said to the
Big Medicine Elk:

"That is all proud talk. But I must have the Strongarm back,
for he catches my fish."

But the Big Medicine Elk said he would not give Moh-Kwa
back the Strongarm.

"Why should I?" asked the Big Medicine Elk.

"Did not I save you in the Yellowstone," said Moh-Kwa, "when
as you swam the river a drifting tree caught in your antlers an'

held down your head to drown you? An' did you not bawl to me who searched for berries on the bank; an' did I not swim to you an' save you from the tree?" Still the Big Medicine Elk shook his antlers.

"What you say is of another day. You saved me an' that is ended. I will not give you back the Strongarm for that. One does not drink the water that is gone by."

Moh-Kwa then grew so angry his eyes burned red like fire, an' he threatened to kill the Big Medicine Elk. But the Big Medicine Elk laughed like the fish laughed, for he said he could not be killed by any who lived on the land.

"Then we will go to the water," said Moh-Kwa; an' with that he took the Big Medicine Elk in his great hairy arms an' carried him kicking an' struggling to the Yellowstone; for Moh-Kwa could hold the Big Medicine Elk though he could not hurt him.

When Moh-Kwa had carried the Big Medicine Elk to the river, he sat down on the bank an' waited with the Big Medicine Elk in his arms until a tree came floating down. Then Moh-Kwa swam with the Big Medicine Elk to the tree an' tangled the branches in the antlers of the Big Medicine Elk so that he was fast with his nose under the water an' was sure to drown.

"Now you are as you were when I helped you," said Moh-Kwa.

An' the Catfish people in the river came with joy an' bit the legs of the Big Medicine Elk, an' said, "Thank you, Moh-Kwa; you do well to bring us food now an' then since you eat so many fish."

As Moh-Kwa turned to swim again to the bank, he said over his shoulder to the Big Medicine Elk:

"Now you may sing your death song, for Pauguk, the Death, is in the river with you an' those are Pauguk's catfish which gnaw your legs."

At this the Big Medicine Elk said between his cries of grief an' fear that if Moh-Kwa would save him out of the river, he would tell him how to have the Strongarm back. So Moh-Kwa went again an' freed the Big Medicine Elk from the tree an' carried him to the bank, while the Catfish people followed, angrily crying:

"Is this fair, Moh-Kwa? Do you give an' then do you take away? Moh-Kwa! you are a Pawnee!"

When the Big Medicine Elk had got his breath an' wiped the tears from his eyes, he told Moh-Kwa that the only way to bring the Strongarm back to be a hunter from being one of the hunted was for Feather-foot, his son, to cut his throat; an' for the Blossom, his squaw, to burn his elk-body with cedar boughs.

"An' why his son, the Feather-foot?" asked Moh-Kwa.

"Because the Feather-foot owes the Strongarm a life," replied the Big Medicine Elk. "Is not Strongarm the Feather-foot's father an' does not the son owe the father his life?"

Moh-Kwa saw this was true talk, so he let the Big Medicine Elk go free.

"I will even promise that the Strongarm," said Moh-Kwa, as the two parted, "when again he is a Sioux on two legs, shall never hunt the Elk people."

But the Big Medicine Elk, who was licking his fetlocks where the Catfish people had hurt the skin, shook his antlers an' replied:

"It is not needed. The Strongarm has been one of the Elk people an' will feel he is their brother an' will not hurt them."

Moh-Kwa found it a hard task to capture Strongarm when now he was an elk with the elk-fear in his heart. For Strongarm had already learned the elk's warning which is taught by all the Elk people, an' which says:

Look up for danger and look down for gain;
Believe no wolf's word, and avoid the plain.

Strongarm would look down for the grass with one eye, while he kept an eye up among the branches or along the sides of the canyon for fear of mountain lions. An' he stuck close in among the hills, an' would not go out on the plains where the wolves lived; an' he wouldn't talk with a wolf or listen to his words.

But Strongarm, while he ran an' hid from Moh-Kwa an' the others, was not afraid of the Blossom, who was his squaw, but would come to her gladly if he might find her alone among the trees.

"It is not the first time," said the Wise Bear, "that the hunter has made his trap of love."

With that he told the Blossom to go into the hills an' call Strongarm to her with her love. Then she was to bind his feet so that he might not get away an' run.

The Blossom called Strongarm an' he came; but he was fearful an' suspicious an' his nose an' his ears an' his eyes kept guard until the Blossom put her hand on his neck; an' then Strongarm's great love for the Blossom smothered out his caution as one might smother a fire with a robe; an' the Blossom tied all his feet with thongs an' bound his eyes with her blanket so that Strongarm might not see an' be afraid.

Then came Feather-foot, gladly, an' cut Strongarm's throat with his knife; for Feather-foot did not know he killed his father—for that was a secret thing with Moh-Kwa an' the Blossom—an' thought only how he killed a great Elk.

When Strongarm was dead, Moh-Kwa toiled throughout the day carrying up the big cedar; an' when a pile like a hill was made, Moh-Kwa put Strongarm's elk-body on its top, an' brought fire from his house in the rocks, an' made a great burning.

In the morning, the Blossom who had stayed with Moh-Kwa through the night while the fire burned, said, "Now, although the big elk is gone into ashes, I do not yet see the Strongarm." But Moh-Kwa said, "You will find him asleep in the lodge." An' that was a true word, for when Moh-Kwa an' the Blossom went to the lodge, there they found Strongarm whole an' good an' as sound asleep as a tree at midnight.

Outside the lodge they met the little Feather-foot who cried, "Where is the big elk, Moh-Kwa, that I killed?" An' the Blossom showed him his father, Strongarm, where he slept, an' said, "There is your big elk, Feather-foot; an' this will ever be your best hunting for it found you your father again."

When Moh-Kwa saw that everything was settled an' well, an' that he would now have always his regular fish, he wiped the sweat out of his eyes with his paws which were all singed fur an' ashes, an' said, "I am the weariest bear along the whole length of the Yellowstone, for I carried some heavy trees an' have worked hard. Now I will sleep an' rest."

An' with that Moh-Kwa lay down an' snored an' slept four days; then he arose an' eat up the countless fish which Strong-arm had speared to be ready for him. This done, Moh-Kwa lighted his pipe of kinnikinick, an' softly rubbing his stomach where the fish were, said: "Fish give Moh-Kwa a good heart."

Wolfville, With a Difference, and others

Sandburrs *(1900) was a curiosity in the Wolfville saga, in that it contained five Wolfville stories* not *told by the Old Cattleman. They give us some check on Lewis' techniques, and his effectiveness in handling the same themes with an without the Old Cattleman, as in the following tale, and (p. 115) in "Wagon Mound Sal."*

CHEYENNE BILL

Cheyenne Bill is out of luck. Ordinarily his vagaries are not regarded in Wolfville. His occasional appearance in its single street in a voluntary of nice feats of horsemanship, coupled with an exhibition of pistol shooting, in which old tomato cans and passé beer bottles perform as targets, has hitherto excited no more baleful sentiment in the Wolfville bosom than disgust.

"Shootin' up the town a whole lot!" is the name for this engaging pastime, as given by Cheyenne Bill, and up to date the exercise has passed unchallenged.

But today it is different. Camps like individuals have moods, now light, now dark; and so it is with Wolfville. At this time Wolfville is experiencing a wave of virtue. This may have come spontaneously from those seeds of order which, after all, dwell sturdily in the Wolfville breast. It may have been excited by the presence of a pale party of Eastern tourists, just now abiding at the O. K. Hotel; persons whom the rather sanguine sentiment of Wolfville credits with meditating an investment of treasure in her rocks and rills. But whatever the reason, Wolfville virtue is aroused; a condition of the public mind which makes it a bad day for Cheyenne Bill.

The angry sun smites hotly in the deserted causeway of Wolfville. The public is within doors. The Red Light Saloon is thriving mightily. Those games which generally engross public thought are drowsy enough; but the counter whereat the citizen of Wolf-

ville gathers with his peers in absorption of the incautious com-
pounds of the place, is fairly sloppy from excess of trade. Not-
withstanding the torrid heat this need not sound strangely; Wolfville leaning is strongly homœopathic. *"Similia similibus curan-
tur,"* says Wolfville; and when it is blazing hot, drinks whiskey.

But today there is further reason for this consumption. Wolfville is excited, and this provokes a thirst. Cheyenne Bill, render-
ing himself prisoner to Jack Moore, rescue or no rescue, has by
order of that sagacious body been conveyed by his captor before
the vigilance committee, and is about to be tried for his life.

What was Cheyenne Bill's immediate crime? Certainly not a
grave one. Ten days before it would have hardly earned a com-
ment. But now in its spasm of virtue, and sensitive in its memories of the erratic courses of Cheyenne Bill aforetime, Wolfville
has grimly taken possession of that volatile gentleman for punishment. He has killed a Chinaman. Here is the story:

"Yere comes that prairie dog, Cheyenne Bill, all spraddled out,"
says Dave Tutt.

Dave Tutt is peering from the window of the Red Light, to
which lattice he has been carried by the noise of hoofs. There is
a sense of injury disclosed in Dave Tutt's tone, born of the
awakened virtue of Wolfville.

"It looks like this camp never can assoome no airs," remarks
Cherokee Hall in a distempered way, "but this yere miser'ble
Cheyenne comes chargin' up to queer it."

As he speaks, that offending personage, unconscious of the
great change in Wolfville morals, sweeps up the street, expressing
gladsome and ecstatic whoops, and whirling his pistol on his fore-
finger like a thing of light. One of the tourists stands in the door
of the hotel smoking a pipe in short, brief puffs of astonishment,
and reviews the amazing performance. Cheyenne Bill at once and
abruptly halts. Gazing for a disgruntled moment on the man
from the East, he takes the pipe from its owner's amazed mouth
and places it in his own.

"Smokin' of pipes," he vouchsafes in condemnatory explanation, "is onelegant an' degradin'; an' don't you do it no more in my presence. I'm mighty sensitive that a-way about pipes, an' I don't aim to tolerate 'em none whatever."

This solution of his motives seems satisfactory to Cheyenne Bill. He sits puffing and gazing at the tourist, while the latter stands dumbly staring with a morsel of the ravished meerschaum still between his lips.

What further might have followed in the way of oratory or overt acts cannot be stated, for the thoughts of the guileless Cheyenne suddenly receive a new direction. A Chinaman, voluminously robed, emerges from the New York store, whither he has been drawn by dint of soap.

"Whatever is this Mongol doin' in camp, I'd like for to know?" inquires Cheyenne Bill disdainfully. "I shore leaves orders when I'm yere last, for the immejit removal of all sech. I wouldn't mind it, but with strangers visitin' Wolfville this a-way, it plumb mortifies me to death."

"Oh well!" he continues in tones of weary, bitter reflection, "I'm the only public-sperited gent in this yere outfit, so all reforms falls nacheral to me. Still, I plays my hand! I'm simply a pore, lonely white, but jest the same, I makes an example of this speciment of a sudsmonger to let 'em know whatever a white man is, anyhow."

Then comes the short, emphatic utterance of a six-shooter. A puff of smoke lifts and vanishes in the hot air, and the next census will be short one Asiatic.

In a moment arrives a brief order from Enright, the chief of the vigilance committee, to Jack Moore. The last-named official proffers a Winchester and a request to surrender simultaneously, and Cheyenne Bill, realizing fate, at once accedes.

"Of course, gents," says Enright, apologetically, as he convenes the committee in the Red Light bar; "I don't say this Cheyenne is held for beefin' the Chinaman sole an' alone. The fact is, he's been havin' a mighty sight too gay a time of late, an' so I thinks it's a good, safe play, bein' as it's a hot day an' we has the time, to sorter call the committee together an' ask its views, whether we better hang this yere Cheyenne yet or not?"

"Mr. Pres'dent," responds Dave Tutt, "if I'm in order, an' to get the feelin' of the meetin' to flowin' smooth, I moves we takes this Cheyenne an' proceeds with his immolation. I ain't basin' it on nothin' in partic'lar, but lettin' her slide as fulfillin' a long-felt want."

"Do I note any remarks?" asks Enright. "If not I takes Mr. Tutt's very excellent motion as the census of this meetin', an' it's hang she is."

"Not intendin' of no interruption," remarks Texas Thompson, "I wants to say this: I'm a quiet gent myse'f, an' nacheral aims to keep Wolfville a quiet place likewise. For which-all I shorely favours a-hangin' of Cheyenne. He's given us a heap of trouble. Like Tutt I don't make no p'int on the Chinaman; we spares the Chink too easy. But this Cheyenne is allers a-ridin', an' a-yellin', an' a-shootin' up this camp till I'm plumb tired out. So I says let's hang him, an' su'gests as a eligible, as well as usual nook tharfore, the windmill back of the dance hall."

"Yes," says Enright, "the windmill is, as exper'ence has showed, amply upholstered for sech plays; an' as delays is aggravatin', the committee might as well go wanderin' over now, an' get this yere ceremony off its mind."

"See yere, Mr. Pres'dent!" interrupts Cheyenne Bill in tones of one ill-used, "what for a deal is this I rises to ask?"

"You can gamble this is a squar' game," replies Enright confidently. "You're entitled to your say when the committee is done. Jest figure out what kyards you needs, an' we deals to you in a minute."

"I solely wants to know if my voice is to be regarded in this yere play, that's all," retorts Cheyenne Bill.

"Gents," says Doc Peets, who has been silently listening. "I'm with you on this hangin'. These Eastern sharps is here in our midst. It'll impress 'em that Wolfville means business, an' it's a good, safe, quiet place. They'll carry reports East as will do us credit, an' thar you be. As to the propriety of stringin' Cheyenne,

little need be said. If the Chinaman ain't enough, if assaultin' of
an innocent tenderfoot ain't enough, you can bet he's done
plenty besides as merits a lariat. He wouldn't deny it himse'f if
you asks him."

There is a silence succeeding the rather spirited address of Doc
Peets, on whose judgment Wolfville has been taught to lean. At
last Enright breaks it by inquiring of Cheyenne Bill if he has
anything to offer.

"I reckons it's your play now, Cheyenne," he says, "so come
a-runnin'."

"Why!" urges Cheyenne Bill, disgustedly, "these proceedin's
is ornery an' makes me sick. I shore objects to this hangin'; an'
all for a measly Chinaman too! This yere Wolfville outfit is gettin'
a mighty sight too stylish for me. It's growin' that per-dad-binged-
'tic'lar it can't take its reg'lar drinks, an'——"

"Stop right thar!" says Enright, with dignity, rapping a shoe-
box with his six-shooter; "don't you cuss the chair none, 'cause
the chair won't have it. It's parliamentary law, if any gent cusses
the chair he's out of order, same as it's law that all chips on the
floor goes to the house. When a gent's out of order once, that
settles it. He can't talk no more that meetin'. Seein' we're aimin'
to eliminate you, we won't claim nothin' on you this time. But
be careful how you come trackin' 'round ag'in, an' don't fret us!
Sabe? Don't you-all go an' fret us none!"

"I ain't allowin' to fret you," retorts Cheyenne Bill. "I don't
have to fret you. What I says is this: I s'pose I sees fifty gents
stretched by one passel of Stranglers or another between yere
an' The Dalls, an' I never does know a party who's roped yet on
account of no Chinaman. An' I offers a side bet of a blue stack,
it ain't law to hang people on account of downin' no Chinaman.
But you-alls seems sot on this, an' so I tells you what I'll do.
I'm a plain gent an' thar's no filigree work on me. If it's all congenial to the boys yere assembled—not puttin' it on the grounds
of no miser'ble hop slave, but jest to meet public sentiment half-
way—I'll gamble my life, hang or no hang, on the first ace turned
from the box, Cherokee deal. Does it go?"

Wolfville tastes are bizarre. A proposition original and new finds in its very novelty an argument for Wolfville favour. It befalls, therefore, that the unusual offer of Cheyenne Bill to stake his neck on a turn at faro is approvingly criticised. The general disposition agrees to it; even the resolute Enright sees no reason to object.

"Cheyenne," says Enright, "we don't have to take this chance, an' it's a-makin' of a bad preceedent which the same may tangle us yereafter; but Wolfville goes you this time, an' may Heaven have mercy on your soul. Cherokee, turn the kyards for the ace."

"Turn squar', Cherokee!" remarks Cheyenne Bill with an air of interest. "You wouldn't go to sand no deck, nor deal with kyards at a clatter, ag'in perishin' flesh an' blood?"

"I should say, no!" replies Cherokee. "I wouldn't turn queer for money, an' you can gamble! I don't do it none when the epeesode comes more onder the head of reelaxation."

"Which the same bein' satisfact'ry," says Cheyenne Bill, "roll your game. I'm eager for action; also, I plays it open."

"I dunno!" observes Dan Boggs, meditatively caressing his chin; "I'm thinkin' I'd a-coppered;—that's whatever!"

The deal proceeds in silence, and as may happen in that interesting sport called faro, a split falls out. Two aces appear in succession.

"Ace lose, ace win!" says Cherokee, pausing. "Whatever be we goin' to do now, I'd like to know?"

There is a pause.

"Gents," announces Enright, with dignity, "a split like this yere creates a doubt; an' all doubts goes to the pris'ner, same as a maverick goes to the first rider as ties it down, an' runs his brand onto it. This camp of Wolfville abides by law, an' blow though it be, this yere Cheyenne Bill, temp'rarily at least, goes free. However, he should remember this yere graze an' restrain his methods yereafter. Some of them ways of his is onhealthful, an' if he's wise he'll shortly alter his system from now on."

"Which the camp really lose! an' this person Bill goes free!" says Jack Moore, dejectedly. "I allers was ag'in faro as a game.

Where we-all misses it egreegious, is we don't play him freeze-out."

"Do you know, Cherokee," whispers Faro Nell, as her eyes turn softly to that personage of the deal box, "I don't like killin's none! I'd sooner Cheyenne goes loose, than two bonnets from Tucson!"

At this Cherokee Hall pinches the cheek of Faro Nell with a delicate accuracy born of his profession, and smiles approval.

Another of Lewis' tales from the actual chronicles of the West. It appeared in The Black Lion Inn and shows the Old Cattleman once more talking to a varied audience, rather than, as in the Wolfville stories proper, to his alter ego.

As always, it is best to take the tale as art, rather than as record. The cowboys were as shrewd as any of their shrewder eastern compatriots in putting the best face possible on a situation. They tended their own counsel, and muddled truth in order to advance their own reputations or interests. "Wild Bill"—"Hickox" is a curiosity for Hickok - had more reason to do so than many other adventurers, and we will never entirely know the truth behind many of his assertions.

THE WIPING OUT OF M'CANDLAS

Tell you-all a tale of blood? It shore irritates me a heap, gents, when you eastern folks looks allers to the west for stories red an' drippin' with murder. Which mighty likely now the west is plenty peaceful compared with this yere east itse'f. Thar's one thing you can put in your mem'randum book for footure ref'rence, an' that is, for all them years I inhabits Arizona an' Texas an' sim'lar energetic localities, I never trembles for my life, an' goes about plumb furtive, expectin' every moment is goin' to be my next that a-way, ontil I finds myse'f camped on the sunrise side of the Alleghenies.

Nacherally, I admits, thar has been a modicum of blood shed west an' some slight share tharof can be charged to Arizona. No, I can't say I deplores these killin's none. Every gent has got to die. For one, I'm mighty glad the game's been rigged that a-way. I'd shore hesitate a lot to be born onless I was shore I'd up an' some day cash in. Live forever? No, don't confer on me no sech gloomy outlook. If a angel was to appear in our midst an' saw off on me the news that I was to go on an' on as I be now, livin' forever like that Wanderin' Jew, the information would stop my clock right thar. I'd drop dead in my moccasins.

It don't make much difference, when you gives yourse'f to a ca'm consid'ration of the question as to when you dies or how you dies. The important thing is to die as becomes a gent of sperit who has nothin' to regret. Every one soon or late comes to his trail's end. Life is like a faro game. One gent has ten dollars, another a hundred, another a thousand, and still others has rolls big enough to choke a cow. But whether a gent is weak or strong, poor or rich, it's written in advance that he's doomed to go broke final. He's doomed to die. Tharfore, when that's settled, of what moment is it whether he goes broke in an hour, or pikes along for a week—dies to-day or postpones his funeral for years an' mebby decades?

Holdin' to these yere views, you can see without my tellin' that a killin', once it be over, ain't likely to harass me much. Like the rest of you-all, I've been trailin' out after my grave ever since I was foaled—on a hunt for my sepulcher, you may say—an' it ought not to shock me to a showdown jest because some pard tracks up ag'inst his last restin' place, spreads his blankets an' goes into final camp before it come my own turn.

But, speakin' of killin's, the most onusual I ever hears of is when Wild Bill Hickox cleans up the Jake McCandlas gang. This Bill I knows intimate; he's not so locoed as his name might lead a gent to concloode. The truth is, he's a mighty crafty, careful form of sport; an' he never pulled a gun ontil he knew what for an' never onhooked it ontil he knew what at.

An' speakin' of the latter—the onhookin' part—that Wild Bill never missed. That's his one gift; he's born to make a center shot whenever his six-shooter expresses itse'f.

This McCandlas time is doorin' them border troubles between Missouri an' Kansas. Jest prior tharunto, Bill gets the ill-will of the Missouri outfit by some gun play he makes at Independence, then the eastern end of the old Santa Fe trail. What Bill accomplishes at Independence is a heap effectual an' does him proud. But it don't endear him none to the Missouri heart. Moreover, it starts a passel of resentful zealots to lookin' for him a heap f'rocious, an' so he pulls his freight.

It's mebby six months later when Bill is holdin' down a stage station some'eres over in Kansas—it's about a day's ride at a road-gait from Independence—for Ben Holiday's overland line. Thar's the widow of a *compadre* of Bill who has a wickeyup about a mile away, an' one day Bill gets on his hoss, Black Nell, an' goes romancin' over to see how the widow's gettin' on. This Black Nell hoss of Bill's is some cel'brated. Black Nell is tame as a kitten an' saveys more'n a hired man. She'd climb a pa'r of steps an' come sa'nterin' into a dance hall or a hurdy gurdy if Bill calls to her, an' I makes no doubt she'd a-took off her own saddle an' bridle an' gone to bed with a pa'r of blankets, same as folks, if Bill said it was the proper antic for a pony.

It's afternoon when Bill rides up to pow-wow with this relict of his pard. As he comes into the one room—for said wickeyup ain't palatial, an' consists of one big room, that a-way, an' a jim-crow leanto—Bill says:

"Howdy, Jule?" like that.

"Howdy, Bill?" says the widow. "Light an' rest your hat, while I roam 'round an' rustle some chuck." This widow has the right idee.

While Bill is camped down on a stool waitin' for the promised *carne* an' flap-jacks, or whatever may be the grub his hostess is aimin' to onloose, he casts a glance outen the window. He's interested at once. Off across the plains he discerns the killer, McCandlas an' his band p'intin' straight for the widow's. They're from Missouri; thar's 'leven of 'em, corral count, an' all "bad."

As they can see his mare, Black Nell, standin' in front of the widow's, Bill argues jestly that the McCandlas outfit knows he's thar; an' from the speed they're makin' in their approach, he likewise dedooces that they're a heap eager for his company.

Bill don't have to study none to tell that thar's somebody goin' to get action. It's likely to be mighty onequal, but thar's no h'ep; an' so Bill pulls his gun-belt tighter, an' organizes to go as far as he can. He has with him only one six-shooter; that's a severe setback. Now, if he was packin' two the approaching warjig would have carried feachers of comfort. But he's got a nine-inch bowie, which is some relief. When his six-shooter's empty, he can fall back on the knife, die hard, an' leave his mark.

As Bill rolls the cylinder of his gun to see if she's workin' free, an' loosens the bowie to avoid delays, his eye falls on a rifle hangin' above the door.

"Is it loaded, Jule?" asks Bill.

"Loaded to the gyards," says the widow.

"An' that ain't no fool of a piece of news, neither," says Bill, as he reaches down the rifle. "Now, Jule, you-all better stampede into the cellar a whole lot ontil further orders. Thar's goin' to be heated times 'round yere an' you'd run the resk of gettin' scorched."

"I'd sooner stay an' see, Bill," says the widow. "You-all knows how eager an' full of cur'osity a lady is," an' here the widow beams on Bill an' simpers coaxin'ly.

"An' I'd shore say stay, Jule," says Bill, "if you could turn a trick. But you sees yourse'f, you couldn't. An' you'd be in the way."

Thar's a big burrow out in the yard; what Kansas people dee-nominates as a cyclone cellar. It's like a cave; every se'f-respectin' Kansas fam'ly has one. They may not own no bank account; they may not own no good repoote; but you can gamble, they've got a cyclone cave.

Shore, it ain't for ornament, nor yet for ostentation. Thar's allers a breeze blowin' plenty stiff across the plains. Commonly, it's strenyous enough to pick up a empty bar'l an' hold it ag'inst the side of a buildin' for a week. Sech is the usual zephyr. Folks don't heed them none. But now an' then one of these yere cyclones jumps a gent's camp, an' then it's time to make for cover. Thar's nothin' to be said back to a cyclone. It'll take the water outen a well, or the money outen your pocket, or the ha'r off your head; it'll get away with everything about you incloodin' your address. Your one chance is a cyclone cellar; an' even that refooge ain't no shore-thing, for I knowed a cyclone once that simply feels down an' pulls a badger outen his hole. Still, sech as the last, is onfrequent.

The widow accepts Bill's advice an' makes for the storm cave. This leaves Bill happy an' easy in his mind, for it gives him plenty of room an' nothin' to think of but himse'f. An' Bill shore admires a good fight.

He don't have long to wait after the widow stampedes. Bill hears the sweep of the 'leven McCandlas hosses as they come chargin' up. No, he can't see; he ain't quite that weak-minded as to be lookin' out the window.

As the band halts, Bill hears McCandlas say:

"Shore, gents; that's Wild Bill's hoss. We've got him treed an' out on a limb; to-morry evenin' we'll put that long-ha'red skelp of his in a showcase in Independence." Then McCandlas gives a whoop, an' bluffs Bill to come out. "Come out yere, Bill; we needs you to decide a bet," yells McCandlas. "Come out; thar's no good skulkin'."

"Say, Jake," retorts Bill; "I'll gamble that you an' your hoss thieves ain't got the sand to come after me. Come at once if you comes; I despises delays, an' besides I've got to be through with you-all an' back to the stage station by dark."

"I'll put you where thar ain't no stage lines, Bill, long before dark," says McCandlas. An' with that he comes caperin' through the window, sash, glass, an' the entire lay-out, as blithe as May an' a gun in each hand.

Bill cuts loose the Hawkins as he's anxious to get the big gun off his mind. It stops McCandlas, "squar' in the door," as they says in monte; only it's the window. McCandlas falls dead outside.

"An' I'm sorry for that, too," says Bill to himse'f. "I'm preemature some about that shot. I oughter let Jake come in. Then I could have got his guns."

When McCandlas goes down, the ten others charges with a whoop. They comes roarin' through every window; they breaks in the door; they descends on Bill's fortress like a 'possum on a partridge nest!

An' then ensoos the busiest season which any gent ever cuts in upon. The air is heavy with bullets an' thick with smoke. The walls of the room later looks like a colander.

It's a mighty fav'rable fight, an' Bill don't suffer none in his repoote that Kansas afternoon. Faster than you can count, his gun barks; an' each time thar's a warrior less. One, two, three, four, five, six; they p'ints out after McCandlas an' not a half second between 'em as they starts. It was good luck an' good shootin' in combination.

It's the limit; six dead to a single Colt's! No gent ever approaches it but once; an' that's a locoed sharp named Metzger in Raton. He starts in with Moulton who's the alcade, an' beefs five an' creases another; an' all to the same one gun. The public, before he can reload, hangs Metzger to the sign in front of the First National Bank, so he don't have much time to enjoy himse'f reviewin' said feats.

Rifle an' six-shooter empty; seven dead an' done, an' four to take his knife an' talk it over with! That's the situation when Bill pulls his bowie an' starts to finish up.

It shore ain't boy's play; the quintette who's still prancin' about the field is as bitter a combination as you'd meet in a long day's ride. Their guns is empty, too; an' they, like Bill, down to the steel. An' thar's reason to believe that the fight from this p'int on is even more interestin' than the part that's gone before. Thar's no haltin' or hangin' back; thar ain't a bashful gent in the herd. They goes to the center like one man.

Bill, who's as quick an' strong as a mountain lion, with forty times the heart an' fire, grips one McCandlas party by the wrist. Thar's a twist an' a wrench an' Bill onj'ints his arm.

That's the last of the battle Bill remembers. All is whirl an' smoke an' curse an' stagger an' cut an' stab after that, with tables crashin' an' the wreck an' jangle of glass.

But the end comes. Whether the struggle from the moment when it's got down to the bowies lasts two minutes or twenty, Bill never can say. When it's over, Bill finds himse'f still on his feet, an' he's pushin' the last gent off his blade. Split through the heart, this yere last sport falls to the floor in a dead heap, an' Bill's alone, blood to both shoulders.

Is Bill hurt? Gents, it ain't much likely he's put 'leven fightin' men into the misty beyond, the final four with a knife, an' him plumb scatheless! No, Bill's slashed so he wouldn't hold hay; an' thar's more bullets in his frame than thar's pease in a pod. The Doc who is called in, an' who prospects Bill, allers allowed that it's the mistake of his life he don't locate Bill an' work him for a lead mine.

When the battle is over an' peace resoomes its sway, Bill begins to stagger. An' he's preyed on by thirst. Bill steadies himse'f along the wall; an' weak an' half blind from the fogs of fightin', he feels his way out o' doors.

Thar's a tub of rain-water onder the eaves; it's the only thing Bill's thinkin' of at the last. He bends down to drink; an' with that, faints an' falls with his head in the tub.

It's the widow who rescoos Bill; she emerges outen her cyclone cellar an' saves Bill from drownin'. An' he lives, too; lives to be downed years afterward when up at Deadwood a timid party who don't dare come 'round in front, drills Bill from the r'ar. But what can you look for? Folks who lives by the sword will perish by the sword as the scripters sets forth, an' I reckons now them warnin's likewise covers guns.

Another novelty, from The Black Lion Inn: *the Old Cattleman recounting a political incident not out of Arizona, but Missouri, where he (as well as Lewis) had spent time in his youth. See also (p. 130), "When the Capitol Was Moved."*

THE GREAT STEWART CAMPAIGN

As I states, I saveys nothin' personal of politics. Thar's mighty little politics gets brooited about Wolfville, an' I ain't none shore but it's as well. The camp's most likely a heap peacefuller as a commoonity. Shore, Colonel Sterett discusses politics in that Coyote paper he conducts; but none of it's nearer than Washin'ton, an' it all seems so plumb dreamy an' far away that while it's interestin', it can't be regyarded as replete of the harrowin' excitement that sedooces a public from its nacheral rest an' causes it to set up nights an' howl.

Rummagin' my mem'ry, I never does hear any politics talked local but once, an' that's by Dan Boggs. It's when the Colonel asks Dan to what party he adheres in principle—for thar ain't no real shore-enough party lurkin' about in Arizona much, it bein' a territory that a-way an' mighty busy over enterprises more calc'lated to pay—an' Dan retorts that he's hooked up with no outfit none as yet, but stands ready as far as his sentiments is involved to go buttin' into the first organization that'll cheapen nose-paint, 'liminate splits as a resk in faro-bank, an' raise the price of beef. Further than them tenets, Dan allows he ain't got no principles.

Man an' boy I never witnesses any surplus of politics an' party strife. In Tennessee when I'm a child every decent gent has been brought up a Andy Jackson man, an' so continyoos long after that heroic captain is petered. As you-all can imagine, politics onder sech conditions goes all one way like the currents of the Cumberland. Thar's no bicker, no strife, simply a vast Andy Jackson yooniformity.

The few years I puts in about Arkansaw ain't much different. Leastwise we-all don't have issues; an' what contests does arise is gen'rally personal an' of the kind where two gents enjoys a j'int debate with their bowies or shows each other how wrong they be with a gun. An' while politics of the variety I deescribes is thrillin', your caution rather than your intellects gets appealed to, while feuds is more apt to be their frootes than any drawin' of reg'lar party lines. Wherefore I may say it's only doorin' the one year I abides in Missouri when I experiences troo politics played with issues, candidates, mass-meetin's an' barbecues.

For myse'f, my part is not spectacyoolar, bein' I'm new an' raw an' young; but I looks on with relish, an' while I don't cut no hercoolean figger in the riot, I shore saveys as much about what's goin' on as the best posted gent between the Ozarks an' the Iowa line.

What you-all might consider as the better element is painted up to beat Old Stewart who's out sloshin' about demandin' re-election to Jeff City for a second term. The better element says Old Stewart drinks. An' this accoosation is doubtless troo a whole lot, for I'm witness myse'f to the following colloquy which takes place between Old Stewart an' a jack-laig doctor he crosses up with in St. Joe. Old Stewart's jest come forth from the tavern, an' bein' on a joobilee the evenin' before, is lookin' an' mighty likely feelin' some seedy.

"Doc," says Old Stewart, openin' his mouth as wide as a young raven, an' then shettin' it ag'in so's to continyoo his remarks, "Doc, I wish you'd peer into this funnel of mine."

Then he opens his mouth ag'in in the same egreegious way, while the scientist addressed scouts about tharin with his eyes, plenty owley. At last the Doc shows symptoms of bein' ready to report.

"Which I don't note nothin' onusual, Gov'nor, about that mouth," says the Doc, "except it's a heap voloominous."

"Don't you discern no signs or signal smokes of any foreign bodies?" says Old Stewart, a bit pettish, same as if he can't onderstand sech blindness.

"None whatever!" observes the Doc.

"It's shore strange," retorts Old Stewart, still in his complainin' tones; "thar's two hundred niggers, a brick house an' a thousand acres of bottom land gone down that throat, an' I sort o' reckons some traces of 'em would show."

That's the trouble with Old Stewart from the immacyoolate standpoint of the better classes; they says he overdrinks. But while it's convincin' to sooperior folks an' ones who's goin' to church an' makin' a speshulty of it, it don't sep'rate Old Stewart from the warm affections of the rooder masses—the catfish an' quinine aristocracy that dwells along the Missouri; they're out for him to the last sport.

"Suppose the old Gov'nor does drink," says one, "what difference does that make? Now, if he's goin' to try sootes in co't, or assoome the pressure as a preacher, thar'd be something in the bluff. But it don't cut no figger whether a gov'nor is sober or no. All he has to do is pardon convicts an' make notaries public, an' no gent can absorb licker s'fficient to incapac'tate him for sech trivial dooties."

One of the argyments they uses ag'in Old Stewart is about a hawg-thief he pardons. Old Stewart is headin' up for the state house one mornin', when he caroms on a passel of felons in striped clothes who's pesterin' about the grounds, tittivatin' up the scenery. Old Stewart pauses in front of one of 'em.

"What be you-all in the pen'tentiary for?" says Old Stewart, an' he's profoundly solemn.

Tharupon the felon trails out on a yarn about how he's a innocent an' oppressed person. He's that honest an' upright—hear him relate the tale—that you'd feel like apol'gizin'. Old Stewart listens to this victim of intrigues an' outrages ontil he's through; then he goes romancin' along to the next. Thar's five wronged gents in that striped outfit, five who's as free from moral taint or stain of crime as Dave Tutt's infant son, Enright Peets Tutt.

But the sixth is different. He admits he's a miscreant an' has done stole a hawg.

"However did you steal it, you scoundrel?" demands Old Stewart.

"I'm outer meat," says the crim'nal, "an' a band of pigs comes pirootin' about, an' I nacherally takes my rifle an' downs one."

"Was it a valyooable hawg?"

"You-all can gamble it ain't no runt," retorts the crim'nal. "I shore ain't pickin' out the worst, an' I'm as good a jedge of hawgs as ever eats corn pone an' cracklin'.'"

At this Old Stewart falls into a foamin' rage an' turns on the two gyards who's soopervisin' the captives.

"Whatever do you-all mean," he roars, "bringin' this common an' confessed hawg-thief out yere with these five honest men? Don't you know he'll corrupt 'em?"

Tharupon Old Stewart reepairs to his rooms in the state house an' pardons the hawg convict with the utmost fury.

"An' now, pull your freight," says Old Stewart, to the crim'nal. "If you're in Jeff City twenty-four hours from now I'll have you shot at sunrise. The idee of compellin' five spotless gents to continyoo in daily companionship with a low hawg-thief! I pardons you, not because you merits mercy, but to preserve the morals of our prison."

The better element concloods they'll take advantage of Old Stewart's willin'ness for rum an' make a example of him before the multitoode. They decides they'll construct the example at a monstrous meetin' that's schedyooled for Hannibal, where Old Stewart an' his opponent—who stands for the better element mighty excellent, seein' he's worth about a million dollars with a home-camp in St. Looey, an' never a idee above dollars an' cents—is programmed for one of these yere j'int debates, frequent in the politics of that era. The conspiracy is the more necessary as Old Stewart, mental, is so much swifter than the better element's candidate, that he goes by him like a antelope. Only two days prior at the town of Fulton, Old Stewart comes after the better element's candidate an' gets enough of his hide, oratorical,

to make a saddle-cover. The better element, alarmed for their gent, resolves on measures in Hannibal that's calc'lated to redooce Old Stewart to a shorething. They don't aim to allow him to wallop their gent at the Hannibal meetin' like he does in old Callaway. With that, they confides to a trio of Hannibal's sturdiest sots—all of 'em acquaintances an' pards of Old Stewart—the sacred task of gettin' that statesman too drunk to orate.

This yere Hannibal barbecue, whereat Old Stewart's goin' to hold a open-air discussion with his aristocratic opponent, is set down for one in the afternoon. The three who's to throw Old Stewart with copious libations of strong drink, hunts that earnest person out as early as sun-up at the tavern. They invites him into the bar-room an' bids the bar-keep set forth his nourishment.

Gents, it works like a charm! All the mornin', Old Stewart swings an' rattles with the plotters an' goes drink for drink with 'em, holdin' nothin' back.

For all that the plot falls down. When it's come the hour for Old Stewart to resort to the barbecue an' assoome his share in the exercises, two of the Hannibal delegation is spread out cold an' he'pless in a r'ar room, while Old Stewart is he'pin' the third —a gent of whom he's partic'lar fond—upstairs in Old Stewart's room, where he lays him safe an' serene on the blankets. Then Old Stewart takes another drink by himse'f, an' j'ins his brave adherents at the picnic grounds. Old Stewart is never more loocid, an' ag'in he peels the pelt from the better element's candidate, an' does it with graceful ease.

Old Stewart, however, is regyarded as in peril of defeat. He's mighty weak in the big towns where the better element is entrenched, an' churches grow as thick as blackberries. Even throughout the rooral regions, wherever a meetin' house pokes up its spire, it's onderstood that Old Stewart's in a heap of danger.

It ain't that Old Stewart is sech a apostle of nose-paint neither; it ain't whiskey that's goin' to kill him off at the ballot box. It's the fact that the better element's candidate—besides bein' rich, which is allers a mark of virchoo to a troo believer—is a church member, an' belongs to a congregation where he passes the plate, an' stands high up in the papers. This makes the better element's gent a heap pop'lar with church folk, while pore Old Stewart, who's a hopeless sinner, don't stand no show.

This grows so manifest that even Old Stewart's most locoed supporters concedes that he's gone; an' money is offered at three to one that the better element's entry will go over Old Stewart like a Joone rise over a tow-head. Old Stewart hears these yere misgivin's an' bids his folks be of good cheer.

"I'll fix that," says Old Stewart. "By election day, my learned opponent will be in sech disrepoote with every church in Missouri he won't be able to get clost enough to one of 'em to give it a ripe peach." Old Stewart onpouches a roll which musters fifteen hundred dollars. "That's mighty little; but it'll do the trick."

Old Stewart's folks is mystified; they can't make out how he's goin' to round up the congregations with so slim a workin' cap'tal. But they has faith in their chief; an' his word goes for all they've got. When he lets on he'll have the churches arrayed ag'inst the foe, his warriors takes heart of grace an' jumps into the collar an' pulls like lions refreshed.

It's the fourth Sunday before election when Old Stewart, by speshul an' trusted friends presents five hundred dollars each to a church in St. Looey, an' another in St. Joe, an' still another in Hannibal; said gifts bein' in the name an' with the compliments of his opponent an' that gent's best wishes for the Christian cause.

Thar's not a doubt raised; each church believes itse'f favored five hundred dollars' worth from the kindly hand of the millionaire candidate, an' the three pastors sits pleasantly down an' writes that amazed sport a letter of thanks for his moonificence. He don't onderstand it none; but he decides it's wise to accept this accidental pop'larity, an' he waxes guileful an' writes back an' says that while he don't clearly onderstand, an' no thanks is his doo, he's tickled to hear he's well bethought of by the good Christians of St. Looey, St. Joe an' Hannibal, as expressed in them missives. The better element's candidate congratulates himse'f on his good luck, stands pat, an' accepts his onexpected wreaths. That's jest what Old Stewart, who is as cunnin' as a fox, is aimin' at.

In two days the renown of them five-hundred-dollar gifts goes over the state like a cat over a back roof. In four days every church in the state hears of these largesses. An' bein' plumb alert financial, as churches ever is, each sacred outfit writes on to the better element's candidate an' desires five hundred dollars of that onfortunate publicist. He gets sixty thousand letters in one week an' each calls for five hundred.

Gents, thar's no more to be said; the better element's candidate is up ag'inst it. He can't yield to the fiscal demands, an' it's too late to deny the gifts. Whereupon the other churches resents the favoritism he's displayed about the three in St. Looey, St. Joe an' Hannibal. They regyards him as a hoss-thief for not rememberin' them while his weaselskin is in his hand, an' on election day they comes down on him like a pan of milk from a top shelf! You hear me, they shorely blots that onhappy candidate off the face of the earth, an' Old Stewart is Gov'nor ag'in.

WAGON MOUND SAL

It was Wagon Mound Sal—she got the prefix later and was plain "Sal" at the time—who took up laundry labours when Benson Annie became a wife. And this tells of the wooing and wedding of Riley Bent with Sallie of Wagon Mound.

Wagon Mound Sal prevailed, as stated, the mistress of a laundry. And it was there Riley Bent first beheld her, as she was putting a tubful of the blue woollen shirts affected by the males of her region through a second suds. On this occasion Riley's appearance was due to a misunderstanding. He was foggy with drink, and looked in on a theory that the place was a store which made a specialty of the sale of shirts.

"What for a j'int is this?" asked Riley as he entered.

"It's a laundry," replied Sal; and then observing that Riley Bent was in his cups, she continued with delicate firmness; "an' if you-all ain't mighty keerful how you line out, you'll shorely get a smoothin' iron direct."

Nothing daunted by the lady's candour, Riley Bent sat down on a furloughed tub which reposed bottom up in one corner. In the course of a conversation, whereof he furnished the questions, and Sal the short, inhospitable replies, it occurred that she and Riley Bent became mutually, albeit dimly, known to one another.

During the three months following, Riley Bent was much and persistently in the laundry of Wagon Mound Sal. Wolfville, eagle-eyed in the softer and more dulcet phenomena of life, looked

confidently for a wedding. So in truth did Sal, emulous of Benson Annie. Also Sal was a clear-minded, resolute young lady; and
having one day concluded to take Riley Bent for better or for
worse, she lost no time in bringing matters to a focus.

"You're a maverick?" she one day asked, suddenly looking up
from her ironing. Sal's tones were steady and cool, but it was
noticed that she burnt a hole in the bosom of Doc Peet's shirt
while waiting a reply. "You-all ain't married none?"

"Thar ain't no squaw has ever been able to rope, throw an'
run her brand on me!" said Riley Bent. "Which I'm shorely a
maverick!"

"Whatever then is the matter of you an' me dealin'?" asked
Sal, coming around to Riley Bent's side of the ironing table.

That personage surveyed her in a thoughtful maze.

"You're a longhorn, an' for that much so be I," he said at last,
as one who meditates. "Neither of us would grade for corn-fed
in anybody's yards!"

Then came another long pause, during which, with his eyes
fixedly gazing into Wagon Mound Sal's, Riley Bent gave himself
to the unwonted employment of thinking. At last he shook his
head until the little gold bells on his bullion hatband tinkled in a
dubious, uncertain way, as taking their tone from the wearer.

"Which the idee bucks me plumb off!" he remarked, with a
final deep breath; and then with no further word Riley repaired
to the Red Light Saloon and became dejectedly yet deeply drunk.

For a month Wolfville saw naught of Riley Bent. He was supposed to be two-score miles away on the range with his cattle.
Wagon Mound Sal, with a trace of grimness about the mouth,
conducted her laundry, and, in the absence of competition,
waxed opulent. She looked confidently for the return of Riley
Bent; as what woman, knowing her spells and powers, would
have not.

At last he came. Sal, as well as Wolfville, learned of his presence
by a mellow whoop at the far end of the single street. Sal was
subsequently gratified by a view of him as he and a comrade, one

Rice Hoskins, slid from their saddles and entered the Red Light
Saloon.

Wagon Mound Sal was offended at this; he should have come
straight to her. But beyond slamming her irons unreasonably as
she replaced them on the range, she made no sign.

To give Riley Bent justice, he had done little during the month
of his absence save think of Wagon Mound Sal. Whether he pur-
sued the evanescent steer, or organised the baking powder biscuit
of his day and kind, Wagon Mound Sal ran ever in his thoughts
like a torrent. But he couldn't bring himself to the motion of a
wife; not even if that favoured woman were Wagon Mound Sal.

"Seems like bein' married that a-way," he explained to Rice
Hoskins, as they discussed the business about their camp-fire, "is
so onnacheral."

"That's whatever!" assented Rice Hoskins.

"But," said Riley Bent after a pause; "I reckon I'd better ride
in an' tell her she don't get me none, an' end the game."

"That's whatever!"

It was the deference to this view which gained Wolfville the
pleasure of the presence of Riley Bent and Rice Hoskins on the
occasion named. It had been Riley Bent's plan—having first ac-
quired what stimulant he might crave—to leave Rice Hoskins to
the companionship of the barkeeper, while he repaired briefly
to Wagon Mound Sal, and expressed a determination never to
wed. But after the first drink he so far modified the programme
as to decide, instead, to write a letter.

"You see!" he said, "writin' a letter shows a heap more respect.
An' then ag'in, if I goes personal, she might get all wrought up
an' lay for me permiscus a whole lot."

The flaw in this letter plan became apparent. Neither Riley
Bent nor Rice Hoskins could write. They made application to
Black Jack, the barkeeper, to act as amanuensis. But he saw ob-
jection, and hesitated.

"I reckon I'll pass the deal, gents," said Black Jack, "if you-alls
don't mind. The grand jury is goin' to begin their round-up over

in Tucson next week, an' they'd jest about call it forgery."

At last as a solution, Rice Hoskins drew a rude picture in ink of a woman going one way, and a man with a big hat and disreputable spurs, going the other; what he called an "Injun letter." This work of art he regarded with looks of sagacity and satisfaction.

"If she was an Injun," said the artist, "she'd *sabe* that picture mighty quick. That means: 'You-all take your trail an' I'll take mine.' "

"Which it does seem plain as old John Chisholm's 'Fence-rail Brand,' " remarked Riley Bent. "Now jest make a tub by her, an' mark me with a 4-bar-J, the same bein' my brand; then she'll shorely tumble. Thar's nothin' like ropin' with a big loop; then if you miss the horns, you're mighty likely to fasten by the feet."

The missive was despatched to Wagon Mound Sal by hand of a Mexican. Then Riley Bent and Rice Hoskins restored their flagged spirits with liquor.

Riley Bent and Rice Hoskins drank a vast deal. And it came to pass, by virtue of this indiscretion, that Rice Hoskins later, while Riley Bent was still thoughtfully over his cups at the Red Light, rode his broncho into the New York Store. In the plain line of objection to this, Jack Moore, the Marshall, shot Rice Hoskins' pony. As the animal fell it pinned Rice Hoskins to the floor by his leg; in this disadvantageous position he emptied his pistol at Jack Moore, and of course missed.

Moore was in no sort an idle target. He was a painstaking Marshal, and showed his sense of duty at this time by putting four bullets through the reckless bosom of Rice Hoskins; the staccate voices of their Colt's six-shooters melted into each other until they sounded as one.

"I never could shoot none with a pony on my laig," observed Rice Hoskins.

Then a splash of blood stained his sun-coloured moustache; his empty pistol rattled on the board floor; his head dropped on his arm, and Rice Hoskins was dead.

It was at this crisis that Riley Bent, startled by the artillery as

he sat in the Red Light, came whirling to the scene on his pony. The duel was over before he set foot in stirrup. He saw at a glance that Rice Hoskins was only a memory. Had he been romantic, or a sentimentalist, Riley Bent would have shot out the hour with Jack Moore, the Marshal. And had there been one spark of life in the heart of Rice Hoskins to have fought over, Riley Bent would have stood in the smoke of his own six-shooter all day and taken what Fate might send. As it was, however, he curbed his broncho in mid-speed so bluntly, the Spanish bit filled its mouth with blood. It spun on its hind hoofs like a top. Then, as the long spurs dug to its ribs, it whizzed off in the opposite direction; out of camp like an arrow. The last bullet in Jack Moore's pistol splashed on a silver dollar in Riley Bent's pocket as he turned his pony.

"Whenever I reloads my pistol," said Jack Moore to Old Man Enright, who had come up, "I likes to reload her all around; so I don't regyard that last cartridge as no loss."

Wagon Mound Sal was deep in a study of Rice Hoskins' "Injun letter" when the shooting took place. The missive's meaning was not so easy to make out as its hopeful authors had believed. When the deeds of Jack Moore were related to her, however, the brow of Wagon Mound Sal took on an angry flush. She sent a message to Jack Moore asking him to call at once.

"Whatever do you mean?" she demanded of Jack Moore, as he entered the laundry, "a-stampedin' of Riley Bent out of camp that a-way? Don't you know I was intendin' to marry him? Yere he's been gone a month, an' yet the minute he shows up you have to take to cuttin' the dust 'round his moccasins with your six-shooter, an' away he goes ag'in. He jest nacherally seizes on your gun-play for a good excuse. It's shore enough to drive one plumb loco!"

Jack Moore looked decidedly bothered.

"Of course, Sal," he said at last in a deprecatory way, "you-all onderstands that when I takes to shakin' the loads outen my six-shooter at Riley Bent, I does it offishul. An' I'm free to say, that I was wropped and preoccupied like with my dooties as Marshal at the time, I never thinks once of them nuptials you med'tates with Riley Bent. If I had I would have downed his pony with that last shot an' turned him over to you. But perhaps it ain't too late."

It was the next afternoon. Riley Bent was reclining in his camp in the *Tres Hermanas*. Grey, keen eyes watched him from behind a point of rocks. Suddenly a mouthful of white smoke puffed from the point of rocks, and something hard and positive broke Riley Bent's leg just above the knee. The blow of the bullet shocked him for a moment, but the next, with a curse in his mouth, and a six-shooter in each hand, he tumbled in behind a boulder to do battle with his assailant. With the crack of the Winchester which accompanied the phenomena of smoke-puff and broken leg, came the voice of Jack Moore, Marshal.

"Hold up your hands, thar!" said Moore. "Up with 'em; I shan't say it twice!"

Riley Bent could not obey; he had taken ten seconds off to faint.

When he revived Jack Moore had claimed his pistols and was calmly setting the bones of the broken leg; devoting the woollen shirts in the war-bags on his saddle to be bandages, and making splints of cedar bark. These folk of the plains and mountains, far from the surgeon, often set each other's, or, for that matter, their own bones, when a fall from a pony, or some similar catastrophe, furnishes the call.

"If you-all needed me," observed Riley Bent peevishly, when a little later Jack Moore was engaged over bacon and flap-jacks for the sundown meal, "whatever was the matter of sayin' so? This yere idee of shootin' up a gent without notice or pow-wow is plumb onlegal. An' I'll gamble on it, ten to one!"

"Well!" said Jack Moore, as he deftly tossed a flap-jack in the air and caught it in the frying-pan again, "I didn't aim to take no chances of chagrinin' one who loves you, by lettin' you get away. Then, ag'in, my own notion is that it might sorter hasten the bridal some. Thar's nothin' like a bullet in a party's frame for makin' him feel romantic an' sentimental. It softens his nature a heap, an' sets him to yearnin' for female care."

"Which you've been shootin me up to be married!" responded Riley Bent in tones of disgust.

"That's straight!" retorted Jack Moore, as he slid the last flap-jack into the invalid's tin plate. "You've been pesterin' round Wagon Mound Sal ontil that lady has become wropped in you. She confides to me cold that she's anxious to make a weddin' of it, which is all the preliminary necessary in Arizona. You are goin' back to Wolfville with me tomorry on a buckboard,—which will be sent on yere from the stage station,—an' after Doc Peets goes over your laig ag'in, you an' Wagon Mound Sal are goin' to become man an' wife like a landslide. You have bred hopes in that lady's bosom, an' you've got to make 'em good. That's all thar is to this play; an' you don't get your guns ag'in ontil you're a married man."

Jack Moore, firm, direct and decided, had a great effect in fixing the wandering fancies of Riley Bent. He thoughtfully masticated his flap-jack a moment, and then asked:

"S'pose I arches my back an' takes to buckin' at these yere abrupt methods in my destinies; s'pose I quits the deal cold?"

"In which eevent," responded Jack Moore, with an air of iron confidence, "we merely convenes the Stranglers an' hangs you for luck."

But Riley Bent was softened and his mind made fully up. Whether it was the sentimental influence of Jack Moore's bullet, which Doc Peets subsequently dug out; or whether Riley was touched by the fact that Wagon Mound Sal, herself, brought over the buckboard to convey him to Wolfville, may never be known. What was certain, however, was that Riley Bent came finally to the conclusion to wed. He told Wagon Mound Sal so while on the buckboard going back.

"Which it's shorely doubtful," said Wagon Mound Sal, "if any man is worth the trouble. An' this yere is my busiest day, too!"

There was great rejoicing in the wareroom of the New York Store. A whole box of candles blazed gloriously from the walls. Old Man Enright gave the bride away, Benson Annie appeared to look on, while Faro Nell supported Sal as bridesmaid. As usual, in any hour of sacred need, a preacher was obtained from Tucson.

"An' you can bet that pastor knows his business!" said Old Monte, the stage driver, who had been commissioned to bring one over. "He's a deep-water brand, an' he's all right! I takes my steer when I seelects him from the barkeep of the Golden Rod saloon, an' he'd no more give me the wrong p'inter, that a-way, than he'd give me the wrong bottle."

Doc Peets's offering to the bride was a bullet. It was formerly the property of Jack Moore. It was the one he conferred on Riley Bent that evening in the foothills of the *Tres Hermanas.*

"Keep it!" said Doc Peets to the bride. "It's what sobers him, an' takes the frivolity outen him, an' makes him know his own heart."

"An' I shorely reckons you're right that a-way, Doc," said Jack Moore, some hours after the wedding as the two turned from the laundry whither Moore had repaired to return Riley Bent his pistols; "I shore reckons you're right a whole lot. I knows a gent in the states, an' he tells me himse'f how he goes projectin' 'round, keepin' company with a lady for a year, an' ain't thinkin' none speshul of marryin' her. One day somebody gets plumb tired of the play an' shoots him some, after which he simply goes about pantin' to lead that lady to the altar; that's straight!"

THE LUCK OF COLD-SOBER SIMMS

From *The Black Lion Inn*

Which this yere tale is mighty devious, not to say disj'inted, because, d'you see! from first to last, she's all the truth. Now, thar is folks sech as Injuns an' them sagacious sports which we-all terms philosophers, who talks of truth bein' straight. Injuns will say a liar has a forked tongue, while philosophers will speak of a straight ondeviatin' narrative, meanin' tharby to indooce you to regyard said story as the emanation of honesty in its every word. For myse'f I don't subscribe none to these yere phrases. In my own experience it's the lies that runs in a straight line like a bullet, whereas the truth goes onder an' over, an' up an' down, doubles an' jumps sideways a dozen times before ever it finally finds its camp in what book-sharps call the "climax." Which I says ag'in that this tale, bein' troo, has nacherally as many kinks in it as a new lariat.

Bein' thoughtful that a-way, an' preyed on by a desire to back-track every fact to its fountain-head, meanwhile considerin' how different the kyards would have fallen final if something prior had been done or left ondone, has ever been my weakness. It's allers so with me. I can recall as a child how back in Tennessee I deevotes hours when fishin' or otherwise uselessly engaged, to wonderin' whoever I'd have been personal if my maw had died in her girlhood an' pap had wedded someone else. It's plumb too many for me; an' now an' then when in a sperit of onusual cog'ta-tion, I ups an' wonders where I'd be if both my maw an' pap

had cashed in as colts, I'd jest simply set down he'pless, onquali-
fied to think at all. It's plain that in sech ontoward events as
my two parents dyin', say, at the age of three, I sort o' wouldn't
have happened none. This yere solemn view never fails to give
me the horrors.

I fixes the time of this story easy as bein' that eepock when
Jim East an' Bob Pierce is sheriffs of the Panhandle, with head-
quarters in Tascosa, an' Bob Roberson is chief of the L I T ranch.
These yere evidences of merit on the parts of them three gents
has not, however, anything to do with how Cold-sober Simms
gets rich at farobank; how two hold-ups plots to rob him; how
he's saved by the inadvertent capture of a bob-cat who's strange
to him entire; an' how the two hold-ups in their chagrin over
Cold-sober's escape an' the mootual doubts it engenders, pulls on
each other an' relieves the Stranglers from the labor of stringin'
'em to a cottonwood.

These doin's whereof I gives you a rapid rehearsal, has their
start when Old Scotty an' Locoed Charlie gets drunk in Tascosa
prior to startin' west on their buckboard with the mailbags of
the Lee-Scott ranch. Locoed Charlie an' Old Scotty is drunk when
they pulls out; Cold-sober Simms is with 'em as a passenger. At
their night camp half way to the Lee-Scott, Locoed Charlie,
whose head can't stand the strain of Jenkins' nose-paint, makes
war-medicine an' lays for Old Scotty all spraddled out. As the
upcome of these yere hostilities, Old Scotty confers a most elab'-
rate beatin' on Locoed Charlie; after which they-all cooks their
grub, feeds, an' goes to sleep.

But Locoed Charlie don't go to sleep; he lays thar drunk an'
disgruntled an' hungerin' to play even. As a good revengeful
scheme, Locoed Charlie allows he'll get up an' secrete the mailbag, thinkin' tharby to worry Old Scotty till he sweats blood.
Locoed Charlie packs the mailbag over among some rocks which
is thick grown with cedar bresh. When it comes sun-up an' Locoed Charlie is sober an' repents, an' tells Old Scotty of his little
game, neither he nor Scotty can find that mailbag nohow. Locoed
Charlie shore hides her good.

Locoed Charlie an' Scotty don't dare go on without it, but stays an' searches; Cold-sober Simms—who is given this yere nom-de-guerre, as Colonel Sterett terms it, because he's the only sport in the Panhandle who don't drink—stays with 'em to help on the hunt. At last, failin' utter to discover the missin' mail, Locoed Charlie an' Old Scotty returns to Tascosa in fear an' tremblin', not packin' the nerve to face McAllister, who manages for the Lee-Scott, an' inform him of the yoonique disposition they makes of his outfit's letters. This return to Tascosa is, after all, mere proodence, since McAllister is a mighty emotional manager, that a-way, an' it's as good as even money he hangs both of them culprits in that first gust of enthoosiasm which would be shore to follow any explanation they can make. So they returns; an' because he can't he'p himse'f none, bein' he's only a passenger on that buckboard, Cold-sober Simms returns with 'em. No, the mailbag is found a week later by a Lee-Scott rider, an' for the standin' of Locoed Charlie an' Scotty it's as well he does.

Cold-sober is some sore at bein' baffled in his trip to the Lee-Scott since he aims to go to work thar as a rider. To console himse'f, he turns in an' bucks a faro game that a brace of onknown black-laigs who shows in Tascosa from Fort Elliot the day prior, has onfurled in James' s'loon. As sometimes happens, Cold-sober plays in all brands an' y'earmarks of luck, an' in four hours breaks the bank. It ain't overstrong, no sech institootion of finance in fact as Cherokee Hall's faro game in Wolfville, an' when Cold-sober calls the last nine-king turn for one hundred, an' has besides a hundred on the nine, coppered, an' another hundred open on the king, tharby reapin' six hundred dollars as the froots of said feat, the sharp who's dealin' turns up his box an' tells Cold-sober to set in his chips to be cashed. Cold-sober sets 'em in; nine thousand five hundred dollars bein' the roundup, an' the dealer-sharp hands over the dinero. Then in a sperit of resentment the dealer-sharp picks up the faro-box an' smashes it ag'in the wall.

"Thar bein' nothin' left," he says to his fellow black-laig, who's settin' in the look-out's chair, "for you an' me but to prance out an' stand up a stage, we may as well dismiss that deal-box from our affairs. I knowed that box was a hoodoo ever since Black Morgan gets killed over it in Mobeetie; an' so I tells you, but you-all wouldn't heed."

Cold-sober is shore elated about his luck; them nine thousand odd dollars is more wealth than he ever sees; an' how to dispose of it, now he's got it, begins to bother Cold-sober a heap. One gent says, "Hive it in Howard's Store!" another su'gests he leave it with old man Cohn; while still others agrees it's Cold-sober's dooty to blow it in.

"Which if I was you-all," says Johnny Cook of the L I T outfit, "I'd shore sally forth an' buy nose-paint with that treasure while a peso remained."

But Cold-sober turns down these divers proposals an' allows he'll pack said roll in his pocket a whole lot, which he accordin' does.

Cold-sober hangs 'round Tascosa for mighty near a week, surrenderin' all thought of gettin' to the Lee-Scott ranch, feelin' that he's now too rich to punch cattle. Doorin' this season of idleness an' ease, Cold-sober bunks in with a jimcrow English doctor who's got a 'doby in Tascosa an' who calls himse'f Chepp. He's a decent form of maverick, however, this yere Chepp, an' him an' Cold-sober becomes as thick as thieves.

Cold-sober's stay with Chepp is brief as I states; in a week he gets restless ag'in for work; whereupon he hooks up with Roberson, an' goes p'intin' south across the Canadian on a L I T hoss to hold down one of that brand's sign-camps in Mitchell's canyon. It's only twenty miles, an' he's thar in half a day—him an' Wat Peacock who's to be his mate. An' Cold-sober packs with him that fortune of ninety-five hundred.

The two black-laigs who's been depleted that a-way still hankers about Tascosa; but as mighty likely they don't own the riches to take 'em out o' town, not much is thought. Nor does it ruffle the feathers of commoonal suspicion when the two disappears a few days after Cold-sober goes ridin' away to assoome them L I T reesponsibilities in Mitchell's canyon. The public is too busy to bother itse'f about 'em. It comes out later, however, that the goin' of Cold-sober has everything to do with the exodus of them hold-ups, an' that they've been layin' about since they loses their roll on a chance of gettin' it back. When Cold-sober p'ints south for Mitchell's that time, it's as good as these outlaws asks. They figgers on trailin' him to Mitchell's an' hidin' out ontil some hour when Peacock's off foolin' about the range; when they argues Cold-sober would be plumb easy, an' they'll kill an' skelp him an' clean him up for his money, an' ride away.

"In fact," explains the one Cold-sober an' Peacock finds alive, "It's our idee that the killin' an' skelpin' an' pillagin' of Cold-sober would get layed to Peacock, which would mean safety for us an' at the same time be a jest on Peacock that would be plumb hard to beat." That was the plan of these outlaws; an' the cause of its failure is the follerin' episode, to wit:

It looks like this Doc Chepp is locoed to collect wild anamiles that a-way.

"Which I wants," says this shorthorn Chepp, "a speciment of every sort o' the fauna of these yere regions, savin' an' exceptin' polecats. I knows enough of the latter pungent beast from an encounter I has with one, to form notions ag'in 'em over which not even the anxious cry of science can preevail. Polecats is barred from my c'llections. But," an' said Chepp imparts this last to Cold-sober as the latter starts for Mitchell's, "if by any sleight or dexterity you-all accomplishes the capture of a bob-cat, bring the interestin' creature to me at once. An' bring him alive so I may observe an' note his pecooliar traits."

It's the third mornin' in Mitchell's when a bob-cat is seen by Cold-sober an' Peacock to go sa'nterin' up the valley. Mebby this yere bob'cat's homeless; mebby he's a dissoloote bob-cat an' has been out all night carousin' with other bob-cats an' is simply late gettin' in; be the reason of his appearance what it may, Cold-sober remembers about Doc Chepp's wish to own a bob-cat, an' him an' Peacock lets go all holds, leaps for their ponies an' gives chase. Thar's a scramblin' run up the canyon, then Peacock gets his rope onto it, an' next Cold-sober fastens with his rope, an' you hear me, gents, between 'em they almost rends this year on-happy bob-cat in two. They pauses in time, however, an' after a fearful struggle they succeeds in stuffin' the bob-cat into Pea-cock's leather laiggin's, which the latter gent removes for that purpose. Bound hand an' foot, an' wropped in the laiggin's so tight he can hardly squawl, that bob-cat's put before Cold-sober on his saddle; an' this bein' fixed, Cold-sober heads for Tascosa to present him to his naturalist friend, Chepp, Peacock scamper-in' cheerfully along like a drunkard to a barbecue regyardin' the racket as a ondeniable excuse for gettin' soaked.

This adventure of the bob-cat is the savin' clause in the case of Cold-sober Simms. As the bob-cat an' him an' Peacock rides away, them two male-factors is camped not five miles off, over by the Serrita la Cruz, an' arrangin' to go projectin' 'round for Cold-sober an' his ninety-five hundred that very evenin'. In truth, they execootes their scheme; but only to find when they jumps his camp in Mitchell's that Cold-sober's done vamosed a whole lot.

It's then trouble begins to gather for the two rustlers. The one who deals the game that time is so overcome by Cold-sober's absence, he peevishly puts it up that his pard gives Cold-sober warnin' with the idee of later whackin' up the roll with him by way of a reward for his virchoo. Nacherally no se'f-respectin' miscreant will submit to sech impeachments, an' the accoosed makes a heated retort, punctuatin' his observations with his gun. Tharupon the other proceeds to voice his feelin's with his six-shooter; an' the mootual remarks of these yere dispootants is so well aimed an' ackerate that next evenin' when Cold-sober an' Peacock returns, they finds one dead an' t'other dyin' with even an' exact jestice broodin' over all.

As Cold-sober an' Peacock is settin' by their fire that night, restin' from their labors in plantin' the two hold-ups, Cold-sober starts up sudden an' says:

"Yereafter I adopts a bob-cat for my coat-o'-arms. Also, I changes my mind about Howard, an' to-morry I'll go chargin' into Tascosa an' leave said ninety-five hundred in his iron box. Thar's more 'bad men' at Fort Elliot than them two we plants, an' mebby some more of 'em may come a-weavin' up the Canadian with me an' my wealth as their objective p'int."

Peacock endorses the notion enthoosiastic, an' declar's himse'f in on the play as a body-guard; for he sees in this yere second expedition a new o'casion for another drunk, an' Peacock jest nacherally dotes on a debauch.

WHEN THE CAPITOL WAS MOVED

When the joobilant Texans set down to kyarve out the destinies of that empire they wrests from the feeble paws of the Mexicans an' Santa Anna, they decides on Austin for the Capitol an' Old Houston to be President. An' I'll say right yere, Old Houston, by all roomer an' tradition, is mighty likely the most presidential president that ever keeps a republic guessin' as to whatever is he goin' to do next. Which he's as full of surprises as a night in Red Dog.

About the first dash outen the box, Old Houston gets himse'f into trouble with two Lone Star leadin' citizens whose names, respective, is Colonel Morton an' Jedge Webb.

Old Houston himse'f on the hocks of them vict'ries he partic'-pates in, an' bein' selected president like I say, grows as full of vanity as a prairie dog. Shore! he's a hero; the drawback is that his notion of demeanin' himse'f as sech is to spread his tail feath-ers an' strut. Old Houston gets that puffed up, an' his dignity is that egreegious, he feels crowded if a gent tries to walk on the same street with him.

Colonel Morton an' Jedge Webb themse'fs wades through that carnage from soda to hock freein' Texas, an' they sort o' figgers that these yere services entitles them to be heard some. Old Houston, who's born with a notion that he's doo to make what public uproar every o'casion demands, don't encourage them two patriots. He only listens now an' then to Morton; an' as for Jedge Webb, he jest won't let that jurist talk at all.

"An' for these yere followin' reasons to wit," explains Old Houston, when some Austin sports puts it to him p'lite, but steadfast, that he's onjust to Webb. "I permits Morton to talk some, because it don't make a splinter of difference what Morton says. He can talk on any side of any subject an' no one's ediot enough to pay the least attention to them remarks. But this sit-yooation is changed when you-all gets to Webb. He's a disaster. Webb never opens his mouth without subtractin' from the sum total of hooman knowledge."

When Morton hears of them remarks he regyards himse'f as wronged.

"An' if Old Houston," observes Morton, who's a knife fighter an' has sliced offensive gents from time to time; "an' if Old Houston ain't more gyarded in his remarks, I'll take to disapprovin' of his conduct with a bowie."

As I intimates, Old Houston is that pride-blown that you-all couldn't stay on the same range where he is. An' he's worried to a standstill for a openin' to onload on the Texas public a speciment of his dignity. At last, seein' the chances comin' some slow, he ups an' constructs the opportunity himse'f.

Old Houston's home-camp, that a-way, is at a hamlet named Washin'ton down on the Brazos. It's thar he squanders the heft of his leesure when not back of the game as President over to Austin. Thar's a clause in the constitootion which, while pitchin' onto Austin as the public's home-ranche or capitol, permits the President in the event of perils onforeseen or invasions or sech, to round up the archives an' move the capitol camp a whole lot. Old Houston, eager to be great, seizes onto this yere tenet.

"I'll jest sort o' order the capitol to come down yere where I live at," says Old Houston, "an' tharby call the waverin' attention of the Lone Star public to who I be."

As leadin' up to this atrocity an' to come within the constitootion, Old Houston allows that Austin is menaced by Comanches. Shore, it ain't menaced none; Austin would esteem the cleanin' out of that entire Comanche tribe as the labors of a holiday. But it fills into Old Houston's hand to make this bluff as a excuse.

An' with that, he issues the order to bring the whole gov'ment layout down to where he lives.

No, as I tells you-all before, Austin ain't in no more danger of Comanches than she is of j'inin' the church. Troo, these yere rannikaboo savages does show up in paint an' feathers over across the Colorado once or twice; but beyond a whoop or two an' a little permiscus shootin' into town which nobody minds, them vis'tations don't count.

To give you-all gents a idee how little is deemed of Comanches by them Texas forefathers, let me say a word of Bill Spence who keeps a store in Austin. Bill's addin' up Virg Horne's accounts one afternoon in his books.

"One pa'r of yaller-top, copper-toe boots for Virg, joonior, three dollars, one red cal'co dress for Missis Virg, two dollars," goes on Bill.

At this epock Bill hears a yowl; glancin' out of the winder, he counts a couple of hundred Injuns who's proselytin' about over on t'other side of the river. Bill don't get up none; he jests looks annoyed on account of that yellin' puttin' him out in his bookkeepin'.

As a bullet from them savages comes singin' in the r'ar door an' buries itse'f in a ham, Bill even gets incensed.

"Hiram," he calls to his twelve-year old son, who's down cellar drawin' red-eye for a customer; "Hiram, you-all take pop's rifle, raise the hindsight for three hundred yards, an' reprove them hostiles. Aim low, Hiram, an' if you fetches one, pop'll give you a seegyar an' let you smoke it yourse'f."

Bill goes back to Virg Horne's account, an' Hiram after slammin' away with Bill's old Hawkins once or twice comes in an' gets his seegyar.

No; Old Houston does wrong when he flings forth this yere ukase about movin' the capitol. Austin, even if a gent does have to dodge a arrer or duck a bullet as he prosecootes his daily tasks, is as safe as a camp-meetin'.

When Old Houston makes the order, one of his Brazos pards reemonstrates with him.

"Which Austin will simply go into the air all spraddled out," says this pard.

"If Austin sails up in the air an' stays thar," says Old Houston, "still you-all can gamble that this yere order goes."

"You hears," says another, "Elder Peters when he tells of how a Mexican named Mohammed commands the mountain to come to him? But the mountain calls his bluff; that promontory stands pat, an' Mohammed has to go to the mountain."

"My name's Sam Houston an' it ain't Mohammed," retorts Old Houston. "Moreover, Mohammed don't have no written constitootion."

Nacherally, when Austin gets notice of Old Houston's plan, that meetropolis r'ars back an' screams. The faro-bank folks an' the tavern folks is speshul malignant, an' it ain't no time before they-all convenes a meetin' to express their views on Old Houston. Morton an' Jedge Webb does the oratory. An' you hear me! that assembly is shore sultry. Which the epithets they applies to Old Houston kills the grass for twenty rods about.

Austin won't move.

Austin resolves to go to war first; a small army is organized with Morton in command to gyard the State House an' the State books that a-way, an' keep Old Houston from romancin' over an' packin' 'em off a heap.

Morton is talkin' an' Webb is presidin' over this yere convocation—which the said meetin' is that large an' enthoosiastic it plumb chokes up the hall an' overflows into the street—when all of a sudden a party comes swingin' through the open winder from the top of a scrub-oak that grows alongside the buildin', an' drops light as a cat onto the platform with Morton an' Webb. At this yere interruption, affairs comes to a halt, an' the local sports turns in to consider an' count up the invader.

This gent who swoops through the winder is dark, big, bony, an' tall; his ha'r is lank an' long as the mane of a hoss; his eyes is deep an' black; his face, tanned like a Injun's, seems hard as iron. He's dressed in leather from foretop to fetlock, is shod with a pa'r of Comanche moccasins, an' besides a 'leven inch knife in his belt, packs a rifle with a 48-inch bar'l. It will weigh twenty pounds, an' yet this stranger handles it like it's a willow switch.

As this darksome gent lands in among Morton an' Webb, he stands thar without sayin' a word. Webb, on his part, is amazed, while Morton glowers.

"Whatever do you-all regyard as a market price for your skelp?" says Morton to the black interloper, at the same time loosenin' his knife.

The black stranger makes no reply; his hand flashes to his bowie, while his face still wears its iron look.

Webb, some hurried, pushes in between Morton an' the black stranger. Webb is more for peace an' don't believe in beginnin' negotiations with a knife.

Webb dictates a passel of p'lite queries to this yere black stranger. Tharupon, the black stranger bows p'lite an' formal, an' goin' over to the table writes down in good English, "I'm deef an' dumb." Next, he searches outen his warbags a letter. It's from Old Houston over on the Brazos. Old Houston allows that onless Austin comes trailin' in with them records within three days, he'll ride over a whole lot an' make the round-up himse'f. Old Houston declar's that Austin by virchoo of them Comanches is as onsafe as a Christian in Mississippi, an' he don't aim to face no sech dangers while performin' his dooties as President of the Commonwealth.

After the black stranger flings the letter on the table, he's organizin' to go out through the winder ag'in. But Morton sort o' detains him. Morton writes on the paper that now the black stranger is through his dooties as a postman, he will, if he's a dead game sport, stay over a day, an' him an' Morton will entertain themse'fs by pullin' off a war of their own. The idee strikes the black stranger as plenty good, an' while his face still wears its ca'm, hard look, he writes onder Morton's bluff:

"Rifles; no'th bank of the Colorado; sun-down, this evenin'."

The next moment he leaps from the platform to the winder an' from thar to the ground, an' is gone.

"But Colonel Morton," reemonstrates Webb, who's some scand'lized at Morton hookin' up for blood with this yere black stranger; "you-all shorely don't aim to fight this party? He's deef an' dumb, which is next to bein' locoed outright. Moreover, a gent of your standin' can't afford to go ramblin' about, lockin' horns with every onknown miscreant who comes buttin' in with a missif from President Houston, an' then goes stampedin' through a winder by way of exit."

"Onknown!" retorts Morton. "That letter-packin' person is as well known as the Rio Grande. That's Deef Smith."

"Colonel Morton," observes Webb, some horrified when he learns the name of the black stranger, "this yere Deef Smith is a shore shot. They say he can empty a Comanche saddle four times in five at three hundred yards."

"That may be as it may," returns Morton. "If I downs him, so much the more credit; if he gets me, at the worst I dies by a famous hand."

The sun is restin' on the sky-line over to the west. Austin has done crossed the Colorado an' lined up to witness this yere dooel. Deef Smith comes ridin' in from some'ers to the no'th, slides outen the saddle, pats his hoss on the neck, an' leaves him organized an' ready fifty yeard to one side. Then Deef Smith steps to the center an' touches his hat, mil'tary fashion, to Morton an' Webb.

These yere cavaliers is to shoot it out at one hundred yards. As they takes their places, Morton says:

"Jedge Webb, if this Deef Smith party gets me, as most like he will, send my watch to my mother in Looeyville."

Then they fronts each other; one in brown leather, the other in cloth as good as gold can buy. No one thinks of any difference between 'em, however, in a day when courage is the test of aristocracy.

Since one gent can't hear, Webb is to give the word with a handkerchief. At the first flourish the rifles fall to a hor'zontal as still an' steady as a rock. Thar's a brief pause; then Webb drops his handkerchief.

Thar is a crack like one gun; Deef Smith's hat half turns on his head as the bullet cuts it, while Morton stands a moment an' then, without a sound, falls dead on his face. The lead from Deef Smith's big rifle drills him through the heart. Also, since it perforates that gold repeater, an' as the blood sort o' clogs the works, the Austin folks decides it's no use to send it on to Looey-ville, but retains it that a-way as a keepsake.

With the bark of the guns an' while the white smoke's still hangin' to mark the spot where he stands, Deef Smith's hoss runs to him like a dog. The next instant Deef Smith is in the saddle an' away. It's jest as well. Morton's plenty pop'lar with the Austin folks an' mebby some sharp, in the first hysteria of a great loss, overlooks what's doo to honor an' ups an' plugs this yere Deef Smith.

The Old Cattleman

THE TREACHERY OF CURLY BEN

"Yere! you black boy, Tom!" and the Old Cattleman's voice rose loudly as he commanded the approach of that bouyant servitor, who supervised his master's destinies, and performed in the triangular role of valet, guardian and friend. "Yere, you; go to the barkeep of this tavern an' tell him to frame me up a pitcher of that peach brandy an' honey the way I shows him how. An' when he's got her organized, bring it out to us with two glasses by the fire. You-all ain't filin' no objections to a drink, be you?" This last was to me. "As for me, personal," he continued, "you can put down a bet I'm as dry as a covered bridge."

I readily assented to peach and honey. I would agree to raw whiskey if it were needed to appease him and permit me to remain in his graces.

"Thar's one thing, one redeemin' thing I might say, about the East," he went on, when the peach and honey appeared, "an' the same claims my respects entire; that's its nose-paint. Which we shorely suffers in the Southwest from beverages of the most ornery kind."

"There's a word I've wanted to ask you about more than once," I said. "What do you mean by 'ornery,' and where do you get it?"

"Where do I get it?" he responded, with a tinge of scorn. "Where do I rope onto any word? I jest nacherally reaches out an' acquires it a whole lot, like I do the rest of the language I employs. As for what it means, I would have allowed that any gent who escapes bein' as weak-minded as Thompson's colt—an' that cayouse is that imbecile he used to swim a river to get a drink—would hesitate with shame to ask sech questions.

" 'Ornery' is a word the meanin' whereof is goin' to depend a heap on what you brands with it." This was said like an oracle. "Also, the same means more or less, accordin' to who-all puts the word in play. I remembers a mighty decent sort of sport, old Cape Willingham it is; an' yet Dan Boggs is forever referrin' to old Cape as 'ornery.' An' I reckon Dan thinks he is. Which the trouble with Cape, from Dan's standp'int, is this: Cape is one of these yere precise parties, acc'rate as to all he does, an' plenty partic'lar about his looks. An Osage buck, paintin' for a dance, wouldn't worry more over his feachers, an' the way the ocher should be streaked on.

"Now this yere Cape is shy an eye, where an Apache pokes it out with a lance, back in Cochise's time; an', as he regyards his countenance as seemin' over rocky, bein' redooced to one eye as I relates, he sends East an' gets a glass eye. This ain't where Cape's technical'ties about his looks trails in, however; an', if he had paused thar in his reehabilitations, Boggs allers put it up he'd a-found no fault. But Cape notices that about tenth drink time his shore-enough eye begins for to show up bloodshot, an' is a bad mate for the glass eye, the same bein' onaffected by drink. So what does Cape do but have a bloodshot eye made, an' takes to packin' the same on his person constant. As Cape drinks his forty drops all commodious, he sort o' keeps tabs on himse'f in the lookin' glass back of the bar; an' when the good eye commences to turn red with them libations he's countin' into the corral, he ups an' shifts his bresh; digs out the white eye an' plants the drunken eye in the place.

"Shore! none of us cares except Dan Boggs; but Dan feels it to that extent, it's all Colonel Sterett an' Doc Peets an' Old Man Enright can do, added to Dan's bein' by nacher a born gent that a-way, to keep Dan from mentionin' it to old Cape.

" 'A gent who comes from a good fam'ly, like you-all,' says Old Man Enright to Dan, sort o' soothin' of him, 'oughter be removed above makin' comments on pore old Cape shiftin' his optics. Troo! it's a weakness, but where is the sport who hasn't weaknesses likewise. Which you-all is a mighty sight to one side of bein' perfect yourse'f, Dan, an' yet we don't go 'round breakin' the information off in you every time you makes a queer play. An' you must b'ar with Cape, an' them caprices of his.' "

" 'I ain't denyin' nothin',' declar's Dan. 'I'm the last longhorn in Wolfville to be revilin' old Cape, an' refoosin' him his plain American right to go pirootin' 'round among his eyes as suits his taste. But I'm a mighty nervous man that a-way, an' Cape knows, or oughter know, how, as I states, I'm nacherally all onstrung, an' that his carryin's on with them eyes gives me the fantods. Onder all the circumstances, I claims his conduct is ornery, an' not what a invalid like me has a right to expect.'

"No; Dan never says nothin' to Cape; or does anythin' 'cept talk to Enright an' the rest of us about how he can't stand Cape shiftin' them eyes. An' it ain't affectation on the part of Dan; he shorely feels them shifts. Many a time, when it's got to be red eye time with Cape, an' as the latter is scroop'lously makin' said transfers, have I beheld Dan arise in silent agony, an' go to bite hunks outen a pine shelf that is built on the Red Light wall.

" 'Which that ornery Cape,' says Dan, as he picks the splinters from his mouth after sech exercises, 'would drive me as locoed as a coyote if I don't take refooge in some sech play like that.' "

"But, as I su'gests about this term 'ornery;' it depends a lot on who uses it, an' what for. Now Dan never refers to old Cape except as 'ornery;' while Enright an' the rest of us sees nothin' from soda to hock in Cape, doorin' them few months he mingles with us, which merits sech obloquys.

"No; ornery is a word that means what it says an' is shore deescriptif. Coyotes is ornery, sheep is ornery; an' them low-flung hoomans who herds sheep is ornery, speshul. Of course, the term has misapplications; as an extreme case, I've even heard ign'rant tenderfeet who alloodes to the whole West as 'ornery.'

But them folks is too debased an' too darkened to demand comments."

"You are very loyal to the West," I remarked.

"Which I shorely oughter be," retorted the old gentleman. "The West has been some loyal to me. Troo! it stands to reason that a party fresh from the East, where the horns has been knocked offen everythin' for two or three hundred years, an' conditions gen'ral is as soft as a goose-ha'r pillow, is goin' to notice some turgid changes when he lands in Arizona. But a shorthorn, that a-way, should reserve his jedgment till he gets acquainted, or gets lynched, or otherwise experiences the West in its troo colors. While Arizona, for speciment, don't go up an' put her arms about the neck of every towerist that comes chargin' into camp, her failure to perform said rites arises rather from dignity than hauteur. Arizona don't put on dog; but she has her se'f-respectin' ways, an' stands a pat hand on towerists.

"If I was called on to lay out a system to guide a tenderfoot who is considerin' on makin' Arizona his home-camp, I'd advise him to make his deboo in that territory in a sperit of ca'm an' silent se'f-reliance. Sech a gent might reside in Wolfville, say three months. He might meet her citizens, buck her faro-banks, drink her nose-paint, shake a hilarious hoof in her hurdy gurdies, ask for his letters, or change in whatever sums seems meet to him at the New York Store for shirts. Also, he might come buttin' along into the O. K. Restauraw three times a day with the balance of the band, an' Missis Rucker would shorely turn her grub-game for him, for the limit if he so pleased. But still, most likely every gent in camp would maintain doorin' his novitiate a decent distance with this yere stranger; they wouldn't onbuckle an' be drunk with him free an' social like, an' with the bridle off, like pards who has crossed the plains together an' seen extremes. All this, with a chill onto it, a tenderfoot would find himse'f ag'inst for the first few months in Wolfville.

"An' yet, my steer to him would be not to get discouraged, The camp's sizin' him up; that's all. If he perseveres, ca'm an' c'llected like I states, along the trail of his destiny, he'll shore come winner on the deal. At the end of three months, or mebby in onusual cases four months, jest as this yere maverick is goin' into the dance hall, or mebby the Red Light, some gent will chunk him one in the back with his shet fist an' say, 'How be you? You double-dealin', cattle-stealin', foogitive son of a murdererin' hoss-thief, how be you?''

"Now, right thar is whar this yere shorthorn wants to maintain his presence of mind. He don't want to go makin' no vain plays for his six-shooter, or indulge in no sour ranikaboo retorts. That gent likes him. With Wolfville social conditions, this yere greetin' is what you sports who comes from the far No'th calls 'the beginnin' of the thaw.' The ice is breakin' up; an' if our candidate sets in his saddle steady an' with wisdom at this backthumpin', name-callin' epock, an' don't take to millin' 'round for trouble, in two minutes him an' that gregar'ous gent who's accosted him is drinkin' an' fraternizin' together like two stage hold-ups in a strange camp. The West ain't ornery; she's simply reserved a whole lot.

"Mighty likely now," continued my friend, following a profound pause which was comfortably filled with peach and honey; "it's mighty likely now, comin' down to folks, that the most ornery party I ever knows is Curly Ben. This yere Ben is killed, final; downed by old Captain Moon. Thar's a strange circumstance attendin', as the papers say, the obliteration of this Curly Ben, an' it makes a heap of an impression on me at the time. It shows how the instinct to do things, that a gent is allers carryin' 'round in his mind, gets sort o' located in his nerves mebby, an' he'll do 'em without his intellects ridin' herd on the play—do 'em like Curly Ben does, after his light is out complete.

"This yere is what I'm trailin' up to: When Captain Moon fetches Curly Ben that time, Curly is playin' kyards. He's jest dealin', when, onbeknown to him, Moon comes Injunin' up from the r'ar surreptitious, an' drills Curly Ben through the head; an' the bullet bein' a '45 Colt's—for Moon ain't toyin' with Curly an' means business—goes plumb through an' emerges from onder Curly Ben's off eye. For that matter, it breaks the arm of a party

who's playin' opp'site to Curly, an' who is skinnin' his paste-
boards at the time, thinkin' nothin' of war. Which the queer part
is this: Curly, as I states—an' he never knows what hits him an'
is as dead as Santa Anna in a moment—is dealin' the kyards. He's
got the deck in his hands. An' yet, when the public picks Curly
off the floor, he's pulled his two guns, an' has got one cocked.
Now what do you-all deem of that for the workin' of a left-over
impulse when a gent is dead?

"But, as I remarks yeretofore, Curly Ben is the most ornery
person I ever overtakes, an' the feelin's of the camp is in nowise
laid waste when Moon adds him to the list that time in the Red
Light bar. It's this a-way:

"It's about a month before, when Captain Moon an' his nephy,
with two 8-mule teams and four big three-an'-a-half Bain wagons,
two lead an' two trail they be, comes freightin' out of Silver
City with their eyes on Wolfville. It's the fourth night out, an'
they're camped near a Injun agency. About midnight a half dozen
of the bucks comes scoutin' 'round their camp, allowin' to a
moral certainty they'll see what's loose an' little enough for 'em
to pull. The aborigines makes the error of goin' up the wind
from Moon's mules, which is grazin' about with hobbles on, an'
them sagacious anamiles actoofally has fits. It's a fact, if you
want to see a mule go plumb into the air an' remain, jest let him
get a good ample, onmistakable smell of a Injun! It simply on-
hinges his reason; he ain't no more responsible than a cimmaron
sheep. No, it ain't that the savage is out to do anything oncom-
mon to the mule; it's merely one of the mule's illoosions, as I've
told you once before. Jest the same, if them Injuns is comin' to
braid his tail an' braid it tight, that mule couldn't feel more
frantic.

"When these yere faithful mules takes to surgin' about the
scene on two feet, Moon's nephy grabs a Winchester an' pumps
a load or so into the darkness for gen'ral results. An' he has a
heap of luck He shorely stops one of them Apaches in his lopin'
up an' down the land for good an' all.

"In less than no time the whole tribe is down on Captain Moon an' his nephy, demandin' blood. Thar's plenty of some sorts of wisdom about a savage, an' these yere Apaches ain't runnin' right in on Moon an' his relatif neither. They was perfeckly familiar with the accoomulation of cartridges in a Winchester, an' tharfore goes about the stirrin' up of Moon an' that nephy plumb wary.

"Moon an' the boys goes in between the wagons, blazin' an' bangin' away at whatever moves or makes a noise; an' as they've been all through sech festivals before, they regyards their final chances to be as good as an even break, or better.

"While them Apaches is dodgin' about among the rocks, an' howlin' contempt, an' passin' resolootions of revenge touchin' the two Moons, the Injun agent comes troopin' along. He seeks to round-up his savages an' herd 'em back to the agency. The Apaches, on their side, is demandin' the capture of the nephy Moon for sp'ilin' one of their young men.

"The agent is a prairie dog jest out from the East, an' don't know half as much about what's goin' on inside of a Apache as a horned toad. He comes down to the aige of hostil'ties, as you-all might call it, an' makes Moon an' his Winchester workin' nephy a speech. He addresses 'em a whole lot on the enormity of downin' Apaches who goes prowlin' about an' scarin' up your mules at midnight, in what this yere witless agent calls a 'motif of childish cur'osity;' an' he winds up the powwow with demandin' the surrender of the 'hom'cide.'

" 'Surrender nothin'!' says Captain Moon. 'You tell your Injuns to line out for their camp; an' don't you youse'f get too zealous neither an' come too clost, or as shore as I casts my first vote for Matty Van Buren, I'll plug you plumb center.'

"But the nephy, he thinks different. In spite of Captain Moon's protest, he gives himse'f up to the agent on the promise of protection.

" 'You're gone, lad,' says Moon, when the nephy insists on yieldin'; 'you won't last as long as a pint of whiskey in a five-hand poker game.'

"But this yere young Moon is obdurate an' goes over an' gives

himse'f to the agent, who puts it up he'll send him to Prescott to
be tried in co't for beefin' the mule-thief Apache that a-way.

"Shore! it turns out jest as Captain Moon says. Before they'd
gone a half mile, them wards of the gov'ment, as I once hears a
big chief from Washin'ton call 'em, takes the nephy from this
yere fallacious agent an' by fourth drink time that mornin', or
when it's been sun-up three hours, that nephy is nothin' but a
mem'ry.

"How do they kill him? In a fashion which, from the coigne
your Apache views things, does 'em proud. That nephy is im-
molated as follows: They ropes him out, wrist an' ankle, with
four lariats; pegs him out like he's a hide they're goin' to dry.
Thar's a big ant hill close at hand; it's with reference to this yere
ant colony that the nephy is staked out. In three hours from the
time them ants gets the word from the Apaches, they've done
eat the nephy up, an' the last vestitch of him plumb disappears
with the last ant, as the latter resoomes his labors onder the
earth.

"Why, shore! these yere ants'll eat folks. They regyards sech
reepasts as festivals, an' seasons of reelaxation from the sterner
dooties of a ant. I recalls once how we loses Locoed Charlie,
which demented party I b'lieve I mentions to you prior. This
yere Charlie takes a day off from where he's workin'—at least he
calls it labor—at the stage corrals, an' goes curvin' over to Red
Dog. Charlie tanks up on the whiskey of that hamlet, compared
to which the worst nose-paint ever sold in Wolfville is nectar.
They palms off mebby it's a quart of this jooce on Charlie, an'
then he p'ints out for Wolfville.

"That's the last of the pore drunkard. His pony is nickerin'
about the corral gates, pleadin' with the mules inside to open
'em, in the mornin', but no sign or smoke of Locoed Charlie. An'
he never does show up no more.

"If it's Enright or Cherokee Hall, or any valyooed citizen, thar
would have issooed forth a war party, an' Red Dog would have
been sacked an' burned but what the missin' gent would have
been turned out. But it's different about Locoed Charlie. He

hadn't that hold on the pop'lar heart; didn't fill sech a place in the gen'ral eye; an' so, barrin' a word or two of wonder, over their drinks at the Red Light, I don't reckon now the Wolfville folks disturbs themse'fs partic'lar about the camp bein' shy Charlie.

"It's the second day when a teamster, trackin' over from Red Dog, developes what's left of Locoed Charlie. He falls off his hoss, with that load of Red Dog whiskey, an' every notion or idee or sensation absolootely effaced. An' where Charlie loses is, he falls by a ant hill. Yes; they shorely takes Charlie in. Thar's nothin' left of him when the teamster locates the remainder, but his clothes, his spurs an' his 'natomy. The r'ar gyard of them ants has long since retired with the final fragments of Locoed Charlie.

"You-all might o' seen the story. Colonel Sterett writes it up in the *Coyote*, an' heads it, 'Hunger is a Terrible Thing.' This sot Charlie comin' to his death that a-way puts a awful scare over Huggins an' Old Monte. It reforms 'em for more'n two hours. Huggins, who is allers frontin' up as one who possesses public sperit, tries to look plumb dignified about it, an' remarks to Dave Tutt in the New York Store as how he thinks we oughter throw in around an' build a monument to Locoed Charlie. Dave allows that, while he's with Huggins in them projecks, he wants to add a monument to the ants. The founders of the scheme sort o' splittin' at the go-in that a-way, it don't get no further, an' the monument to Locoed Charlie, as a enterprise, bogs down. But to continyoo on the trail of Captain Moon.

"Moon comes rumblin' into Wolfville, over-doo mebby it's two weeks, bringin' both teams. Tharupon he relates them outrages. Thar's but one thought; that agent has lived too long.

" 'If he was the usual common form of felon,' says Enright, 'ondoubted—for it would be their dooty—the vig'lance committee local to them parts would string him up. But that ain't possible; this yere miscreant is a gov'ment official an' wears the gov'ment brand, an' even the Stranglers, of whatever commoonity, ain't strong enough, an' wouldn't be jestified in stackin' in ag'in the gov'ment. Captain Moon's only show is a feud. He oughter caper over an', as private as possible, arrogate to himse'f the skelp of this yere agent who abandons his relatif to them hostiles.'

"Wolfville listens to Captain Moon's hist'ry of his wrongs; but aside from them eloocidations of Enright, no gent says much, Thar's some games where troo p'liteness consists in sayin' nothin' an' knowin' less. But the most careless hand in camp can see that Moon's aimin' at reprisals.

"This Curly Ben is trackin' about Wolfville at the time. Curly ain't what you-all would call a elevated character. He's a rustler of cattle, an' a smuggler of Mexican goods, an' Curly an' the Yoonited States marshals has had more turn-ups than one. But Curly is dead game; an' so far, he manages to either out-luck or out-shoot them magistrates; an', as I says, when Moon comes wanderin' in that time, mournin' for his nephy, Curly has been projectin' about camp for like it's a week.

"Moon sort o' roominates on the play, up an' down for a day or so, makin' out a plan. He don't want to go back himse'f; the agent knows him, an' them Injuns knows him, an' it's even money, if he comes pokin' into their bailiwick, they'll tumble to his errant. In sech events, they're shore doo to corral him an' give them ants another holiday. It's the ant part that gives pore Captain Moon a chill.

" 'I'll take a chance on a bowie knife,' says Moon to Dan Boggs,—Dan, bein' a sympathetic gent an' takin' nacherally to folks in trouble, has Moon's confidence from the jump; 'I'll take a chance on a bowie knife; an' as for a gun, I simply courts the resk. But them ants dazzles me—I lay down to ants, an' I looks on it as no disgrace to a gent to say so.'

" 'Ants shorely do sound poignant,' admits Dan: 'speshully them big black an' red ants that has stingers like hornets an' pinchers like bugs. Sech insecks, armed to the teeth as they be, an' laid out to fight both ways from the middle, is likewise too many for me. I would refoose battle with 'em myse'f.'

"It ain't long before Captain Moon an' Curly Ben is seen confidin' an' conferrin' with one another, an' drinkin' by themse'fs;

an' no one has to be told that Moon's makin' negotiations with Curly to ride over an' down the agent. The idee is pecooliarly grateful to Wolfville. It stands to win no matter how the kyards lay in the box. If Curly fetches the agent flutterin' from his limb, thar's one miscreant less in Arizona; if the agent gets the drop an' puts out Curly Ben, it comes forth jest the same. It's the camp's theery that, in all that entitles 'em to death, the case stands hoss an' hoss between the agent an' Curly Ben.

" 'An' if they both gets downed, it's a whip-saw; we win both ways;' says Cherokee Hall, an' the rest of us files away our nose-paint in silent assent tharwith.

"It comes out later that Moon agrees to give Curly Ben fifteen hundred dollars an' a pony, if he'll go over an' kill off the agent. Curly Ben says the prop'sition is the pleasantest thing he hears since he leaves the Panhandle ten years before; an' so he accepts five hundred dollars an' the pony—the same bein' in the nacher of payments in advance—an' goes clatterin' off up the canyon one evenin' on his mission of jestice. An' then we hears no more of Curly Ben for about a month. No one marvels none at this, however, as downin' any given gent is a prop'sition which in workin' out is likely to involve delays.

"One day, with onruffled brow an' an air all careless an' free, Curly Ben rides into Wolfville an' begins orderin' whiskey at the Red Light before he's hardly cl'ar of the saddle. Thar ain't no-body in camp, from Doc Peets to Missis Rucker, but what's eager to know the finish of Curly's expedition, but of course every-body hobbles his feelin's in them behalfs. It's Captain Moon's fooneral, an' he oughter have a first, oninterrupted say. Moon comes up to Curly Ben where Curly is cuttin' the alkali dust outen his throat at the Red Light bar.

" 'Did you get him?' Moon asks after a few p'lite preeliminar-ies. 'Did you bring back his ha'r an' y'ears like we agrees?'

" 'Have you-all got the other thousand ready,' says Curly Ben, 'in the event I do?'

" 'Right yere in my war-bags,' says Moon, 'awaitin' to make

good for your time an' talent an' trouble in revengin' my pore nephy's deemise by way of them insecks.' An' Moon slaps his pocket as locatin' the *dinero.*

" 'Well, I don't get him,' says Curly Ben ca'mly, settin' his glass on the bar.

"Thar's a pause of mebby two minutes, doorin' which Moon looks cloudy, as though he don't like the way the kyards is comin'; Curly Ben, on his part, is smilin' like what Huggins calls 'one of his songstresses' over in the Bird Cage Op'ry House. After a bit, Moon resoomes them investigations.

" 'Don't I give you four stacks of reds an' a pony,' he says, 'to reepair to that murderer an' floor-manage his obsequies? An' don't I promise you eight stacks more when you reports with that outcast's y'ears an' ha'r as showin' good faith?'

" 'C'rrect; every word,' says Curly Ben, lightin' a seegyar an then leanin' his elbows on the bar, a heap onmoved.

" 'Which I would admire to know, then,' says Moon, an' his eyes is gettin' little an' hard, 'why you-all don't made good them compacts.'

" 'Well, I'll onfold the reasons an' make it as plain an' cl'ar an' convincin' as a spade flush,' says Curly Ben. 'When I gets to this yere victim of ours, I finds him to be a mighty profoose an' lavish form of sport. The moment I'm finished explainin' to him my mission, an' jest as I onlimbers my six-shooter to get him where he lives, he offers me five thousand dollars to come back yere an' kill you. Nacherally, after that, me an' this yere subject of our plot takes a few drinks, talks it over, an' yere I be.'

" 'But what be you aimin' to do?' asks Moon.

" 'What be you aimin' to do?' responds Curly Ben. As I states, he's shore the most ornery coyote!

" 'I don't onderstand,' says Moon.

" 'Why it's as obv'ous,' retorts Curly Ben, 'as the Fence Rail brand, an' that takes up the whole side of a cow. The question now is, do you raise this yere gent? He raises you as I explains; now do you quit, or tilt him, say, a thousand better?'

" 'An' suppose I don't?' says Moon, sort o' figgerin' for a moment or so. 'What do you reckon now would be your next move?'

" 'Thar would be but one thing to do,' says Curly Ben mighty placid; 'I'd shorely take him. I would proceed with your destruction at once, an' return to this agent gent an' accept that five thousand dollar honorarium he offers.'

"Curly Ben is 'bad' plumb through, an' the sights as they says in the picturesque language of the Southwest, has been filed from his guns for many years. Which this last is runnin' in Moon's head while he talks with his disgustin' emmissary. Moon ain't out to take chances on gettin' the worst of it. An' tharfore, Moon at once waxes cunnin' a whole lot.

" 'I'm a pore man,' he says, 'but if it takes them teams of mine, to the last tire an' the last hoof, I've got to have this agent's ha'r an' y'ears. You camp around the Red Light awhile, Curly, till I go over to the New York Store an' see about more money. I'll be back while you're layin' out another drink.'

"Now it's not to the credit of Curly, as a crim'nal who puts thought into his labors, that he lets Captain Moon turn his flank the easy way he does. It displays Curly as lackin' a heap in mil'-tary genius. I don't presoome to explain it; an' it's all so dead on-nacheral at this juncture that the only s'lootion I'm cap'ble of givin' it is that it's preedestinated that a-way. Curly not only lets Moon walk off, which after he hangs up that bluff about takin' them terms of the agent's is mighty irreg'lar, but he's that ob-toose he sits down to play kyards, while he's waitin', with his back to the door. Why! it's like sooicide!

"Moon goes out to his wagons an' gets, an' buckles on, his guns. Quick, crafty, brisk as a cat an' with no more noise, Moon comes walkin' into the Red Light door. He sees Curly where he sits at seven-up, with his back turned towards him.

" 'One for jack!' says Curly, turnin' that fav'rite kyard. Moon sort o' drifts to his r'ar.

" 'Bang!' says Moon's pistol, an' Curly falls for'ards onto the table, an' then onto the floor, the bullet plumb through his head, as I informs you.

"Curly Ben never has the shadow of a tip; he's out of the Red

Light an' into the regions beyond, like snappin' your thumb an' finger. It's as sharp as the buck of a pony; he's Moon's meat in a minute.

"No; thar's nothin' for Wolfville to do. Moon's jestified. Which his play is the one trail out; for up to that p'int where Moon onhooks his guns, Curly ain't done nothin' to put him in reach of the Stranglers. Committees of vig'lance, that a-way like shore-enough co'ts, can't prevent crime; they only punish it, an' up to where Moon gets decisive action, thar's no openin' by which the Stranglers could cut in on the deal. Yes, Enright convenes his committee an' goes through the motions of tryin' Moon. They does this to preserve appearances, but of course they throws Moon loose. An' as thar's reasons, as any gent can see, why no one cares to have the story as it is, be made a subject of invidious gossip in Red Dog, an' other outfits envious of Wolfville, at Enright's su'gestion, the Stranglers bases the acquittal of Moon on the fact that Curly Ben deloodes Moon's sister, back in the States, an' then deserts her. Moon cuts the trail of the base sedoocer in Wolfville, an' gathers him in accordin', an' as a brother preyed on by his sister's wrongs is shorely expected to do."

"But Curly Ben never did mislead Moon's sister, did he?" I asked, for the confident fashion wherewith my old friend reeled off the finding of Wolfville's vigilance committee, and the reasons, almost imposed on me.

"Which you can bet the limit," he observed fiercely, as he prepared to go into the hotel; "which you can go the limit open, son, Curly ain't none too good."

There is more to the following tale than I give here, but we cannot display the Old Cattleman entire, and there is no reason why we should try. Anyhow, here he is again, philosophizing in all directions, setting up mental trails in his southwestern country, for those who might wish to follow them. . . .

HOW PRINCE HAL GOT HELP

"Come yere, you boy Tom." It was the Old Cattleman addressing his black satellite. "Stampede up to them rooms of mine an'
fetch me my hat; the one with the snakeskin band. My head
ain't feelin' none too well, owin' to the barkeep of this hostelry
changin' my drinks, an' that rattlesnake band oughter absorb
them aches an' clar'fy my roominations a heap. Now, *vamos!*"
he continued, as Tom seemed to hesitate, "the big Stetson with
the snakeskin onto it."

"An' how be you stackin' up yourse'f?" observed the old gentleman, turning to me as his dark agent vanished in quest of
head-gear. "Which you shorely looks as worn an' weary as a calf
jest branded. It'll do you good to walk a lot; better come with
me. I sort o' orig'nates the notion that I'll go swarmin' about
permiscus this mornin' for a hour or so, an cirk'late my blood,
an' you-all is welcome to attach yourse'f to the scheme. Thar's
nothin' like exercise, that a-way, as Grief Mudlow allows when
he urges his wife to take in washin'. You've done heard of Grief
Mudlow, the laziest maverick in Tennessee?"

I gave my word that not so much as a rumor of the person
Mudlow had reached me. My friend expressed surprise. It was
now that the black boy Tom came up with the desired hat. Tom
made his approach with a queer backward and forward shuffle,
crooning to himself the while:

> "Rain come wet me, sun come dry me,
> Take keer, white man, don't come nigh me."

"Stop that double-shufflin' an' wing dancin'," remonstrated
the old gentleman severely, as he took the hat and fixed it on his
head. "I don't want no frivolities an' merry-makin's 'round me.
Which you're always jumpin' an' dancin' like one of these yere
snapjack bugs. I ain't aimin' at pompousness none, but thar's a
sobriety goes with them years of mine which I proposes to maintain if I has to do it with a blacksnake whip. So you-all boy
Tom, you look out a whole lot! I'm goin' to break you of them
hurdy-gurdy tendencies, if I has to make you wear hobbles an'
frale the duds off your back besides."

Tom smiled toothfully, yet in confident fashion, as one who
knows his master and is not afraid.

"So you never hears of Grief Mudlow?" he continued, as we
strolled abroad on our walk. "I reckons mebby you has, for they
shore puts Grief into a book once, commemoratin' of his lazi-
ness. How lazy is he? Well, son, he could beat Mexicans an' let
'em deal. He's raised away off east, over among the knobs of old
Knox County, Grief is, an' he's that lazy he has to leave it on
account of the hills.

" 'She's too noomerous in them steeps an' deecliv'ties,' says
Grief. 'What I needs is a landscape where the prevailin' feacher is
the hor'zontal. I was shorely born with a yearnin' for the level
ground.' An' so Grief moves his camp down on the river bottoms,
where thar ain't no hills.

"He's that mis'rable idle an' shiftless, this yere Grief is, that
once he starts huntin' an' then decides he won't. Grief lays down
by the aige of the branch, with his moccasins towards the water.
It starts in to rain, an' the storm prounces down on Grief like
a mink on a settin' hen. One of his pards sees him across the
branch an' thinks he's asleep. So he shouts an' yells at him.

" 'Whoopee, Grief!' he sings over to where Grief's layin' all
quiled up same as a water-moccasin snake, an' the rain peltin' into him like eternal wrath; 'wake up thar an' crawl for cover!'"

" 'I'm awake,' says Grief.

" 'Well, why don't you get outen the rain?'

" 'I'm all wet now an' the rain don't do no hurt,' says Grief.

"An' this yere lazy Grief Mudlow keeps on layin' thar. It ain't no time when the branch begins to raise; the water crawls up about Grief's feet. So his pard shouts at him some more:

" 'Whoopee, you Grief ag'in!' he says. 'If you don't pull your freight, the branch'll get you. It's done riz over the stock of your rifle.'

" 'Water won't hurt the wood none,' says Grief.

" 'You Grief over thar!' roars the other after while; 'your feet an' laigs is half into the branch, an' the water's got up to the lock of your gun.'

" 'Thar's no load in the gun,' says Grief, still a-layin', 'an' besides she needs washin' out. As for them feet an' laigs, I never catches cold.'

"An' thar that ornery Grief reposes, too plumb lazy to move, while the branch creeps up about him. It's crope up so high, final, that his y'ears an' the back of his head is in it. All Grief does is sort o' lift his chin an' lay squar', to keep his nose out so' he can breathe.

"An' he shorely beats the game; for the rain ceases, an' the branch don't rise no higher. This yere Grief lays thar ontil the branch runs down an' he's high an' dry ag'in, an' then the sun shines out an' dries his clothes. It's that same night when Grief has drug himse'f home to supper, he says to his wife, "Thar's nothin' like exercise,' an' then counsels that lady over his corn pone an' chitlins to take in washin' like I relates."

We walked on in mute consideration of the extraordinary indolence of the worthless Mudlow. Our silence obtained for full ten minutes. Then I proposed "courage" as a subject, and put a question.

"Thar's fifty kinds of courage," responded my companion, "an' a gent who's plumb weak an' craven, that a-way, onder certain circumstances, is as full of sand as the bed of the Arkansaw onder others. Thar's hoss-back courage an' thar's foot courage, thar's day courage an' night courage, thar's gun courage an' knife courage, an' no end of courages besides. An' then thar's the courage of vanity. More'n once, when I'm younger, I'm swept down

by this last form of heroism, an' I even recalls how in a sperit of
vainglory I rides a buffalo bull. I tells you, son, that while that
frantic buffalo is squanderin' about the plains that time, an' me
onto him, he feels a mighty sight like the ridge of all the yooni-
verse. How does it end? It's too long a tale to tell walkin' an'
without reecooperatifs; suffice it that it ends disastrous. I shall
never ride no buffalo ag'in, leastwise without a saddle, onless
it's a speshul o'casion.

"No, indeed, that word 'courage' has to be defined new for
each case. Thar's old Tom Harris over on the Canadian. I beholds
Tom one time at Tascosa do the most b'ar-faced trick; one which
most sports of common sens'bilities would have shrunk from.
Thar's a warrant out for Tom, an' Jim East the sheriff puts his
gun on Tom when Tom's lookin' t'other way.

" 'See yere, Harris!' says East, that a-way.

"Tom wheels, an' is lookin' into the mouth of East's six-shooter
not a yard off.

" 'Put up your hands!' says East.

"But Tom don't. He looks over the gun into East's eye; an' he
freezes him. Then slow an' delib'rate, an' glarin' like a mountain
lion at East, Tom goes back after his Colt's an' pulls it. He lays
her alongside of East's with the muzzle p'intin' at East's eye.
An' thar they stands.

" 'You don't dar' shoot!' says Tom; an' East don't.

"They breaks away an' no powder burned; Tom stands East
off.

" 'Warrant or no warrant,' says Tom, 'all the sheriffs that ever
jingles a spur in the Panhandle country, can't take me! Nor all
the rangers neither!' An' they shore couldn't.

"Now this yere break-away of Tom's, when East gets the drop
that time, takes courage. It ain't one gent in a thousand who
could make that trip but Tom. An' yet this yere Tom is feared
of a dark room.

"Take Injuns;—give 'em their doo, even if we ain't got room
for them miscreants in our hearts. On his lines an' at his games,
a Injun is as clean strain as they makes. He's got courage, an' can

die without battin' an eye or waggin' a y'ear, once it's come his turn. An' the squaws is as cold a prop'sition as the bucks. After a fight with them savages, when you goes 'round to count up an' skin the game, you finds most as many squaws lyin' about an' bullets through 'em, as you finds bucks.

"Courage is sometimes knowledge, sometimes ignorance; sometimes courage is desp'ration, an' then ag'in it's innocence.

"Once, about two miles off, when I'm on the Staked Plains, an' near the aige where thar's pieces of broken rock, I observes a Mexican on foot, frantically chunkin' up somethin'. He's left his pony standin' off a little, an' has with him a mighty noisy form of some low kind of mongrel dog, this latter standin' in to worry whatever it is the Mexican's chunkin' at, that a-way. I rides over to investigate the war-jig; an' I'm a mesquite digger! if this yere transplanted Castillian ain't done up a full-grown wild cat! It's jest coughin' its last when I arrives. Son, I wouldn't have opened a game on that feline—the same bein' as big as a coyote, an' as thoroughly organized for trouble as a gatling—with anythin' more puny than a Winchester. An' yet that guileless Mexican lays him out with rocks, and regyards sech feats as trivial. An American, too, by merely growlin' towards this Mexican, would make him quit out like a jack rabbit.

"As I observes prior, courage is frequent the froots of what a gent don't know. Take grizzly b'ars. Back fifty years, when them squirrel rifles is preevalent; when a acorn shell holds a charge of powder, an' bullets runs as light an' little as sixty-four to the pound, why son! you-all could shoot up a grizzly till sundown an' hardly gain his disdain. It's a fluke if you downs one. That sport who can show a set of grizzly b'ar claws, them times, has fame. They're as good as a bank account, them claws be, an' entitles said party to credit in dance hall, bar room an' store, by merely slammin' 'em on the counter.

"At that time the grizzly b'ar has courage. Whyever does he have it, you asks? Because you couldn't stop him; he's out of hoomanity's reach—a sort o' Alexander Selkirk of a b'ar, an' you couldn't win from him. In them epocks, the grizzly b'ar treats a gent contemptuous. He swats him, or he claws him, or he hugs him, or he crunches him, or he quits him accordin' to his moods, or the number of them engagements which is pressin' on him at the time. An' the last thing he considers is the feelin's of that partic'lar party he's dallyin' with. Now, however, all is changed. Thar's rifles, burnin' four inches of this yere fulminatin' powder, that can chuck a bullet through a foot of green oak. Wisely directed, they lets sunshine through a grizzly b'ar like he's a pane of glass. An', son, them b'ars is plumb onto the play.

"What's the finish? To-day you can't get clost enough to a grizzly to hand him a ripe peach. Let him glimpse or smell a white man, an' he goes scatterin' off across hill an' canyon like a quart of licker among forty men. They're shore apprehensife of them big bullets an' hard-hittin' guns, them b'ars is; an' they wouldn't listen to you, even if you talks nothin' but bee-tree an' gives a bond to keep the peace besides. Yes, sir; the day when the grizzly b'ar will stand without hitchin' has deeparted the calendar a whole lot. They no longer attempts insolent an' coarse familiar'-ties with folks. Instead of regyardin' a rifle as a rotton cornstalk in disguise, they're as gun-shy as a female institoote. Big b'ars an' little b'ars, it's all sim'lar; for the old ones tell it to the young, an' the lesson is spread throughout the entire nation of b'ars. An' yere's where you observes, enlightenment that a-way means a-weakenin' of grizzly-b'ar courage.

"What's that, son? You-all thinks my stories smell some tall! You expresses doubts about anamiles conversin' with one another? That's where you're ignorant. All anamiles talks; they commoonicates the news to one another like hoomans. When I've been freightin' from Dodge down towards the Canadian, I had a eight-mule team. As shore as we're walkin'—as shore as I'm pinin' for a drink, I've listened to them mules gossip by the hour as we swings along the trail. Lots of times I saveys what they says. Once I hears the off-leader tell his mate that the jockey stick is sawin' him onder the chin. I investigates an' finds the complaint troo an' relieves him. The nigh swing mule is a wit; an' all day long he'd be throwin' off remarks that keeps a ripple of

laughter goin' up an' down the team. You-all finds trouble cred-
itin' them statements. Fact, jest the same, I've laughed at the
jokes of that swing mule myse'f; an' even Jerry, the off wheeler,
who's a cynic that a-way, couldn't repress a smile. Shore! anamiles talks all the time; it's only that we-all hoomans ain't eddicated to understand. . . .

Lewis' regard for Mexicans was no more pretentious than it was for Indians, but it was as rich and as remunerative. There were things Lewis did not understand. He could not, for instance, have written The Negro Cowboys, by Philip Durham and Everett L. Jones (1965), though I have no doubt he would have read it, if his own times had been able to produce it. One thing is certain: his was not the barren liberalism which sacrifices reality to diplomacy, and lacks feeling for human nature.

Once again, it helps to notice the art by which Lewis varied humor and anecdotes with serious incidents in order to set the scene for tragedy.

DEATH AND THE DONNA ANNA

"Locoweed? Do I savey loco?" The Old Cattleman's face offered full hint of his amazement as he repeated in the idiom of
his day and kind the substance of my interrogatory. "Why, son,"
he continued, "every longhorn who's ever cinched a Colorado
saddle, or roped a steer, is plumb aware of locoweed. Loco is
Mexicano for mad—crazy. An' cattle or mules or ponies or anythin' else, that makes a repast of locoweed—which as a roole they
don't, bein' posted instinctif that loco that a-way is no *bueno*—
goes crazy; what we-all in the Southwest calls 'locoed.'

"Whatever does this yere plant resemble? I ain't no sharp on
loco, but the brand I encounters is green, bunchy, stiff, an'
stands taller than the grass about it. An' it ain't allers thar when
looked for, loco ain't. It's one of these yere migratory weeds;
you'll see it growin' about the range mebby one or two seasons,
an' then it sort o' pulls its freight. Thar won't come no more loco
for years.

"Mostly, as I observes prior, anamiles disdains loco, an' passes
it up as bad medicine. They're organized with a notion ag'inst it,
same as ag'inst rattle snakes. An' as for them latter reptiles, you
can take a preacher's hoss, foaled in the lap of civilization, who
ain't seen nothin' more broadenin' than the reg'lar church service,
with now an' then a revival, an' yet he's born knowin' so much
about rattlesnakes in all their hein'ousness, that he'll hunch his
back an' go soarin' 'way of yonder at the first *Zizz-z-z-z*.

"Doc Peets informs me once when we crosses up with some locoweed over by the Cow Springs, that thar's two or three breeds of this malignant vegetable. He writes down for me the scientific name of the sort we gets ag'inst. Thar she is."

And my friend produced from some recess of a gigantic pocket-book a card whereon the learned Peets had written *Oxytropis Lamberti.*

"That's what Peet says loco is," he resumed, as I handed back the card. "Of course, I don't go surgin' off pronouncin' no sech words; shorely not in mixed company. Some gent might take it personal an' resent it. But I likes to pack 'em about, an' search 'em out now an' then, jest to gaze on an' think what a dead cold scientist Doc Peets is. He's shorely the high kyard; thar never is that drug-sharp in the cow country in my day who's fit to pay for Peets' whiskey. Scientific an' eddicated to a feather aige, Peets is.

"You-all oughter heard him lay for one of them cliff-climbin', bone-huntin' stone c'llectors who comes out from Washin'ton for the Gov'ment. One of these yere deep people strikes Wolfville on one of them rock-roundups he's makin', an' for a-while it looks like he's goin' to split things wide open. He's that contrary about his learnin', he won't use nothin' but words of four syllables —words that runs about eight to the pound. He comes into the New York Store where Boggs an' Tutt an' me is assembled, an', you hear me, son! that savant has us walkin' in a cirkle in a minute.

"It's Peets who relieves us. Peets strolls up an' engages this person in a debate touchin' mule-hoof hawgs; the gov'ment sport maintainin' thar ain't no sech swine with hoofs like a mule, be-cause he's never heard about 'em; an' Peets takin' the opp'site view because he's done met an' eat 'em a whole lot.

" 'The mere fact,' says Peets to this scientist, 'that you mav-ericks never knows of this mule-hoof hawg, cannot be taken as proof he does not still root an' roam the land. Thar's more than one of you Washin'ton shorthorns who's chiefly famed for what he's failed to know. The mule-hoof hawg is a fact; an' the igno-rance of closet naturalists shall not prevail ag'inst him. His back is arched like a greyhound's, he's about the thickness of a bowie-knife, he's got hoofs like a mule, an' sees his highest deevelopment in the wilds of Arkansaw.'

"But speakin' of locoweed, it's only o'casional that cattle or mules or broncos partakes tharof. Which I might repeat for the third time that, gen'ral, they eschews it. But you-all never will know how wise a anamile is till he takes to munchin' loco. Once he's plumb locoed, he jest don't know nothin'; then it dawns on you, by compar'son like, how much he saveys prior. The change shows plainest in mules; they bein'—that is, the mule normal an' before he's locoed—the wisest of beasts. Wise, did I say? A mule is more than wise, he's sagacious. An' thar's a mighty sight of difference. To be simply wise, all one has to do is set 'round an' think wise things, an' mebby say 'em. It's only when a gent goes trackin' 'round an' does wise things, you calls him sagacious. An' mules *does* wisdom.

"Shore! I admits it; I'm friendly to mules. If the Southwest ever onbends in a intellectual competition—whites barred—mules will stand at the head. The list should come out, mules, coyotes, Injuns, Mexicans, ponies, jack rabbits, sheep-herders, an' pra'ry dogs, the last two bein' shorely imbecile.

"Yes, son; you can lean up ag'inst the intelligence of a mule an' go to sleep. Not but what mules hasn't their illoosions, sech as white mares an' sim'lar reedic'lous inflooences; but them's weaknesses of the sperit rather than of mind.

"While mules don't nacherally go scoutin' for loco, an' commonly avoids said weed when found, if they ever does taste it once, they never quits it as long as they lives. It's like whiskey to Huggins an' Old Monte; the appetite sort o' goes into camp with 'em an' takes possession. No; a locoed mule ain't vicious nor voylent; it's more like the treemors—he sees spectacles that ain't thar none. I've beheld a locoed mule that a-way, standin' alone on the level plains in the sun, kickin' an' pitchin' to beat a straight flush. He thinks he's surrounded by Injuns or other hostiles; he's that crazy he don't know grass from t'rant'lers. An' their mem'ry's wiped out; they forgets to eat an' starves to death. That's the way they dies, onless some party who gets worked up seein' 'em about, takes a Winchester an' pumps a bullet into 'em.

"Yes; Peets says if a gent was to take to loadin' up on loco, or deecoctions tharof, he'd become afflicted by bats, same as cattle an' mules. But no one I knows of, so far as any news of it ever comes grazin' my way, is that ongyarded. I never hears tell in detail of sech a case but onct; an' that's a tale that Old Man Enright sets forth one evenin' in the Red Light.

"We-all is settin' 'round the faro layout at the time. Cherokee Hall is back of the box, with Faro Nell on the look-out's stool; but nobody's feelin' playful, an' no money's bein' changed in. It's only about first drink time in the evenin', which, as a season, is prematoor for faro-bank. It's Dave Tutt who brings up the matter with some remarks he makes touchin' the crazy-hoss conduct of a party who works over to the stage company's corral. This hoss-hustler is that eccentric he's ediotic, an' is known as 'Locoed Charlie.' It's him who final falls a prey to ants that time.

" 'An' it's my belief,' asserts Tutt, as he concloodes his relations of the ranikaboo breaks of this party, 'that if this Charlie, speakin' mine fashion, was to take his intellects over to the assay office in Tucson, they wouldn't show half a ounce of idee to the ton; wouldn't even show a color. Which he's shore locoed.'

" 'Speakin' of being locoed that a-way,' says Enright, 'recalls an incident that takes place back when I'm a yearlin' an' assoomes my feeble part in the Mexican War. That's years ago, but I don't know of nothin' sadder than that story, nothin' more replete of sobs. Not that I weeps tharat, for I'm a thoughtless an' a callous yooth, but, all the same, it glooms me up a heap.'

" 'Is it a love story, Daddy Enright?' asks Faro Nell, all eager, an' bendin' towards Enright across the layout.

" 'It shows brands an' y'ear marks as sech, Nellie,' says Enright; 'love an' loco makes up the heft of it.'

" 'Then tell it,' urges Faro Nell. 'I'm actooally hungerin' for a love story,' an' she reaches down an' squeezes Cherokee's hand onder the table.

"Cherokee squeezes hers, an' turns his deal box on its side to show thar's no game goin', an' leans back with the rest of us to listen. Black Jack, who knows his mission on this earth, brings over a bottle with glasses all 'round.

" 'Yere's to you, Nellie,' says Texas Thompson, as we shoves the nose-paint about. 'While that divorce edict my wife wins back in Laredo modifies my interest in love tales, an' whereas I don't feel them thrills as was the habit of me onct, still, in a subdooed way I can drink happiness to you.'

"Texas,' says Boggs, settin' down his glass an' bendin' a eye full of indignant reproach on Thompson; 'Texas, before I'd give way to sech onmanly weakness, jest because my wife's done stampeded, I'd j'ine the church. Sech mush from a cow-man is disgraceful. You'll come down to herdin' sheep if you keeps on surrenderin' yourse'f to sech sloppy bluffs.'

" 'See yere, Dan,' retorts Thompson, an' his eye turns red on Boggs; 'my feelin's may be bowed onder losses which sech nachers as yours is too coarse to feel, but you can gamble your bottom dollar, jest the same, I will still resent insultin' criticisms. I advises you to be careful an' get your chips down right when you addresses me, or you may quit loser on the deal.'

" 'Now you're a couple of fine three-year-olds!' breaks in Jack Moore. 'Yere we be, all onbuckled an' fraternal, an' Enright on the brink of a love romance by the ardent requests of Nell, an' you two longhorns has to come prancin' out an' go pawin' for trouble. You know mighty well, Texas, that Boggs is your friend an' the last gent to go harassin' you with contoomely.'

" 'Right you be, Jack,' says Boggs plenty prompt; 'if my remarks to Texas is abrupt, or betrays heat, it's doo to the fact that it exasperates me to see the most elevated gent in camp—for so I holds Texas Thompson to be—made desolate by the wild breaks of a lady who don't know her own mind, an' mighty likely ain't got no mind to know.'

" 'I reckons I'm wrong, Dan,' says Thompson, turnin' apol'-getic. 'Let it all go to the diskyard. I'm that peevish I simply ain't fit to stay yere nor go anywhere else. I ain't been the same person since my wife runs cimmaron that time an' demands said sep'ration.'

" 'Bein' I'm a married man,' remarks Dave Tutt, sort o' gen'ral, but swellin' out his chest an' puttin' on a lot of dog at the same time, 'an' wedded to Tucson Jennie, the same bein' more or less known, I declines all partic'pation in discussions touchin' the sex. I could, however, yoonite with you-all in another drink, an' yereby su'gests the same. Bar-keep, it's your play.'

" 'That's all right about another drink,' says Faro Nell, 'but I wants to state that I sympathizes with Texas in them wrongs. I has my views of a female who would up an' abandon a gent like Texas Thompson, an' I explains it only on the theery that she shorely must have been coppered in her cradle.'

" 'Nellie onderstands my feelin's,' says Texas, an' he's plumb mournful, 'an' I owes her for them utterances. However, on second thought, an' even if it is a love tale, if Enright will resoome his relations touchin' that eepisode of the Mexican War, I figgers that it may divert me from them divorce griefs I alloodes to. An', at any rate, win or lose, I assures Enright his efforts will be regyarded.'

"Old Man Enright takes his seegyar out of his mouth an' rouses up a bit. He's been wropped in thought doorin' the argyments of Boggs an' Thompson, like he's tryin' to remember a far-off past. As Thompson makes his appeal, he braces up.

" 'Now that Dan an' Texas has ceased buckin',' says Enright, 'an' each has all four feet on the ground, I'll try an' recall them details. As I remarks, it's towards the close of the Mexican War, Whatever I'm doin' in that carnage is a conundrum that's never been solved. I had hardly shed my milk teeth, an' was only 'leven hands high at the time. An' I ain't so strong physical, but I feels the weight of my spurs when I walks. As I looks back to it, I must have been about as valyooable an aid to the gov'ment, as the fifth kyard in a poker hand when four of a kind is held. The most partial an' besotted of critics would have conceded that if I'd been left out entire, that war couldn't have suffered material changes in its results. However, to get for'ard, for I sees that Nellie's patience begins to mill an' show symptoms of comin' stampede.

" 'It's at the close of hostil'ties,' goes on Enright, 'an' the company I'm with is layin' up in the hills about forty miles back from Vera Cruz, dodgin' yellow fever. We was cavalry, what the folks in Tennessee calls a "critter company," an', hailin' mostly from that meetropolis or its vicinity, we was known to ourse'fs at least as the "Pine Knot Cavaliers." Thar's a little Mexican village where we be that's called the "Plaza Perdita." An' so we lays thar at the Plaza Perdita, waitin' for orders an' transportation to take us back to the States.

" 'Which most likely we're planted at this village about a month, an' the Mexicans is beginnin' to get used to us; an' we on our parts is playin' monte, an' eatin' frijoles, an' accommodatin' ourse'fs to the simple life of the place. Onct a week the chaplain preaches to us. He holds that Mexico is a pagan land; an', entertainin' this idee, he certainly does make onusual efforts to keep our morals close-herded, an' our souls bunched an' banded up in the Christian faith, as expressed by the Baptis' church. Candor, however, compels me to say that this yere pulpit person can't be deescribed as a heavy winner on the play.'

" 'Was you-all so awful bad?' asks Faro Nell.

" 'No,' replies Enright, 'we ain't so bad none; but our conduct is a heap onhampered, which is the same thing to the chaplain. He gives it out emphatic, after bein' with the Pine Knot Cavaliers over a year, that he plumb despairs of us becomin' christians.'

"Whatever does he lay down on you-all like that for?' says Faro Nell. 'Couldn't a soldier be a christian, Daddy Enright?'

" 'Why, I reckons he might,' says Enright, he'pin' himse'f to a drink; 'a soldier could be a christian, Nellie, but after all it ain't necessary.

" 'Still, we-all likes the chaplain because them ministrations of his is entertainin'; an', for that matter, he likes us a lot, an' in more reelaxed moments allows we ain't so plumb crim'nal—merely loose like on p'ints of doctrine.'

" 'Baptis' folks is shore strong on doctrines,' says Tutt, coincidin' in with Enright. 'I knows that myse'f. Doctrine is their long suit. They'll go to any len'ths for doctrines, you hear me! I remembers once ridin' into a hamlet back in the Kaintucky mountains. Thar ain't one hundred people in the village, corral count. An' yet I notes two church edifices.

" ' "You-all is plenty opulent on sanctooaries," I says to the barkeep at the tavern where I camps for the night. "It's surprisin', too, when you considers the size of the herd. What be the two deenom'nations that worships at them structures?"

" ' "Both Baptis'," says the barkeep.

" ' "Whyever, since they're ridin' the same range an' runnin' the same brand," I says, "don't they combine like cattle folks an' work their round-ups together?"

"They splits on doctrine," says the barkeep; "you couldn't get 'em together with a gun. They disagrees on Adam. That outfit in the valley holds that Adam was all right when he started, but later he struck something an' glanced off; them up on the hill contends that Adam was a hoss-thief from the jump. An' thar you be! You couldn't reeconcile 'em between now an' the crack of doom. Doctrines to a Baptis' that a-way is the entire check-rack.' "

" 'To ag'in pick up said narratif,' says Enright, when Tutt subsides, 'at the p'int where Dave comes spraddlin' in with them onasked reminiscences, I may say that a first source of pleasure to us, if not of profit, while we stays at the Plaza Perdita, is a passel of Mexicanos with a burro train that brings us our pulque from some'ers back further into the hills.' "

"What's pulque?" I interjected.

It was plain that my old gentleman of cows as little liked my interruption as Enright liked that of the volatile Tutt. He hid his irritation, however, under an iron politeness and explained.

"Pulque is a disapp'intin' form of beverage, wharof it takes a bar'l to get a gent drunk," he observed. And then, with some severity: "It ain't for me to pull no gun of criticism, but I'm amazed that a party of your attainments, son, is ignorant of pulque. It's, as I says, a drink; an' it tastes like glucose an' looks like yeast. It comes from a plant, what the Mexicans calls 'maguey,' an' Peets calls a 'aloe.' The pulque gatherers scoops out the blossom of the maguey while it's a bud. They leaves the place hollow; what wood-choppers back in Tennessee, when I'm a colt, deescribes as 'bucketin' the stump.' This yere hollow fills up with oozin' sap, an' the Mexican dips out two gallons a day an' keeps it for a month. That's straight; sixty gallons from one maguey before ever it quits an' refooses to further turn the game. That's pulque; an' when them Greasers gathers it, they puts it into a pigskin—skinned complete, the pig is; them pulque receptacles is made of the entire bark of the anamile. When the pulque's inside, they packs it, back down an' hung by all four laigs to the saddle, a pigskin on each side of the burro. It's gathered the evenin' previous, an' brought into camp in the night so as to keep it cool.

"When I'm a child, an' before ever I connects myse'f with the cow trade, if thar's a weddin', we-all has what the folks calls a 'infare;' an' I can remember a old lady from the No'th who contreebutes to these yere festivals a drink she calls 'sprooce beer.' An' pulque, before it takes to frettin' and fermentin' 'round, in them pigskins, reminds me a mighty sight of that sprooce beer. Later it most likely reminds you of the pigskin.

"Mexican barkeeps, when they sells pulque, aims to dispose of it two glasses at a clatter. It gives their conceit a chance to spread itse'f an' show. The pulque is in a tub down back of the bar. This yere vain Mexican seizes two glasses between his first an' second fingers, an' with a finger in each glass. Then he dips 'em full backhanded; an' allers comes up with the back of his hand an' the two fingers covered with pulque. He claps 'em on the bar, eyes you a heap sooperior like he's askin' you to note what a acc'rate, highgrade barkeep he is, an' then raisin' his hand, he slats the pulque off his fingers into the two glasses. If he spatters a drop on the bar, it shows he's a bungler, onfit for his high p'sition, an' oughter be out on the hills tendin' goats instead of dealin' pulque.

"What do they do with the sour pulque? Make mescal of it—a sort o' brandy, two hookers of which changes you into a robber. No, thar's mighty few still-houses in Mexico. But that's no set-back to them Greasers when they're out to construct mescal. As a roole Mexicans is slow an' oninventive; but when the question becomes the arrangement of somethin' to be drunk with, they're plenty fertile. Jest by way of raw material, if you'll only confer on a Mexican a kettle, a rifle bar'l, a saddle cover, an' a pigskin full of sour pulque, he'll be conductin' a mescal still in full blast at the end of the first hour. But to go back to Enright's yarn.

" 'These yere pulque people,' says Enright, 'does a fa'rly rapid commerce. For while, as you-all may know, pulque is tame an' lacks in reebound as compared with nose-paint, still when pulque is the best thar is, the Pine Knot Cavaliers of the Plaza Perdita invests heavily tharin. That pulque's jest about a stand-off for the chaplain's sermons.

" 'It's the fourth trip of the pulque sellers, when the Donna Anna shows in the door. The Donna Anna arrives with 'em; an' the way she bosses 'round, an' sets fire to them pulque slaves, notifies me they're the Donna Anna's peonies.

" 'I'm sort o' pervadin' about the plaza when the Donna Anna rides up. Thar's an old she-wolf with her whose name is Magdalena. I'm not myse'f what they calls in St. Looey a "connoshur" of female loveliness, an' it's a pity now that some gifted gent like Doc Peets yere don't see this Donna Anna that time, so's he could draw you her picture, verbal. All I'm able to state is that she's as beautiful as a cactus flower; an' as vivid. She's tall an' strong for a Mexican, with a voice like velvet, graceful as a mountain lion, an' with eyes that's soft an' deep an' black, like a deer's. She's shorely a lovely miracle, the Donna Anna is; an' as dark an' as warm an' as full of life as a night in Joone. She's of the *grande;* for the mule she's ridin', gent-fashion, is worth forty ponies. Its coat is soft, an' shiny like this yere watered silk, while its mane an' tail is braided with a hundred little silver bells. The Donna Anna is dressed half Mexican an' half Injun, an' thar's likewise a row of bells about the wide brim of her Chihuahua hat.

" 'Thar's mebby a half-dozen of us standin' 'round when the Donna Anna comes up. Nacherally, we-all is interested. The Donna Anna, bein' only eighteen an' a Mexican, is not abashed. She waves her hand an' says, "How! how!" Injun fashion, an' gives us a white flash of teeth between her red lips. Then a band of nuns comes out of a little convent, which is one of the public improvements of the Plaza Perdita, an' they rounds up the Donna Anna an' the wrinkled Magdalena, an' takes 'em into camp. The Donna Anna an' the other is camped in the convent doorin' the visit. No, they're not locked up nor gyarded, an' the Donna Anna comes an' goes in an' out of that convent as free as birds. The nuns, too, bow before her like her own peonies.

" 'Thar's a Lootenant Jack Spencer with us; he hails from further up the Cumberland than me—some'ers near Nashville. He's light-ha'red an' light-hearted, Spencer is; an' as straight an' as strong as a pine-tree. S'ciety ain't throwin' out no skirmish lines them days, an' of course Spencer an' the Donna Anna meets up with each other; an' from the onbroken hours they tharafter proceeds to invest in each other's company, one is jestified in assoomin' they experiences a tender interest. The Donna Anna can't talk Americano, but Spencer is a sharp on Spanish; an' you can bet a pony, if he wasn't, he'd set to studyin' the language right thar.

" 'Nothin' much is thought by the Pine Knot Cavaliers of an' concernin' the attitoodes of Spencer an' the Donna Anna touch-in' one another. Love it might be, an' less we cares for that. Our army, when it ain't fightin', is makin' love throughout the entire Mexican War; an' by the time we're at the Plaza Perdita, love, mere everyday love, either as a emotion or exhibition, is plenty commonplace. An' so no one is interested, an' no one keeps tabs on Spencer an' the Donna Anna. Which, if any one had, he'd most likely got ag'inst Spencer's gun; wharfore, it's as well mebby that this yere lack-luster feelin' prevails.

" 'It's about the tenth day since the Donna Anna gladdens us first. Orders comes up from Vera Cruz for the Pine Knot Cavaliers to come down to the coast an' embark for New Orleans. The word is passed, an' our little jimcrow camp buzzes like bees, with us gettin' ready to hit the trail. Spencer asks "leave;" an' then saddles up an' starts at once. He says he's got a trick or two to turn in Vera Cruz before we sails. That's the last we-all ever beholds of Lootenant Jack Spencer.

" 'When Spencer don't show up none in Vera Cruz, an' the ship throws loose without him, he's marked, "missin'," on the company's books. If he's a private, now, it would have been "deserted;" but bein' Spencer's an officer, they makes it "missin'." An' they gets it right, at that; Spencer is shorely missin'. Spencer not only don't come back to Tennessee none; he don't even send no word nor make so much as a signal smoke to let on whar he's at. This yere, to some, is more or less disapp'intin'.

" 'Thar's a lady back in Tennessee which Spencer's made overtures to, before he goes to war that time, to wed. Young she is; beautiful, high-grade, corn-fed, an' all that; an' comes of one of the most clean-bred fam'lies of the whole Cumberland country. I will interject right yere to say that thar's ladies of two sorts. If a loved one, tender an' troo, turns up missin' at roll-call, an' the phenomenon ain't accompanied with explanations, one sort thinks he's quit, an' the other thinks he's killed. Spencer's inamorata is of the former. She's got what the neighbors calls "hoss sense." She listens to what little thar is to tell of Spencer fadin' from our midst that Plaza Perdita day, shrugs her shoulders, an' turns her back on Spencer's mem'ry. An' the next news you gets is of how, inside of three months, she jumps some gent—who's off his gyard an' is lulled into feelin's of false secoority—ropes, throws, ties an' weds him a heap, an' he wakes up to find he's a gone fawn-skin, an' to realize his peril after he's onder its hoofs. That's what this Cumberland lady does. I makes no comments; I simply relates it an' opens a door an' lets her out.

" 'I'm back in Tennessee mighty nigh a year before ever I hears ag'in of Lootenant Jack Spencer of the Pine Knot Cavaliers.

It's this a-way: I'm stoppin' with my old gent near Warwhoop Crossin', the same bein' a sister village to Pine Knot, when he's recalled to my boyish mind. It looks like Spencer ain't got no kin nearer than a aunt, an' mebby a stragglin' herd of cousins. He never does have no brothers nor sisters; an' as for fathers an' mothers an' sech, they all cashes in before ever Spencer stampedes off for skelps in that Mexican War at all.

" 'These yere kin of Spencer's stands his absence ca'mly, an' no one hears of their settin' up nights, or losin' sleep, wonderin' where he's at. Which I don't reckon now they'd felt the least cur'ous concernin' him—for they're as cold-blooded as channel catfish—if it ain't that Spencer's got what them law coyotes calls a "estate," an' this property sort o' presses their hands. So it falls out like, that along at the last of the year, a black-coat party—lawyer he is—comes breezin' up to me in Warwhoop an' says he's got to track this yere Spencer to his last camp, dead or alive, an' allows I'd better sign for the round-up an' accompany the expedition as guide, feelos'pher an' friend—kind o' go 'long an' scout for the campaign.

" 'Two months later me an' that law sharp is in the Plaza Perdita. We heads up for the padre. It's my view from the first dash outen the box that the short cut to find Spencer is to acc'rately discover the Donna Anna; so we makes a line for the padre. In Mexico, the priests is the only folks who saveys anythin'; an', as if to make up for the hoomiliatin' ignorance of the balance of the herd, an' promote a average, these yere priests jest about knows everythin'. An' I has hopes of this partic'lar padre speshul; for I notes that, doorin' them times when Spencer an' the Donna Anna is dazzlin' one another at the Plaza Perdita, the padre is sort o' keepin' cases on the deal, an' tryin' as well as he can to hold the bars an' fences up through some covert steers he vouchsafes from time to time to the old Magdalena.

" 'No; you bet this padre don't at that time wax vocif'rous or p'inted none about Spencer an' the Donna Anna. Which he's afraid if he gets obnoxious that a-way, the Pine Knot Cavaliers will rope him up a lot an' trade him for beef. Shore! don't you-all know that? When we're down in Mexico that time, with old Zach Taylor, an' needs meat, we don't go ridin' our mounts to death combin' the hills for steers. All we does is round up a band of padres, or monks, an' then trade 'em to their par'lyzed congregations for cattle. We used to get about ten steers for a padre; an' we doles out them divines, one at a time, as we needs the beef. It's shorely a affectin' sight to see them parish'ners, with tears runnin' down their faces, drivin' up the cattle an' takin' them religious directors of theirs out o' hock.

" 'We finds the padre out back of his wickeyup, trimmin' up a game-cock that he's matched to fight the next day. The padre is little, fat, round, an' amiable as owls. Nacherally, I has to translate for him an' the law sport.

" ' "You do well to come to me, my children," he says. "The Señor Juan"—that's what the padre calls Spencer—"the Señor Juan is dead. It is ten days since he passed. The Donna Anna? She also is dead an' with the Señor Juan. We must go to the Hacienda Tulorosa, which is the house of the Donna Anna. That will be to-morrow. Meanwhile, who is to protect Juarez, my beloved chicken, in his battle when I will be away? Ah! I remember! The Don Jose Miguel will do. He is skilful of cocks of the game. Also he has bet money on Juarez; so he will be faithful. Therefore, to-morrow, my children, we will go to the Donna Anna's house. There I will tell you the story of the Señor Juan."

" 'The Hacienda Tulorosa is twenty miles back further in the hills. The padre, the law sharp an' me is started before sun-up, an' a good road-gait fetches us to the Hacienda Tulorosa in a couple of hours. It's the sort of a ranch which a high grade Mexican with a strong bank-roll would throw up. It's built all 'round a court, with a flower garden and a fountain in the centre. As we comes up, I observes the old Magdalena projectin' about the main door of the *casa*, stirrin' up some lazy peonies to their daily toil—which, to use the word "toil," however, in connection with a Greaser, is plumb sarcastic. The padre leads us into the *casa,* an' the bitter-lookin' Magdalena hustles us some grub; after which we-all smokes a bit. Then the padre gets up an' leads the way.

" ' "Come, my children," says the padre, "I will show you the graves. Then you shall hear what there is of the Señor Juan an' the Donna Anna."

" 'It's a set-back,' continyoos Enright, as he signals Black Jack the barkeep to show us he's awake; 'it's shorely a disaster that some book-instructed gent like Peets or Colonel Sterett don't hear this padre when he makes them revelations that day. Not that I overlooks a bet, or don't recall 'em none; but I ain't up-holstered with them elegancies of diction needed to do 'em jus-tice now. My language is roode an' corrupted with years of sech surroundin's as cattle an' kyards. It's too deeply freighted with the slang of the plains an' the faro-banks to lay forth a tale of love an' tenderness, as the o'casion demands. Of course, I can read an' write common week-day print; but when thar's a call for more, I'm mighty near as illit'rate that a-way as Boggs.'

" 'Which, as you su'gests, I'm plumb ignorant,' admits Boggs, 'but it ain't the fault none of my bringin' up neither. It jest looks like I never can learn print nohow when I'm young. I'm simply born book-shy, an' is terrified at schools from my cradle. An', say! I'm yere to express my regrets at them weaknesses. If I was a eddicated gent like Doc Peets is, you can put down all you has, I'd be the cunnin'est wolf that ever yelps in Cochise County.'

" 'An' thar ain't no doubt of that, Boggs,' observes Enright, as he reorganizes to go ahead with them Donna Anna mem'ries of his. 'Which if you only has half of Peets' game now, you'd be the hardest thing—mental—to ride that ever invades the South-west. Nacherally, an' in a wild an' ontrained way, you're wise. But to resoome: As much as I can, I'll give the padre in his own words. He takes us out onder a huddle of pine trees, where thar's two graves side by side, an' with a big cross of wood standin' gyard at the head. Thar's quite a heap o' rocks, about as big as your shet hand, heaped up on 'em. It's the Mexicans does that. Every Greaser who goes by, says a pray'r, an' tosses a rock on the grave. When we-all is camped comfortable, the padre begins.

" ' "This is that which was with the Señor Juan and the Donna Anna," he says. "They adored each other with their hearts. It was many months ago when, from the Plaza Perdita, they came together here to the Donna Anna's house, the Hacienda Tulorosa. Who was the Donna Anna? Her mother was an Indian, a Navajo, and the child of a head man. Her father was the Señor Ravel, a captain of war he was, and the Americanos slew him at Buena Vista. No; they were not married, the father and the mother of the Donna Anna. But what then? There are more children than weddings in Mexico. Also the mother of the Donna Anna was a Navajo. The Captain Ravel long ago brought her to the Hacienda Tulorosa for her home—her and the Donna Anna. But the mother lived not long, for the Indian dies in a house. This is years gone by; and the Donna Anna always lived at the *Casa* Tulorosa.

" ' "No; the Señor Juan and the Donna Anna do not marry. They might; but the Señor Juan became like a little child— *muchachito*. This was within a few days after he came here. Then he lived until ten days ago; but always a little child.

" ' "When the Señor Juan is dead, the Donna Anna sends for me. The Señor Juan is ready for the grave when I arrive. "Is it to bury him that I come?" I ask. 'No; it is to bury me,' says the Donna Anna. Ah! she was very beautiful the Donna Anna. You should have seen her, my children.

" ' "When the Señor Juan is laid away, the Donna Anna tells me all. 'He came, the Señor Juan,' says the Donna Anna, 'and I gave him all my love. But in a day he was to have gone to his home far away with the Americanos. Then I would never more see him nor hear him, and my soul would starve and die. There, too, was a Senorita, an Americana; she would have my place. Father, what could I do? I gave him the loco to drink; not much, but it was enough. Then his memory sank and sank; and he forgot the Senorita Americana; and he remembered not to go away to his home; and he became like a little child with me. The good loco drove every one from his heart; and all from his mind—all, save me, the Donna Anna. I was the earth and the life to him.

And so, night and day, since he came until now he dies, my arms and my heart have been about the Señor Juan. And I have been very, very happy with my *muchachito,* the Señor Juan. Yes, I knew he would go; because none may live who drinks the loco. But it would be months; and I did not care. He would be mine, ever my own, the Señor Juan; for when he died, could I not die and follow him? We were happy, these months with the flowers and the fountain and each other. I was happier than he; for I was like the mother, and he like a little child. But it was much peace with love! And we will be happy again to-morrow when I go where he waits to meet me. Father, you are to remain one day, and see that I am buried with the Señor Juan.'

" ' "Then," goes on the padre, "I say to the Donna Anna, 'If you are to seek the Señor Juan, you will first kneel in prayer and in confession, and have the parting rites of the church.' But the Donna Anna would not. 'I will go as went the Señor Juan,' she says; 'else I may find another heaven and we may not meet.' Nor could I move the Donna Anna from her resolution. 'The Señor Juan is a heretic and must now be in perdition,' I say. 'Then will I, too, go there,' replies the Donna Anna, 'for we must be together; I and the Señor Juan. He is mine and I will not give him up to be alone with the fiends or with the angels.' So I say no more to the Donna Anna of the church.

" ' "On the day to follow the burial of the Señor Juan, it is in the afternoon when the Donna Anna comes to me. Oh! she was twice lovely! 'Father,' she says, 'I come to say my *adios.* When the hour is done you will seek me by the grave of my Señor Juan,' Then she turns to go. 'And *adios* to you, my daughter,' I say, as she departs from my view. And so I smoke my cigars; and when the hour is done, I go also to the grave of the Señor Juan— the new grave, just made, with its low hill of warm, fresh earth.

" ' "True! it was as you guess. There, with her face on that little round of heaped-up earth, lay the Donna Anna. And all the blood of her heart had made red the grave of her Señor Juan. The little knife she died by was still in her hand. No, I do not fear for them, my children. They are with the good; the Donna

Anna and her Señor Juan. They were guiltless of all save love; and the good God does not punish love." ' "

HOW JACK RAINEY QUIT

"Customary, we has our social round-ups in the Red Light,"
observed the Old Cattleman; "which I mentions once it does us
for a club. We're all garnered into said fold that time when Dave
Tutt tells us how this yere Jack Rainey quits out.

" 'Rainey gets downed,' says Tutt, 'mainly because his system's
obscoore, an' it chances that a stranger who finds himse'f im-
meshed tharin takes it plumb ombrageous; an' pendin' explanations, gets tangled up with a pard of Rainey's, goes to a gun play,
an' all accidental an' casooal Rainey wings his way to them
regions of the blest.

" 'Now I allers holds,' goes on Tutt, 'an' still swings an' rattles
with that decision, that it's manners to ask strangers to drink; an'
that no gent, onless he's a sky-pilot or possesses scrooples otherwise, has a right to refoose. Much less has a gent, bein' thus
s'licited to licker, any license to take it hostile an' allow he's
insulted, an' lay for his entertainers with weepons.'

" 'Well, I don't know, neither,' says Texas Thompson, who's a
heap dispootatious an' allers spraddlin' in on every chance for an
argyment. 'Thar's a party, now deceased a whole lot—the Stranglers over in Socorro sort o' chaperones this yere gent to a cottonwood an' excloodes the air from his lungs with a lariat for mebby
it's an hour—an' this party I'm alloodin' at, which his name is
Fowler, is plumb murderous. Now, it's frequent with him when
he's selected a victim that a-way, an' while he's bickerin' with

him up to the killin' p'int, to invite said sacrifice to take a drink. When they're ag'inst the bar, this yere Fowler we-all strangles would pour out a glass of whiskey an' chuck it in the eyes of that onfortunate he's out to down. Of course, while this party's blind with the nose-paint, he's easy; an' Fowler tharupon c'llects his skelp in manner, form an' time to suit his tastes. Now I takes it that manners don't insist none on no gent frontin' up to a bar on the invite of sech felons as Fowler, when a drink that a-way means a speshul short-cut to the tomb.'

" 'All this yere may be troo,' replies Tutt, 'but it's a exception. What I insists is, Texas, that speakin' wide an' free an' not allowin' none for sports of the Fowler brand, it's manners to ask strangers to stand in on what beverages is goin'; an' that it's likewise manners for said strangers to accept; an' it shows that both sides concerned tharin is well brought up by their folks. Sech p'liteness is manners, goin' an' comin', which brings me with graceful swoops back to how Jack Rainey gets shot up.'

" 'But, after all,' breaks in Texas ag'in, for he feels wranglesome, 'manners is frequent a question of where you be. What's manners in St. Looey may be bad jedgment in Texas; same as some commoonities plays straights in poker, while thar's regions where straights is barred.'

" 'Texas is dead right about his State that a-way,' says Jack Moore, who's heedin' of the talk. 'Manners is a heap more inex'rable in Texas than other places. I recalls how I'm galivantin' 'round in the Panhandle country—it's years ago when I'm young an' recent—an' as I'm ridin' along south of the Canadian one day, I discerns a pony an' a gent an' a fire, an' what looks like a yearlin' calf tied down. I knows the pony for Lem Woodruff's cayouse, an' heads over to say "Howdy" to Lem. He's about half a mile away; when of a sudden he stands up—he's been bendin' over the yearlin' with a runnin' iron in his hand—an' gives a whoop an' makes some copious references towards me with his hands. I wonders what for a game he's puttin' up, an' whatever is all this yere sign-language likely to mean; but I keeps ridin' for'ard. It's then this Woodruff steps over to his pony, an' takin' his Winchester off the saddle, cuts down with it in my direction, an' onhooks her—"Bang!" The bullet raises the dust over about fifty yards to the right. Nacherally I pulls up my pony to consider this conduct. While I'm settin' thar tryin' to figger out Woodruff's system, thar goes that Winchester ag'in, an' a streak of dust lifts up, say, fifty yards to the left. I then sees Lem objects to me. I don't like no gent to go carpin' an' criticisin' at me with a gun; but havin' a Winchester that a-way, this yere Woodruff can overplay me with only a six-shooter, so I quits him an' rides contemptuous away. As I withdraws, he hangs his rifle on his saddle ag'in, picks up his runnin' iron an' goes back content an' all serene to his maverick.' "

" 'What is a maverick?" I asked, interrupting my friend in the flow of his narration.

"Why, I s'posed," he remarked, a bit testily at being halted, "as how even shorthorns an' tenderfeet knows what mavericks is. Mavericks, son, is calves which gets sep'rated from the old cows, their mothers, an' ain't been branded none yet. They're bets which the round-ups overlooks, an' don't get marked. Of course, when they drifts from their mothers, each calf for himse'f, an' no brands nor y'ear marks, no one can tell whose calves they be. They ain't branded, an' the old cows ain't thar to identify 'an' endorse 'em, an' thar you stands in ignorance. Them's mavericks.

"It all comes," he continued in further elucidation of mavericks, "when cattle brands is first invented in Texas. The owners, whose cattle is all mixed up on the ranges, calls a meetin' to decide on brands, so each gent'll know his own when he crosses up with it, an' won't get to burnin' powder with his neighbors over a steer which breeds an' fosters doubts. After every party announces what his brand an' y'ear mark will be, an' the same is put down in the book, a old longhorn named Maverick addresses the meetin', an' puts it up if so be thar's no objection, now they all has brands but him, he'll let his cattle lope without markin', an' every gent'll savey said Maverick's cattle because they won't have no brand. Cattle without brands, that a-way, is to belong to Maverick, that's the scheme, an' as no one sees no reason why not, they lets old Maverick's proposal go as it lays.

"An' to cut her short, for obv'ous reasons, it ain't no time before Maverick, claimin' all the onbranded cattle, has herds on herds of 'em; whereas thar's good authority which states that when he makes his bluff about not havin' no brand that time, all the cattle old Maverick has is a triflin' bunch of Mexican steers an' no semblances of cows in his outfit. From which onpromisin', not to say barren, beginnin', Maverick owns thousands of cattle at the end of ten years. It all provokes a heap of merriment an' scorn. An' ever since that day, onmarked an' onbranded cattle is called 'mavericks.' But to go back ag'in to what Jack Moore is remarkin' about this yere outlaw, Woodruff, who's been bustin' away towards Jack with his Winchester.

" 'It's a week later,' goes on Jack Moore, 'when I encounters this sport Woodruff in Howard's store over in Tascosa. I stands him up an' asks whatever he's shootin' me up for that day near the Serrita la Cruz.

" ' "Which I never sees you nohow," replies this yere Woodruff, laughin'. "I never cuts down on you with no Winchester, for if I did, I'd got you a whole lot. You bein' yere all petulant an' irritated is mighty good proof I never is shootin' none at you. But bein' you're new to the Canadian country an' to Texas, let me give you a few p'inters on cow ettyquette an' range manners. Whenever you notes a gent afar off with a fire goin' an' a yearlin' throwed an' hawg-tied ready to mark up a heap with his own private hieroglyphics, don't you-all go pesterin' 'round him. He ain't good company, sech a gent ain't. Don't go near him. It's ag'in the law in Texas to brand calves lonely an' forlorn that a-way, without stoppin' to herd 'em over to some well-known corral, an' the punishment it threatens, bein' several years in Huntsville, makes a gent when he's violatin' it a heap misanthropic, an' he don't hunger none for folks to come ridin' up to see about whatever he reckons he's at. Mebby later them visitors gets roped up before a co't, or jury, to tell whatever they may

know. So, as I says, an' merely statin' a great trooth in Texas
ettyquette, yereafter on beholdin' a fellow-bein' with a calf laid
out to mark, don't go near him a little bit. It's manners to turn
your back onto him an' ignore him plumb severe. He's a crim'nal,
an' any se'f-respectin' gent is jestified in refoosin' to affiliate
with him. Wherefore, you ride away from every outcast you
tracks up ag'inst who is engaged like you says this onknown
party is the day he fetches loose his Winchester at you over by
the Serrita la Cruz."

" 'That's what this Woodruff says,' concloodes Jack, windin'
up his interruption, 'about what's manners in Texas; an' when
it's made explicit that a-way, I sees the force of his p'sition.
Woodruff an' me buys nose-paint for each other, shakes hearty,
an' drops the discussion. But it shorely comes to this: manners,
as Texas declar's, is sometimes born of geography, an' what goes
for polish an' the p'lite play in St. Looey may not do none for
Texas.'

" 'Mighty likely,' says Old Man Enright, 'what Texas Thompson
an' Jack Moore interjecks yere is dead c'rrect; but after all this
question about what's manners is 'way to one side of the main
trail. I tharfore su'gests at this crisis that Black Jack do his best
with a bottle, an' when every gent has got his p'ison, Dave Tutt
proceeds for'ard with the killin' of this Jack Rainey.'

" 'Goin' on as to said Rainey,' observes Tutt, followin' them
remarks of Enright, 'as I explains when Texas an' Moore runs
me down with them interestin' outbreaks, Rainey gets ag'inst it
over in a jimcrow camp called Lido; an' this yere is a long spell
ago.

" 'Rainey turns in an' charters every bar in Lido, an' gets his
brand onto all the nose-paint. He's out to give the camp an orgy,
an' not a gent can spend a splinter or lose a chip to any bar for a
week. Them's Jack Rainey's commands. A sport orders his forty
drops, an' the barkeep pricks it onto a tab; at the end of a week
Jack Rainey settles all along the line, an' the "saturnalia," as
historians calls 'em, is over. I might add that Jack Rainey gives

way to these yere charities once a year, an' the camp of Lido is plumb used tharto an' approves tharof.

" 'On this sad o'casion when Jack Rainey gets killed, this yere excellent custom he invents is in full swing. Thar's notices printed plenty big, an' posted up in every drink-shop from the dance hall to the Sunflower saloon; which they reads as follows:

RUIN! RUIN! RUIN!
CUT LOOSE!
JACK RAINEY MAKES GOOD
ALL DRINKS
FOR
ONE WEEK.   NAME YOUR POISON!

" 'At this yere time, it's about half through Jack Rainey's week, an' the pop'lace of Lido, in consequence, is plumb happy an' content. They're holdin' co't at the time; the same bein' the first jestice, legal, which is dealt out in Lido.' "

" 'An' do you-all know,' puts in Dan Boggs, who's listenin' to Tutt, 'I'm mighty distrustful of co'ts. You go to holdin' of 'em, an' it looks like everybody gets wrought up to frenzy ontil life where them forums is held ain't safe for a second. I shall shorely deplore the day when a co't goes to openin' its game in Wolfville. It's "adios" to liberty an' peace an' safety from that time.'

" 'You can go a yellow stack,' remarks Texas Thompson, who sets thar plumb loquacious an' locoed to get in a speech, 'that Boggs sizes up right about them triboonals. They're a disturbin' element in any commoonity. I knowed a town in Texas which is that peaceful it's pastoral—that's what it is, it's like a sheep-fold, it's so meek an' easy—ontil one day they ups an' plays a co't an' jedge an' jury on that camp; rings in a herd of law sharps, an' a passel of rangers with Winchesters to back the deal. The town's that fretted tharat it gets full of nose-paint to the brim, an' then hops into the street for gen'ral practice with its guns. In the mornin' the round-up shows two dead an' five wounded, an' all for openin' co't on an outfit which is too frail to stand the strain of so much jestice onexpected.'

" 'As I'm engaged in remarkin',' says Tutt, after Boggs an' Texas is redooced to quiet ag'in—Tutt bein' married most likely is used to interruptions, an' is shore patient that a-way—'as I states, they're holdin' co't, an' this day they emancipates from prison a party named Caribou Sam. They tries to prove this Caribou Sam is a hoss-thief, but couldn't fill on the draw, an' so Caribou works free of 'em an' is what they calls " 'quitted.' "

" 'As soon as ever the marshal takes the hobbles off this Caribou Sam—he's been held a captif off some'ers an' is packed into Lido onder gyard to be tried a lot—this yere malefactor comes bulgin' into the Sunflower an' declar's for fire-water. The barkeep deals to him, an' Caribou Sam is assuaged.

" 'When he goes to pay, a gent who's standin' near shoves back his dust, an' says: "This is Jack Rainey's week—it's the great annyooal festival of Jack Rainey, an' your money's no good."

" ' "But I aims to drink some more *poco tiempo*," says this Caribou Sam, who is new to Lido, an' never yet hears of Jack Rainey an' his little game, "an' before I permits a gent to subsidize my thirst, an' go stackin' in for my base appetites, you can gamble I want to meet him an' make his acquaintance. Where is this yere sport Jack Rainey, an' whatever is he doin' this on?"

" 'The party who shoves Caribou's *dinero* off the bar, tells him he can't pay, an' explains the play, an' exhorts him to drink free an' frequent an' keep his chips in his war-bags.

" ' "As I tells you," says this party to Caribou, "my friend Jack Rainey has treed the camp, an' no money goes yere but his till his further commands is known. Fill your hide, but don't flourish no funds, or go enlargin' on any weakness you has for buyin' your own licker. As for seein' Jack Rainey, it's plumb impossible. He's got too full to visit folks or be visited by 'em; but he's upsta'rs on some blankets, an' if his reason is restored by to-morry, you sends up your kyard an' pays him your regyards—pendin' of which social function, take another drink. Barkeep, pump another dose into this stranger, an' charge the same to Jack."

" ' "This yere sounds good," says Caribou Sam, "but it don't win over me. Ontil I sees this person Rainey, I shall shorely decline all bottles which is presented in his name. I've had a close call about a bronco I stole to-day, an' when the jury makes a verdict that they're sorry to say the evidence ain't enough to convict, the jedge warns me to be a heap careful of the company I maintains. He exhorts me to live down my past, or failin' which he'll hang me yet. With this bluff from the bench ringin' in my y'ears, I shall refoose drinks with all onknown sots, ontil I sees for myse'f they's proper characters for me to be sociable with. Tharfore, barkeep, I renoo my determination to pay for them drinks; at the same time, I orders another round. Do you turn for me or no?"

" ' "Not none you don't," says the friend of Jack Rainey. "You can drink, but you can't pay—leastwise, you-all can't pay without gettin' all sort o' action on your money. This Rainey you're worried about is as good a gent as me, an' not at all likely to shake the standin' of a common hoss-thief by merely buyin' his nose-paint."

" ' "Mine is shorely a difficult p'sition," says Caribou Sam. "What you imparts is scarce encouragin.' If this yere Rainey ain't no improvement onto you, I absolootely weakens on him an' turns aside from all relations of his proposin'. I'm in mighty bad report as the game stands, an' I tharfore insists ag'in on payin' for my own war medicine, as bein' a move necessary to protect my attitoodes before the public."

" 'With these yere observations, Caribou Sam makes a bluff at the barkeep with a handful of money. In remonstratin', Jack Rainey's pard nacherally pulls a gun, as likewise does Caribou Sam. Thar's the customary quantity of shootin', an' while neither Caribou nor his foe gets drilled, a bullet goes through the ceilin' an' sort o' sa'nters in a careless, indifferent way into pore Jack Rainey, where he's bedded down an' snorin' up above.

" 'Shore, he's dead, Rainey is,' concloodes Dave, 'an' his ontimely takin' off makes Lido quit loser for three days of licker free as air. He's a splendid, gen'rous soul, Jack Rainey is; an' as I says at the beginnin', he falls a sacrifice to his love for others, an' in tryin' at his own expense to promote the happiness an' lift them burdens of his fellow-men.'

" 'This yere miscreant, Caribou,' says Texas Thompson, 'is a mighty sight too punctilious about them drinks; which thar's no doubt of it. Do they lynch him?'

" 'No,' says Tutt; 'from the calibre of the gun which fires the lead that snatches Rainey from us, it is cl'ar that it's the gent who's contendin' with Caribou who does it. Still public opinion is some sour over losin' them three days, an' so Caribou goes lopin' out of Lido surreptitious that same evenin', an' don't wait none on Rainey's obsequies. Caribou merely sends regrets by the barkeep of the Sunflower, reiterates the right to pay for them drinks, an' Lido sees him no more.' "

An extract from a longer, and perhaps desultory tale. Lewis recounts a Tennessee tale, complete with folk say, violence, and brag.

From OLD MAN ENRIGHT'S LOVE

. . . "It's in the back room of the New York Store where the casks be, an' Enright, on whose nerves an' sperits Peets' preescriptions of 'no licker' has been feedin' for two full days, sits thar sort o' fidgin' with his fingers an' movin' his feet in a way which shows he's a heap on aige. Thar's a melancholy settles on all, as we camps 'round on crates an' shoe boxes an' silently sympathizes with Enright to see him so redooced. At last the grand old chief starts in to talk without questions or requests.

" 'If you-all don't mind,' says Enright, 'I'll let go a handful of mem'ries touchin' my yooth. Thar's nothin' like maladies to make a gent sentimental, onless it be gettin' shot up or cut up with bullets or bowies; an' these yere visitations, which Peets thinks is alkali an' I holds is the burdens of them years of mine, shore leaves me plumb romantic.

" 'Which I've been thinkin' all day, between times when I'm thinkin' of licker, of Polly Hawks; an' I'll say right yere she's my first an' only love. She's a fine young female, is Polly—tall as a saplin', with a arm on her like a cant-hook. Polly can lift an' hang up a side of beef, an' is as good as two hands at a log-rollin'.

" 'This yere's back in old Tennessee on the banks of the Cumberland. It's about six years followin' on the Mexican war, an' I'm shot up'ards into the semblances of a man. My affections for Polly has their beginnin's in a coon-hunt into which b'ars an' dogs gets commingled in painful profoosion.

" 'I ain't the wonder of a week with a rifle now, since I'm old an' dim, but them times on the Cumberland I has fame as sech. More'n once, ag'inst the best there is in either the Cumberland or the Tennessee bottoms, or on the ridge between, I've won as good as, say, first, second and fifth quarters in a shoot for the beef.'

" 'Whatever do you-all call a fifth quarter of beef?' asks Dan Boggs. 'Four quarters is all I'm ever able to count to the anamile.'

" 'It's yooth an' inexperience,' says Enright, 'that prompts them queries. The fifth quarter is the hide an' tallow; an' also thar's a sixth quarter, the same bein' the bullets in the stump which makes the target, an' which is dug out a whole lot, lead bein' plenty infrequent in them days I'm dreamin' of.

" 'As I'm sayin', when Dan lams loose them thick-head questions, I'm a renowned shot, an' my weakness is huntin' b'ars. I finds 'em an' kills 'em that easy, I thinks thar's nothin' in the world but b'ars. An' when I ain't huntin' b'ars, I'm layin' for deer; an' when I ain't layin' for deer, I'm squawkin' turkeys; an' when I ain't squawkin' turkeys, I'm out nights with a passel of misfit dogs I harbors, a-shakin' up the scenery for raccoons. Altogether, I'm some busy as you-all may well infer.

" 'One night I'm coon huntin'. The dogs trees over on Rapid Run. When I arrives, the whole pack is cirkled 'round the base of a big beech, singin'; my old Andrew Jackson dog leadin' the choir with the air, an' my Thomas Benton dog growlin' bass, while the others warbles what parts they will, indiscrim'nate.

" 'Nacherally, the dogs can't climb the tree none, an' I has to makes that play myse'f. I lays down my gun, an' shucks my belts an' knife, an' goes swarmin' up the beech. It's shorely a teedious enterprise, an' some rough besides. That beech seems as full of spikes an' thorns as a honey locust—it's a sort o' porkypine of a tree.

" 'Which I works my lacerated way into the lower branches, an' then glances up ag'in the firmaments to locate the coon. He ain't vis'ble none; he's higher up an' the leaves an' bresh hides him. I goes on till I'm twenty foot from the ground; then I looks ag'in.

" 'Gents, it ain't no coon; it's a b'ar, black as paint an' as big as a baggage wagon. He ain't two foot above me too; an' the sight of him, settin' thar like a black bale of cotton, an' his nearness, an' partic'larly a few terse remarks he lets drop, comes mighty clost to astonishin' me to death. I thinks of my gun; an' then I lets go all holts to go an' get it. Shore, I falls outen the tree; thar ain't no time to descend slow an' dignified.

" 'As I comes crashin' along through them beech boughs, it inculcates a misonderstandin' among the dogs. Andrew Jackson, Thomas Benton an' the others is convoked about that tree on a purely coon theery. They expects me to knock the coon down to 'em. They shorely do not expect me to come tumblin' none myse'f. It tharfore befalls that when I makes my deboo among 'em, them canines, blinded an' besotted as I say with thoughts of coon, prounces upon me in a body. Every dog rends off a speciment of me. They don't bite twice; they perceives by the taste that it ain't no coon an' desists.

" 'Which I don't reckon their worryin' me would have become a continyoous performance nohow; for me an' the dogs is hardly tangled up that a-way, when we're interfered with by the b'ar. Looks like the example I sets is infectious; for when I lets go, the b'ar lets go; an' I hardly hits the ground an' becomes the ragin' center of interest to Andrew Jackson, Thomas Benton an' them others, when the b'ar is down on all of us like the old Cumberland on a sandbar doorin' a spring rise. I shore regyards his advent that a-way as the day of jedgment.

" 'No, we don't corral him. The b'ar simply r'ars back long enough to put Andrew Jackson an' Thomas Benton into mournin', an' then goes scuttlin' off through the bushes like the grace of heaven through a camp-meetin'. As for myse'f, I lays thar; an' what between dog an' b'ar an' the fall I gets, I'm as completely a thing of the past as ever finds refooge in that strip of timber. As near as I makes out by feelin' of myse'f, I ain't fit to make gourds out of. Of course, she's a mistake on the part of the dogs, an' plumb accidental as far as the b'ar's concerned; but it shore crumples me up as entirely as if this yere outfit of anamiles plots the play for a month.

" 'With the last flicker of my failin' strength, I crawls to my old gent's teepee an' is took in. An' you shore should have heard the language of that household when they sees the full an' awful extent them dogs an' that b'ar lays me waste. Which I'm layed up eight weeks.

" 'My old gent goes grumblin' off in the mornin', an' rounds up old Aunt Tilly Hawks to nurse me. Old Aunt Tilly lives over on the Painted Post, an' is plumb learned in yarbs an' sech as Injun turnips, opydeldock, live-forever, skoke-berry roots, jinson an' whitewood bark. An' so they ropes up Aunt Tilly Hawks an' tells her to ride herd on my wounds an' dislocations.

" 'But I'm plumb weak an' nervous an' can't stand Aunt Tilly none. She ain't got no upper teeth, same as a cow, her face is wrinkled like a burnt boot, an' she dips snuff. Moreover, she gives me the horrors by allers singin' in a quaverin' way:

"Hark from the tombs a doleful sound,
   Mine y'ears attend the cry.
   Ye livin' men come view the ground
   Where you shall shortly lie.

" 'Aunt Tilly sounds a heap like a tea-kettle when she's renderin' this yere madrigal, an' that, an' the words, an' all the rest, makes me gloomy an' dejected. I'm shore pinin' away onder these yere malign inflooences, when my old gent notes I ain't recooperatin', an' so he guesses the cause; an' with that he gives Aunt Tilly a lay-off, an' tells her to send along her niece Polly to take her place.

" 'Thar's a encouragin' difference. Polly is big an' strong like I states; but her eyes is like stars, an' she's as full of sweetness as a bee tree or a bar'l of m'lasses. So Polly camps down by my couch of pain an' begins dallyin' soothin'ly with my heated brow. I commences recoverin' from them attacks of b'ars an' dogs instanter.

" 'This yere Polly Hawks ain't none new to me. I never co'ts her; but I meets her frequent at barn raisin's an' quiltin's, which allers winds up in a dance; an' in them games an' merriments, sech as "bowin' to the wittiest, kneelin' to the prettiest, an' kissin' the one you loves the best," I more than once regyards Polly as an alloorin' form of hooman hollyhock, an' selects her. But thar's no flush of burnin' love; nothin' more than them amiable formalities which befits the o'casion.

" 'While this yere Polly is nursin' me, however, she takes on a different attitoode a whole lot. It looks like I begins to need her permanent, an' every time I sets my eyes on her I feels as soft as b'ar's grease. It's shorely love; that Polly Hawks is as sweet an' luscious as a roast apple.'

" 'Is she for troo so lovely?' asks Faro Nell, who's been hangin' onto Enright's words.

" 'Frankly, Nellie,' says Enright, sort o' pinchin' down his bluff; 'now that I'm ca'mer an' my blood is cool, this yere Polly don't seem so plumb prismatic. Still, I must say, she's plenty radiant.'

" 'Does you-all,' says Dan Boggs, 'put this yere Polly in nom'-nation to be your wife while you're quiled up sick?'

" 'No, I defers them offers to moments when I'm more robust,' says Enright.

" 'You shore oughter rode at her while you're sick that a-way,' remonstrates Boggs. 'That's the time to set your stack down. Females is easy moved to pity, an', as I've heared—for I've nothin' to go by, personal, since I'm never married an' is never sick none—is a heap more prone to wed a gent who's sick, than when he's well a lot.'

" 'I holds them doctrines myse'f,' observes Enright; 'however, I don't descend on Polly with no prop'sitions, neither then nor final, as you-all shall hear, Dan, if you'll only hold yourse'f down. No, I continyoos on lovin' Polly to myse'f that a-way, ontil I'm able to go pokin' about on crutches; an' then, as thar's no more need of her ministrations, Polly lines out for old Aunt Tilly's cabin ag'in.

" 'It's at this yere juncture things happens which sort o' complicates them dreams of mine. While I ain't been sayin' nothin', an' has been plumb reticent as to my feelin's, jest the same, by look or act, or mebby it's a sigh, I tips off my hand. It ain't no time before all the neighbors is aware of my love for Polly Hawks. Also, this Polly has a lover who it looks like has been co'tin' her, an' bringin' her mink pelts an' wild turkeys indeescrim'nate, for months. I never do hear of this gent ontil I'm cripplin' 'round on them stilts of crutches; an' then I ain't informed of him none only after he's informed of me.

" 'Thar's a measley little limberjaw of a party whose name is Ike Sparks; this Ike is allers runnin' about tellin' things an' settin' traps to capture trouble for other folks. Ike is a ornery anamile— little an' furtif—mean enough to suck aigs, an' cunnin' enough to hide the shells. He hates everybody, this Ike does; an' he's as suspicious as Bill Johnson's dog, which last is that doubtful an' suspicious he shore walks sideways all his life for fear someone's goin' to kick him. This low-down Ike imparts to Polly's other lover about the state of my feelin's; an' then it ain't no time when I gets notice of this sport's existence.

" 'It's in the licker room of the tavern at Pine Knot, to which scenes I've scrambled on them crutches one evenin', where this party first meets up with me in person. He's a big, tall citizen with lanky, long ha'r, an' is dressed in a blanket huntin' shirt an' has a coon-skin cap with the tail hangin' over his left y'ear. Also, he packs a Hawkins rifle, bullets about forty to the pound. For myse'f, I don't get entranced none with this person's looks, an' as I ain't fit, physical, for no skrimmage, I has to sing plumb low.

" 'Thar's a band of us settin' 'round when this lover of Polly's shows in the door, drinkin' an' warblin' that entertainin' ditty, which goes:

" ' "Thar sits a dog, by a barn door.
An' Bingo is his name, O !
An' Bingo is his name."

" 'As Polly's other beau comes in, we ceases this refrain. He pitches his rifle to the landlord over the bar, an' calls for a Bald-face whiskey toddy. He takes four or five drinks, contemplatin' us meanwhile a heap disdainful. Then he arches his back, bends his elbows, begins a war-song, an' goes dancin' stiff-laig like a Injun, in front of the bar. This is how this extravagant party sings. It's what Colonel Sterett, yere, to whom I repeats it former, calls "blanket verse."

" ' "Let all the sons of men b'ar witness!" sings this gent, as he goes skatin' stiff-laig about in a ring like I relates, arms bent, an' back arched; "let all the sons of men b'ar witness; an' speshully let a cowerin' varmint, named Sam Enright, size me up an' shudder! I'm the maker of deserts an' the wall-eyed harbinger of desolation! I'm kin to rattlesnakes on my mother's side; I'm king of all the eagles an' full brother to the b'ars! I'm the bloo-eyed lynx of Whiskey Crossin', an' I weighs four thousand pounds! I'm a he-steamboat; I've put a crimp in a cat-a-mount with nothin' but my livin' hands! I broke a full-grown allagator across my knee, tore him asunder an' showered his shrinkin' fragments over a full section of land! I hugged a cinnamon b'ar to death, an' made a grizzly plead for mercy! Who'll come gouge with me? Who'll come bite with me? Who'll come put his knuckles in my back? I'm Weasel-eye, the dead shot; I'm the blood-drinkin', skelp-t'arin', knife-plyin' demon of Sunflower Creek! The flash of my glance will deaden a whiteoak, an' my screech in anger will back the panther plumb off his natif heath! I'm a slayer an' a slaughterer, an' I cooks an' eats my dead! I can wade the Cumberland without wettin' myse'f, an' I drinks outen the spring without touchin' the ground! I'm a swinge-cat; but I warns you not to be misled by my looks! I'm a flyin' bison, an' deevastation rides upon my breath! Whoop! whoop! whoopee! I'm the Purple Blossom of Gingham Mountain, an' where is that son of thunder who'll try an' nip me in the bud! Whoop! whoopee! I'm yere to fight or drink with any sport; ary one or both! Whoopee! Where is the stately stag to stamp his hoof or rap his antlers to my proclamations! Where is that boundin' buck! Whoopee! whoop! whoop!"

" 'Then this yere vociferous Purple Blossom pauses for breath; but keeps up his stilt-laig dance, considerin' me meanwhile with

his eye, plenty baleful. We-all on our parts is viewin' him over a
heap respectful, an' ain't retortin' a word. Then he begins ag'in
with a yelp that would stampede a field of corn.

" ' "Who is thar lovelier than Polly Hawks!" he shouts. "Show
me the female more entrancin', an' let me drop dead at her feet!
Who is lovelier than Polly Hawks, the sweetheart of Flyin' Bison,
the onchained tornado of the hills! Feast your gaze on Polly
Hawks; her beauty would melt the heart of Nacher! I'm the
Purple Blossom of Gingham Mountain; Polly Hawks shall marry
an' follow me to my wigwam! Her bed shall be of b'ar-skins; her
food shall be yearlin' venison, an' wild honey from the tree! Her
gown shall be panther's pelts fringed 'round with wolf-tails an'
eagles' claws! She shall belt herse'f with a rattlesnake, an' her
Sunday bonnet shall be a swarm of bees! When I kiss her it
sounds like the crack of a whip, an' I wouldn't part with her for
twenty cows! We will wed an' pop'late the earth with terror!
Where is the sooicide who'll stand in my way?"

" 'At this p'int the Purple Blossom leaves off dancin' an' fronts
up to me, personal.

" ' "Whoopee!" he says; "say that you don't love the girl an'
I'll give you one hundred dollars before I spills your life!"

" 'Which, of course, all these yere moosical an' terpshicoreen
preeliminaries means simply so much war between me an' this
sperited beau of Polly's, to see who'll own the lady's heart. I
explains that I'm not jest then fit for combat, sufferin' as I be
from that overabundance of dog an' b'ar. The Purple Blossom is
plumb p'lite, an' says he don't hunger to whip no cripples. Then
he names a day two months away when he allows he'll shore
descend from Gingham Mountain, melt me down an' run me into
candles to burn at the weddin' of him an' Polly Hawks. Then we
drinks together, all fraternal, an' he gives me a chew of tobacco
outen a box made of the head of a bald eagle, in token of amity,
that a-way.

" 'But that rumpus between the Purple Blossom an' me never
does come off; an' them rites over me an' Polly is indef'nitely
postponed. The fact is, I has to leave a lot. I starts out to com-

mit a joke, an' it turns out a crime; an' so I goes streakin' it from the scenes of my yoothful frolics for safer stampin' grounds.

" 'It's mebby six weeks followin' them declarations of the Purple Blossom. It's co't day at Warwhoop Crossin', an' the Jedge an' every law-sharp on that circuit comes trailin' into camp. This yere outfit of Warwhoop is speshul fretful ag'inst all forms of gamblin'. Wherefore the Jedge, an' the state's attorney, an' mebby five other speculators, at night adjourns to the cabin of a flat-boat which is tied up at the foot of the levee, so's they can divert themse'fs with a little draw-poker without shockin' the hamlet an' gettin' themse'fs arrested an' fined some.

" 'It's gone to about fourth drink time after supper, an' I'm romancin' about, tryin' to figger out how I'm to win Polly, when as I'm waltzin' along the levee—I'm plumb alone, an' the town itse'f has turned into its blankets—I gets sight of this yere poker festival ragin' in the cabin. Thar they be, antein', goin' it blind, straddlin', raisin' before the draw, bluffin', an' bettin', an' havin' the time of their c'reers.

" 'It's the spring flood, an' the old Cumberland is bank-full an' still a-risin'. The flat boat is softly raisin' an' fallin' on the sobbin' tide. It's then them jocular impulses seizes me, that a-way, an' I stoops an' casts off her one line, an' that flat boat swims silently away on the bosom of the river. The sports inside knows nothin' an' guesses less, an' their gayety swells on without a hitch.

" 'It's three o'clock an' Jedge Finn, who's won about a hundred an' sixty dollars, realizes it's all the money in the outfit, an' gets cold feet plenty prompt. He murmurs somethin' about tellin' the old lady Finn he'd be in early, an' shoves back amidst the scoffs an' jeers of the losers. But the good old Jedge don't mind, an' openin' the door, he goes out into the night an' the dark, an' carefully picks his way overboard into forty foot of water. The yell the Jedge emits as he makes his little hole in the Cumberland is the first news them kyard sharps gets that they're afloat a whole lot.

" 'It ain't no push-over rescooin' Jedge Finn that time. The one hundred an' sixty is in Mexican money, an' he's got a pound or two of it sinkered about his old frame in every pocket; so he goes to the bottom like a kag of nails.

" 'But they works hard, an' at last fishes him out, an' rolls him over a bar'l to get the water an' the money outen him. Which onder sech treatment, the Jedge disgorges both, an' at last comes to a trifle an' is fed whiskey with a spoon.

" 'Havin' saved the Jedge, the others turns loose a volley of yells that shorely scares up them echoes far an' wide. It wakes up a little old tug that's tied in Dead Nigger Bend, an' she fires up an' pushes forth to their relief. The tug hauls 'em back to Warwhoop for seventy dollars, which is paid out of the rescooed treasure of Jedge Finn, the same bein' declar'd salvage by them bandits he's been playin' with.

" 'It's two o'clock in the afternoon when that band of gamblers pulls up ag'in at Warwhoop, an' they're shorely a saddened party as they files ashore. The village is thar in a frownin' an' resentful body to arrest 'em for them voylations, which is accordin' done.

" 'At the same time, I regyards the play as the funniest, ondoubted, that's ever been evolved in Tennessee; but my mood changes as subsequent events assoomes a somber face. Old Jedge Finn goes fumin' about like a wronged lion, an' the rest is as hot as election day in a hornet's nest. Pards, I'm a Mexican! if they don't indict me for piracy on the high seas, an' pledge their words to see me hanged before ever co't adjourns.

" 'That lets me out, right thar! I sees the symptoms of my on-pop'larity in advance, an' don't procrastinate none. I goes sailin' over the divide to the Tennessee, down the Tennessee to the Ohio, down the Ohio to the Mississippi, down the Mississippi to the Arkansaw, up the Arkansaw to Little Rock; an' thar I pauses, exhausted shore, but safe as a murderer in Georgia. Which I never does go back for plumb ten years.

" 'Nacherally, because of this yere exodus, I misses my engagements with the Purple Blossom; also them nuptials I plots about Polly Hawks, suffers the kybosh a whole lot. However, I survives, an' Polly survives; she an' the Purple Blossom hooks up a month later, an' I learns since they shore has offsprings enough to pack a primary or start a public school. It's all over long ago, an' I'm glad the kyards falls as they do. Still, as I intimates, thar's them moments of romance to ride me down, when I remembers my one lone love affair with Polly Hawks, the beauty of the Painted Post.'

"Enright pauses, an' we-all sets still a moment out of respects to the old chief. At last Dan Boggs, who's always bubblin' that a-way, speaks up:

" 'Which I'm shore sorry,' says Dan, 'you don't fetch the moosic of that Purple Blossom's warsong West. I deems that a mighty excellent lay, an' would admire to learn it an' sing it some myse'f. I'd shore go over an' carol it to Red Dog; it would redooce them drunkards to frenzy.' "

Still another extract, this time focussing on the road agent, though without any of the "halo of romance" which sometimes formed about the head of one or another of them, and which good sense will take into account in probing the possibilities of law and order in human affairs. Such recountings as William MacLeod Raine's Famous Sheriffs and Western Outlaws *(1929)* and Stanley Vestal's Dodge City: Queen of Cowtowns *(1952)* are, I think, not calculated to discourage an interest in peace, but to sophisticate it. Incidently, Lewis followed crime in the East, as well as in the West, and has several books on the subject, but they are not the best of him.

From WHEN THE STAGE WAS STOPPED

. . . I had been going over the vigorous details of a Western robbery in the papers. After briefly telling the story as I remembered it, in its broader lines at least, I carried my curiosity to that interesting body politic, the town of Wolfville.

"In the old days," I asked, "did Wolfville ever suffer from stage robberies, or the operations of banditti of the trail?"

"Wolfville," responded my friend, "goes ag'inst the hold-up game so often we lose the count. Mostly, it don't cause more'n a passin' irr'tation. Them robberies an' rustlin's don't, speakin' general, mean much to the public at large. The express company may gnash its teeth some, but comin' down to cases, what is a Wells-Fargo grief to us? Personal, we're out letters an' missifs from home, an' I've beheld individooals who gets that heated about it you don't dar' ask 'em to libate ontil they cools; but as a common thing, we-all don't suffer no practical set-backs. We're shy letters; but sech wounds is healed by time an' other mails to come. We gains what comfort we can from sw'arin' a lot, an' turns to the hopeful footure for the rest. Thar's one time, however, when Wolfville gets wrought up.

"Which the Wolfville temper, usual, is ca'm an' onperturbed that a-way. Thar's a steadiness to the Wolfville that shows the camp has depth; it can lose without thinkin' of sooicide, it can win an' not get drunk. The Wolfville emotions sets squar' an' steady in the saddle, an' it takes more than mere commonplace buckin' to so much as throw its foot loose from a stirrup, let alone send it flyin' from its seat.

"On this yere o'casion, however, Wolfville gets stirred a whole lot. For that matter, the balance of Southeast Arizona gives way likewise, an' excitement is gen'ral an' shorely mounts plumb high. I remembers plain, now my mind is on them topics, how Red Dog goes hysterical complete, an' sets up nights an' screams. Which the vocal carryin's on of that prideless village is a shame to coyotes!

"It's hold-ups that so wrings the public's feelin's. Stages is stood up; passengers, mail-bags an' express boxes gets cleaned out for their last splinter. An' it ain't confined to jest one trail. This festival of crime incloodes a whole region; an' twenty stages, in as many different places an' almost as many days, yields up to these yere bandits. Old Monte, looks like, is a speshul fav'rite; they goes through that old drunkard twice for all thar is in the vehicle. The last time the gyard gets downed.

"No; the stage driver ain't in no peril of bein' plugged. Thar's rooles about stage robbin', same as thar is to faro-bank an' poker. It's onderstood by all who's interested, from the manager of the stage company to the gent in the mask who's holdin' the Winchester on the outfit, that the driver don't fight. He's thar to drive, not shoot; an' so when he hears the su'gestion, 'Hand's up!' that a-way, he stops the team. sets the brake, hooks his fingers together over his head, an' nacherally lets them road agents an' passengers an' gyards, settle events in their own onfettered way. The driver, usual, cusses out the brigands frightful. The laws of the trail accords him them privileges, imposin' no reestrictions on his mouth. He's plumb free to make what insultin' observations he will, so long as he keeps his hands up an' don't start the team none ontil he's given the proper word; the same comin' from the hold-ups or the gyards, whoever emerges winner from said emeutes.

"As I states, the last time Old Monte is made to front the iron, the Wells-Fargo gyard gets plugged as full of lead as a bag of bullets. An' as to that business of loot an' plunder, them miscreants shorely harvests a back load! It catches Enright a heap hard, this second break which these yere felons makes.

"Cherokee Hall an' me is settin' in the Red Light, whilin' away time between bev'rages with argyments, when Enright comes ploddin' along in with the tidin's. Cherokee an' me, by a sing'lar coincidence, is discussin' the topic of 'probity' that a-way, although our loocubrations don't flourish none concernin' stage rustlin'. Cherokee is sayin'.

" 'Now, I holds that trade—what you-all might call commerce, is plenty sappenin' to the integrity of folks. Meanin' no aspersions on any gent in camp, shorely not on the proprietors of the New York Store, what I reiterates is that I never meets up with the party who makes his livin' weighin' things, or who owns a pa'r of scales, who's on the level that a-way. Which them balances, looks like, weaves a spell on a gent's moral princ'ples. He's no longer on the squar'.'

"I'm r'ared back on my hocks organizin' to combat the fal'cies of Cherokee, when Enright pulls up a cha'r. By the clouds on his face, both me an' Cherokee sees thar's somethin' on the old chief's mind a lot, wherefore we lays aside our own dispootes—which after all, has no real meanin', an' is what Colonel William Greene Sterett calls 'ac'demic'—an' turns to Enright to discover whatever is up. Black Jack feels thar's news in the air an' promotes the nose-paint without s'licitation. Enright freights his glass an' then says:

" 'You-all hears of the noomerous stage robberies? Well, Wolfville lose ag'in. I, myse'f, this trip am put in the hole partic'lar. If I onderstands the drift of my own private affairs, thar's over forty thousand dollars of mine on the stage, bein' what balance is doo me from that last bunch of cattle. It's mighty likely though she's in drafts that a-way; an' I jest dispatches one of my best riders with a lead hoss to scatter over to Tucson an' wire informations east, to freeze onto that money ontil further tidin's; said drafts, if sech thar be, havin' got into the hands of these yere diligent hold-ups aforesaid.'

" 'Forty thousand dollars!' remarks Cherokee. 'Which that is a jolt for shore!'"

" 'It shorely shows the oncertainties of things,' says Enright, ag'in referrin' to his glass. 'I'm in the very act of congratulatin' myse'f, mental, that this yere is the best season I ever sees, when a party rides in from the first stage station towards Tucson, with the tale. It's shore a paradox; it's a case where the more I win, the more I lose. However, I'm on the trail of Mack Moore; a conference with Jack is what I needs right now. I'll be back by next drink time;' an' with that Enright goes surgin' off to locate Jack.

"Cherokee an' me, as might be expected, turns our powers of conversation loose with this new last eepisode of the trail.

" 'An' I'm struck speshul,' says Cherokee, 'about what Enright observes at the finish, that it's a instance where the more he wins, the more he loses; an' how this, his best season, is goin' to be his worst. I has experiences sim'lar myse'f onct. Which the cases is plumb parallel!

" 'This time when my own individooal game strikes somethin' an' glances off, is 'way back. I gets off a boat on the upper river at a camp called Rock Island. You never is thar? I don't aim to encourage you-all ondooly, still your failure to see Rock Island needn't prey on you as the rooin of your c'reer. I goes ashore as I relates, an' the first gent I encounters is old Peg-laig Jones. This yere Peg-laig is a madman to spec'late at kyards, an' the instant he sees me, he pulls me one side, plenty breathless with a plan he's evolved.

" ' "Son," says this yere Peg-laig, "how much money has you?"

" 'I tells him I ain't over strong; somethin' like two hundred dollars, mebby.

" ' "That's enough," say Peg-laig. "Son, give it to me. I'll put three hundred with it, an' that'll make a roll of five hundred dollars. With a careful man like me to deal, she shorely oughter be enough."

" ' "Whatever does these yere fiscal bluffs of yours portend?" I asks.

" ' "They portends as follows," says Peg-laig. "This yere Rock

Island outfit is plumb locoed to play faro-bank. I've got a deck of kyards an' a deal box in my pocket. Son, we'll lay over a day an' break the village."

" 'Thar's no use tryin' to head off old Peg-laig. He's the most invet'rate sport that a-way, an' faro-bank is his leadin' weakness. They even tells onct how this Peg-laig is in a small camp in Iowa an' is buckin' a crooked game. A pard sees him an' takes Peg-laig to task.

" ' "Can't you-all see them sharps is skinnin' you?" says this friend, an' his tones is loaded with disgust. "Ain't you wise enough to know this game ain't on the squar', an' them outlaws has a end-squeeze box an' is dealin' two kyards at a clatter an' puttin' back right onder your ignorant nose? Which you conducts yourse'f like you was born last week!"

" ' "Of course, I knows the game is crooked," says Peg-laig, plenty doleful, "an I regrets it as much as you. But whatever can I do?"

" ' "Do!" says his friend; "do! You-all can quit goin' ag'inst it, can't you?"

" ' "But you don't onderstand," says Peg-laig, eager an' warm. "It's all plumb easy for you to stand thar an' say I don't have to go ag'inst it. It may change your notion a whole lot when I informs you that this yere is the only game in town," an' with that this reedic'lous Peg-laig hurries back to his seat.

" 'As I asserts former, it's no use me tryin' to make old Peg-laig stop when once he's started with them schemes of his, so I turns over my two hundred dollars, an' leans back to see whatever Peg-laig's goin' to a'complish next. As he says, he's got a box an' a deck to deal with. So he fakes a layout with a suite of jimcrow kyards he buys, local, an' a oil-cloth table-cover, an' thar he is organized to begin. For chips, he goes over to a store an' buys twenty stacks of big wooden button molds, same as they sews the cloth onto for overcoat buttons. When Peg-laig is ready, you should have beheld the enthoosiasm of them Rock Island folks. They goes ag'inst that brace of Peg-laig's like a avalanche.

" 'Peg-laig deals for mighty likely it's an hour. Jest as he puts it up, he's a careful dealer, an' the result is we win all the big bets an' most all the little ones, an' I'm sort o' estimatin' in my mind that we're ahead about four hundred simoleons. Of a-sudden, Peg-laig stops dealin', up-ends his box and turns to me with a look w.'ich shows he's plumb dismayed. P'intin' at the check-rack, Peg-laig says:

" ' "Son, look thar!"

" 'Nacherally, I looks, an' I at once realizes the roots of that consternation of Peg-laig's. It's this: While thar's more of them button molds in front of Peg-laig's right elbow than we embarks with orig'nal, thar's still twenty-two hundred dollars' worth in the hands of the Rock Island pop'lace waitin' to be cashed. How-ever do they do it? They goes stampedin' over to this yere store-keep an' purchases 'em for four bits a gross. They buys that va-grant out that a-way. They even buys new kinds on us, an' it's a party tryin' to bet a stack of pants buttons on the high kyard that calls Peg-laig's attention to them frauds.

" 'Thar's no he'p for it, however; them villagers is stony an' adamantine, an' so far as we has money they shorely makes us pay. We walks out of Rock Island. About a mile free of the camp, Peg-laig stops an' surveys me a heap mournful.

" ' "Son," he says, "we was winnin', wasn't we?"

" ' "Which we shore was," I replies.

" ' "Exactly," says Peg-laig, shakin' his head, "we was shorely winners. An' I want to add, son, that if we-all could have kept on winnin' for two hours more, we'd a-lost eight thousand dollars."

" 'It's like this yere stage hold-up on Enright,' concloodes Cherokee; 'it's a harassin' instance of where the more you wins, the more you lose.'

"About this time, Enright an' Jack Moore comes in. Colonel Sterett an' Dan Boggs j'ines us accidental, an' we-all six holds a pow wow in low tones.

" 'Which Jack,' observes Enright, like he's experimentin' an' ropin' for our views,' allows it's his beliefs that this yere guileless tenderfoot, Davis, who says he's from Buffalo, an' who's been prancin' about town for the last two days, is involved in them felonies.'

" 'It ain't none onlikely,' says Boggs; 'speshully since he's from Buffalo. I never does know but one squar' gent who comes from Buffalo; he's old Jenks. An' at that, old Jenks gets downed, final, by the sheriff over on Sand Creek for stealin' a hoss.'

" 'You-all wants to onderstand,' says Jack Moore, cuttin' in after Boggs, "I don't pretend none to no proofs. I jest reckons it's so. It's a common scandal how dead innocent this yere short-horn Davis assoomes to be; how he wants Cherokee to explain faro-bank to him; an' how he can't onderstand none why Black Jack an' the dance-hall won't mix no drinks. Which I might, in the hurry of my dooties, have passed by them childish bluffs on-challenged an' with nothin' more than pityin' thoughts of the ignorance of this yere maverick; but gents, this party overplays his hand. Last evenin' he asks me to let him take my gun; says he's cur'ous to see one. That settles it with me; this Davis has been a object of suspicion ever since. No, it ain't that I allows he's out to queer my weepon none, but think of sech a pretence of innocence! I leaves it to you-all, collectif an' individooal, do you reckon now thar's anybody, however tender, who's that guileless as to go askin' a perfect stranger that a-way to pass him out his gun? I says no; this gent is overdoin' them roles. He ain't so tender as he assoomes. An' from the moment I hears of this last stand-up of the stage back in the canyon, I feels that this yere party is somehow in the play. Thar's four in this band who's been spreadin' woe among the stage companies lately, an' thar's only two of 'em shows in this latest racket which they gives Old Monte, an' that express gyard they shot up. Them other two sports who ain't present is shore some'ers; an' I gives it as my opinions one of 'em's right yere in our onthinkin' center, actin' silly, askin' egreegious questions, an' allowin' his name is Davis an' that he hails from Buffalo.'

"While Jack is evolvin' this long talk, we-all is thinkin'; an', son, somehow it strikes us that thar's mighty likely somethin' in this notion of Jack's. We-all agrees, however, thar bein' nothin' def'nite to go on, we can't do nothin' but wait. Still, pro an' con like, we pushes forth in discussion of this person.

" 'It does look like this Davis,' says Colonel Sterett, 'now Jack brings it up, is shorely playin' a part; which he's over easy an' ontaught, even for the East. This mornin', jest to give you-all a sample, he comes sidlin' up to me. "Is thar any good fishin' about yere?" he asks. "Which I shore yearns to fish some."

" ' "Does this yere landscape," I says, wavin' my arm about the hor'zon, "remind you much of fish? Stranger," I says, "fish an' christians is partic'lar sparse in Arizona."

" 'Then this person Davis la'nches out into tales deescriptif of how he goes anglin' back in the States. "Which the eel is the gamest fish," says this Davis. "When I'm visitin' in Virginny, I used to go fishin'. I don't fish with a reel, an' one of them limber poles, an' let a fish go swarmin' up an' down a stream, a-breedin' false hopes in his bosom an' lettin' him think he's loose. Not me; I wouldn't so deloode—wouldn't play it that low on a fish. I goes anglin' in a formal, se'f-respectin' way. I uses a short line an' a pole which is stiff an' strong. When I gets a bite, I yanks him out an' lets him know his fate right thar."

" ' "But eels ain't no game fish," I says. "Bass is game, but not eels."

" ' "Eels ain't game none, ain't they?" says this yere Davis, lettin' on he's a heap interested. "You-all listen to me; let me tell you of a eel I snags onto down by Culpepper. When he bites that time I gives him both hands. That eel comes through the air jest whistlin' an' w'irlin'. I slams him ag'inst the great state of Virginny. Suppose one of them bass you boasts of takes sech a jolt. Whatever would he have done? He'd lay thar pantin' an' rollin' his eyes; mebby he curls his tail a little. That would be the utmost of them resentments of his. What does my eel do? Stranger, he stands up on his tail an' fights me. Game! that eel's game as scorpions! My dog Fido's with me. Fido wades into the eel, an' the commotion is awful. That eel whips Fido in two minutes, Washin'ton time. How much does he weigh? Whatever do I know about it? When he's done put the gaffs into Fido, he nacherally sa'nters back into the branch where he lives at. I don't get him none; I deems I'm plumb lucky when he don't get me. Still, if any gent talks of game fish that a-way, I wants it onderstood, I strings my money on that Culpepper eel." '

" 'Thar, it's jest as I tells you-all, gents!' says Jack Moore a heap disgusted, when Colonel Sterett gets through. 'This yere Davis is a imposter. Which thar's no mortal sport could know as little as he lets on an' live to reach his age.'

"We sets thar an' lays plans. At last in pursooance of them devices, it gets roomored about camp that the next day but one, both Enright an' the New York Store aims to send over to Tucson a roll of money the size of a wagon hub.

" 'Thar's no danger of them hold-ups,' says Enright to this Davis, lettin' on he's a heap confidenshul. 'They won't be lookin' for no sech riches bein' freighted over slap on the heels of this yere robbery. An' we don't aim to put up no gyards alongside of Old Monte neither. Gyards is no good; they gets beefed the first volley, an' their presence on a coach that a-way is notice that thar's plenty of treasure aboard.'

"It's in this way Enright fills that Davis as full of misinforma-tion as a bottle of rum. Also, we deems it some signif'cant when said shorthorn saddles his hoss over to the corral an' goes skally-hootin' for Tucson about first drink time in the mornin'.

" 'I've a engagement in the Oriental S'loon,' he says, biddin' us good-bye plenty cheerful, 'but I'll be back among you-all sports in a week. I likes your ways a whole lot, an' I wants to learn 'em some.'

" 'Which I offers four to one,' says Jack Moore, lookin' after him as he rides away, 'you'll be back yere sooner than that, an' you-all won't know it none, at that.'

"It's the next day when the stage starts; Old Monte is crackin' his whip in a hardened way, carin' nothin' for road agents as long as they don't interfere with the licker traffic. Thar's only one passenger.

"Shore enough, jest as it's closin' in some dark in Apache

Canyon, an' the stage is groanin' an' creakin' along on a up grade, thar's a trio of hold-ups shows on the trail, an' the procession comes to a halt. Old Monte sets the brake, wrops the reins about it, locks his hands over his head, an' turns in to cuss. The hold-ups takes no notice. They yanks down the Wells-Fargo chest, pulls off the letter bag, accepts a watch an' a pocket-book from the gent inside, who's scared an' shiverin' an' scroogin' back in the darkest corner, he's that terror-bit; an' then they applies a few epithets to Old Monte an' commands him to pull his freight. An' Old Monte shorely obeys them mandates, an' goes crashin' off up the canyon on the run.

"Them outlaws hauls the plunder to one side of the trail an' lays for the mail-bag with a bowie. All three is as busy as prairie dogs after a rain, rippin' open letters an' lookin' for checks an' drafts. Later they aims at some op'rations on the express company's box.

"But they never gets to the box. Thar's the lively tones of a Winchester which starts the canyon's echoes to talkin'. That rifle ain't forty foot away, an' it speaks three times before ever you-all, son, could snap your fingers. An' that weepon don't make them observations in vain. It ain't firin' no salootes. Quick as is the work, the sights shifts to a new target every time. At the last, all three hold-ups lay kickin' an' jumpin' like chickens that a-way; two is dead an' the other is too hard hit to respond.

"Whoever does it? Jack Moore; he's that one shiverin' passenger that time. He slides outen the stage as soon as ever it turns the angle of the canyon, an' comes scoutin' an' crawlin' back on his prey. An' I might add, it shore soothes Jack's vanity a lot, when the first remainder shows down as that artless maverick, Davis. Jack lights a pine splinter an' looks him over—pale an' dead an' done.

" 'Which you-all is the victim of over-play,' says Jack to this yere Davis, same as if he hears him. 'If you never asks to see my gun that time, it's even money my suspicions concernin' you might be sleepin' yet.' "

Wolfville Folks *(1908)* differed from other *Wolfville collections* in that it was a continuing tale. Generally speaking, the continuity weakened the force of the individual chapters. Two episodes from it, however, offer their own obvious points of interest.

JAYBIRD HORNE

"As to the size of that bundle Peets inherits," remarked the Old Cattleman, with the painstaking manner of one who would like to be accurate if he could—"As to the actooal size of that bundle, I never has preecise information. Peets himse'f sheds no direct light on it, an' nacherally I don't go proselytin' round askin' him questions, bein' too well raised by my folks. Boggs says once, in talkin' about it, that it's big enough to choke a cow; which statement, while calk'lated to excite admiration, don't go into deetails sufficient to jestify a figger. The clostest any gent ever comes to puttin' it down, book-keep fashion, is Enright, who allows it's fifty thousand dollars. That's a big pot of money, fifty thousand is, an' if you-all don't mind I reckon I'll ring for the licker. The mention of sech giant sums shore leaves my mouth as dry as a covered bridge.

"Fifty thousand dollars!" repeated the old gentleman, after he had been refreshed. Then, musingly: "I recalls the first big money I ever rounds up; which it's a roll of ten thousand. I ain't likely to forget the sensation none. For the first week I thought that ten thousand was a million dollars; after that I simply knowed it was. How do I make it? Well, that's neither yere nor thar. Besides, a gent can't tell two stories at once, more'n a dog can chase two rabbits at once; wharfore, let's stick to the fifty thousand Peets' inherits that time.

"An' yet, to be c'rrect, it ain't a inheritance, emanatin' as it does from folks who's no kin of Peets'. It's not exackly what I'd call a donation neither; it's more like a pick-up, an' sort o' ree-verts to Peets as the legit'mate froots of his eddicational bow an' spear. You frequent hears me mention how Peets is that wise he vis'bly uplifts the mental average of Arizona. This time he proves it; an' it's for that reason I'm allers speshul glad the play comes off. It's refreshin', as markin' the troo valyoo of science, to have a eddicated sport like Peets up an' make a killin', by merely knowin' things at what book-sharps call the croocial moment.

"It's the Deacon who's the instroament seelected by Fate to confer on Peets that treasure; none the less the story, told proper, begins off to one side, with a malignant p'isenous form of hooman varmint, who signs the books as Jaybird Horne. Likewise, the yarn possesses other elements of disj'intedness, doo to its bein' troo. Lies allers flies straight as arrers towards whatever they're aimed at, an' either misses or hurts or kills as the case may be. Trooth is different a whole lot. It's more apt to go wanderin' an' squanderin' an' zigzagin' all over the map, like a pony with its bridle off. An' for causes obv'ous: Lies is artificial, an' framed up for a purpose. As ag'inst this, trooth is nacheral, an' in its 'nitial appearance at least, never has no axe to grind. Which if you'll only stop an' think, you'll see that this yere must be so.

"The commencement of things then is when that outcast Jay-bird, ridin' a pinto pony an' hailin' from Lordsburg, comes bulgin' into camp. He makes a more or less mem'rable deboo; for a Red Dog loonatic called Curly Simpson, who's projectin' 'round Wolfville at the time, pulls his six-shooter, an' takes to cuttin' the dust about Jaybird's moccasins, as soon as ever he hits the ground.

" 'I'm feelin' deepressed an' low,' explains Curly that a-way, 'an' if you'll kindly dance a little, it may serve to cheer me up.'

"As though willin' to yoomer Curly, this Jaybird shore does jump high an' sprightly, like a trant'ler; wharupon Curly gets pleased with his agil'ty, to that degree he cracks off all six loads like the rollin' of a drum. When Curly's final cartridge is gone an' he's plumb inokyoous, Jaybird, assoomin' a rattlesnake grin, prodooces a derringer an' puts a bullet through his foot.

" 'It 'ud be your locoed head,' says Jaybird, 'only most likely sech feats involves me with the stranglers, for which I ain't got time. Likewise, when next you inaug'rates a *baile* of this dee-scription, either pack a second gun, or don't become so lib'rally profoose as to wholly empty the one you has. You sees yourse'f that either you ought to have saved your last cartridge, as a ree-serve ag'inst the onexpected, or been wearin' another pistol so's to be ready, when called on, to back your crazy play. My own notion, private, is to allers have the second gun, as bein' better form. No gent, without sacrificin' his standin', can permit his wardrobe to bog down to where he ain't got a change of guns.'

"Inasmuch as this eepisode comes off in front of the post-office, which is the next edifice to the Red Light, most of us is thar. When Jaybird finishes his oration, Enright, who's strong suit is bein' friendly to strangers an' makin' 'em feel at home, explains that Wolfville don't claim to be reespons'ble for Curly, him hailin' from Red Dog.

" 'An' I certainly hopes,' says Enright, 'that, onder the circum-stance, Curly's capers won't leave no sense of annoyance, nor op'rate with you to queer the town.'

" 'None whatever!' returns Jaybird, mighty gala. Then, to all of us: 'Gents, my name's Horne—Jaybird Horne; an' I makes no doubts but when this Curly Red Dog person gets acquainted with me, he'll reespect me an' walk 'round me like I'm a swamp.'

"Curly is freighted over to Red Dog on a buckboard, by virchoo of his game foot; an' Enright closes the incident by allowin' he's glad he gets it, as a lesson ag'inst bein' so inordinate an' plumb reedundant with his gun.

" 'Leastwise,' says Enright, in concloosion, 'I don't want Curly to come pirootin' over to Wolfville, givin' rein to his witless activities no more.'

" 'Let's go into yon s'loon,' returns Jaybird, indicatin' the Red Light, 'an' forget it over a bowl of snake-water. Neither do I mind admittin', gents, seein' I'm feelin' some languid myse'f when

I rides in, how that little gun-play, so far from irritatin', reely relieves me an' falls in nice with my moods.'

"With the start he makes, if Jaybird has the orig'nal roodiments of a white man in him, he might have climbed to what heights he chooses in public esteem. Wolfville is generous to the p'int of bein' a proverb. It has its tol'rant rooles. You comes to Wolfville; an' it's as though you're beginnin' life anoo. Your past is as nothin' to that hamlet. It begins with you as you steps from the stage. It don't ask your name; it asks 'What may we call you?' an' leaves you, as a proodent gent, to pick out what title is best adapted to your needs. As you go romancin' along from day to day, it watches you; an' final, it endorses you or lynches you as seems jest an' mete. Which I've said all this yere before.

"Bein' moved up into commoonal fellowship, your Wolfville foocher is asshored. Should you go broke, it stakes you; should you marry, it shakes a festive laig at the weddin'; should a papoose be born to call you 'Daddy,' it gets drunk with you; should you fall sick, it sets up with you. Die? Shore, if you dies, it confers on you a hon'rable sepulcher on Boot Hill, an' everybody attends the obsequies—that is everybody who's out of jail. You notes, tharfore, that Jaybird's got the local makin' or breakin' of himse'f wholly in his own hands, an' can stand way up in the pictures if so inclined.

"That he ain't so inclined none, cuts less of a figger in Jaybird's case perhaps, since it's plain from the jump he don't aim to remain. However, in them few days he does stay, he shore creates a black impression.

"An' at that I figgers it's more his atmosphere than what he does. He's plenty reepellant, is this Jaybird outlaw, an' you-all can smell villainy off him same as you smells fire in a house. Physic'ly he's small an' wiry, with bow-laigs from livin' a heap in the saddle. His eyes is small an' has a weaselish look, same as belongs to that egg-suckin' hen-huntin' breed of animals who can see in the dark.

"Most of all, however, it's Jaybird's face that's ag'inst him. For one thing, it peters out into one of them little chins, sharp an' bony at the p'int, broad at the corners of the jaw, like the jaws of snakes of p'isen sort—the chin of a murderer rather than a killer—crooel, skulkin', savage! No discreet gent, after seein' it, would think of takin' off his guns while Jaybird's hankerin' 'round.

"This Jaybird has one redeemin' trait; he's a born gun sharp. Shore! he's among the soonest prop'sitions, when he reaches for a six-shooter, I ever gets ag'inst. Not that I encounters him none lethal; barrin' the foot eepisode, wharin Curly quits loser, he don't offer to shed no blood in Wolfville on that earlier occasion of his trackin' in.

"It's over in Chihuahua, which is that fragment of the Wolfville body pol'tic where the Mexicans herd, that I has a chance of countin' up Jaybird's gun-play. This is what he does;—an' I allers imagines he does it to fix himse'f respectful upon the Greaser mind. He picks up six chips off the lay-out of a saddle-colored party who's dealin' monte, an' tosses 'em up in the air. They spreads out, an' hangs for a moment like six blots ag'inst the sky. That's all Jaybird reequires. As he tosses up the chips, his hand goes to his gun; it's 'bang! bang! bang! bang! bang! bang!' faster than you-all can count, an' when them chips hits the ground ag'in they're in dust an' little pieces.

"Which I witnesses some swift clean gun playin' from time to time, but these yere performances of Jaybird is ondoubted the bloo ribbon outburst of 'em all. Cherokee, who's himse'f a past-master with a Colt's-45, gives it out that, for suddenness an' ackeracy, he himse'f don't stand no more chance with Jaybird than a pa'r of treys in a jack-pot after the draw. That's straight; Jaybird, personal, shore does possess a genius for firearms.

"Throughout the ten days Jaybird sojourns in our midst, he don't do nothin' much. He ain't what you'd call a drinker none, while at poker an' farobank he's even more sparin'. In talk, he don't wax over-commoonicative an' if he beetrays pecooliarities, it's in the way he seems allers to be lookin' for some gent onknown. Not that he goes spyin' about open an' apparent, or takes to overtly rummagin' up the camp. Still it's as plain as printed books he's on some gent's trail. It's this yere hunt for that on-known which takes him over into Chihuahua, the time he busts them monte chips. Hunt as he may, however, Jaybird don't find his man; an' one mornin' he flings the hull onto his little pinto hoss, an' hits the trail for the no'th like he's satisfied he's been dubbin' 'round on a dead kyard.

"Folks in Arizona is so migratory that strangers, in their ad-vents or departures, excites no remark. No one, tharfore, heeds the goin' of Jaybird, more'n perhaps to exper'ence relief, same as if some centipede or stingin' lizard's disappeared. Neither does the camp lift up its astonished gaze none, when, mebby it's a week later, the Deacon comes weavin' in.

"This yere Deacon boy breaks on me first across the supper table at the O. K. Restuaraw; I notices him speshul because he's so plumb callow. His face is as smooth an' young as Faro Nell's; an' he's that innocent for looks, you're overwhelmned with wonder constant as to how he comes to be caperin' about in Arizona at all—Arizona as a region bein' some turgid.

"It's Boggs who names him the 'Deacon;' an', since his pin-feather innocence sort o' gives us a pray'r-meetin' impression, we-all trails in an' calls him the Deacon sim'lar. So far from re-sentin' said title, he nor only answers to it, but acts pleased.

"An' yet, that air of he'pless innocence is a heap misleadin'. This Deacon boy is all the time a more deadly problem even than the Jaybird, an' owns a fitfuller Colt's. Which it goes to prove how deelosive is mere looks that a-way, an' sets a philosophic gent to thinkin'. Laid side an' side, the egg of the eagle ain't in it with a goose egg; but jest the same it holds a eagle.

"The Deacon ain't been a day in town before Jaybird, with his pinto hoss, ag'in comes canterin' in. Not that thar's anythin' irreg'lar or myster'ous in sech return; it's tryin' to read the brands on what follows, which proves sech a puzzle to the pop'lar mind.

"Yere's how eevents takes to pilin' themselves up. It's well into the shank of the evenin', on the day Jaybird gets back, an' we're all a heap onbuckled an' reelaxed. Of a sudden, from some'ers out to the r'ar of Hamilton's dance hall, we hears a gun bark once—short an' sharp, like the single bark of a dog.

" 'Better sa'nter over, Jack,' says Enright, glancin' up from his poker game to Jack Moore—'better sa'nter over an' take a look in. One shot that a-way sounds doobious; I've a notion some maverick's been put over the big jump.'

"Thar's a sentiment of oneasy cur'osity all 'round, which is sharpened when Jack returns, ridin' offishul herd on the Deacon.

" 'It's this yearlin',' says Jack. 'Whatever do you-all reckon now he's done?'

" 'Which I shore can't say none,' observes Enright, layin' down his kyards.

" 'I should gamble not!' Jack retorts. 'I hopes I may be eaten by red ants, if this roothless kid ain't bumped off that Jaybird. The latter prince of pistol shooters is layin' out thar back of a mesquite bush, as dead as Joolius Caesar.'

" 'Him down that Jaybird party!' exclaims Enright, plumb took aback. 'Jack, it ain't feas'ble! It don't lay in his yoothful moccasins!'

" 'Ask him!' says Jack.

" 'It's in se'f defence,' cuts in the Deacon. 'Jaybird goes for his gun, an' I simply beats him to it.'

" 'Do you-all mean to test'fy,' remarks Enright, slow an' p'inted, 'that this Jaybird commences hostil'ties an' that you hives him after he takes to domineerin' at you with his Colt's?'

" 'That's whatever,' replies the Deacon, a heap onshaken. 'An' as to Jaybird bein' sudden with his artillery, you don't want to forget I'm some abrupt myse'f.'

"Enright uplifts a reeprovin' hand. 'Stop,' he says. 'Son, this yere's onhinged you. Thar's gents present who witnesses former what that Jaybird could do. In the light of them exhibitions, I pronounces your statements preepost'rous. My advice is to say no more, but devote yourse'f to silent meditations ontil the stranglers is convened.' "

TOP AND BOTTOM

"Enright su'gests to Tutt that if Tucson Jennie p'rades the street leadin' little Enright Peets Tutt, it would give the camp a quiet domestic look.

" 'The sight of sech a child as Enright Peets,' he says, 'couldn't fail to nootralize any roughness; that done I'd look on vic'try as secure. Also some gent ought to prance over, an' pass the word to Missis Rucker not to tyrranize over pore Rucker too open in the presence of our visitors. But on second thought it would hurt her feelin's an' lead to onpleasant sequels; so mebby it's as well to pass it up.'

"It's yere Doc Peets comes weavin' in, smilin' wide an' complacent. 'It's all right, Sam,' says Peets, addressin' Enright; 'I left 'em gettin' ready for chuck. It don't do to talk to 'em too much at the jump; they might think the camp has designs.'

" 'Right you be, Doc,' breaks in Texas. 'Capitalists that a-way is like antelopes; the way to hunt 'em is to sit still.'

" 'An' Missis Rucker?' urges Enright, sort o' anxious.

" 'Which May mornin's is harsh to her,' returns Peets. 'She's got Rucker out in the kitchen, slicin' salt-hoss an' openin' airtights, an' is preparin' to deal them guests the gastronimic game of the year. Also her attitoode towards Rucker is one of peace an' gentleness; they're gettin' along as congenial as so much milk an' honey.'

"Enright heaves a sigh, lights a seegyar, an' leans back like one

who sees triumph on its windin' way. He beams round on the
boys, an' says:

" 'Bein' no one to count my chickens prematoor, I've ree-
frained from any prophetic bluffs. But after hearin' from the
Doc, I'm yere to say we've got the sityooation treed an' out on
a limb. These cap'talists is ours.'

"It's now, when hope is highest, thar comes a yell that sounds
like an Injun outbreak, an' a pony goes flashin' up the street as
though he's shot out of a gun. Every gent looks up, Enright some
disturbed.

" 'Now what onmuzzled Siwash is that?' he asks, an' his tones
is plenty ferocious. 'Who is it goes promotin' uproar at a crisis
like this?'

" 'It's that exasperatin' Cottonwood,' replies Boggs, 'He's loose
ag'in, an' organizin' to stand the town on its head.'

" 'Jack,' says Enright, wheelin' short an' fierce on Jack Moore,
'go bend a gun over his locoed pate. He'll throw down all our
plans!'

"Before Jack can get to Cottonwood, the worst possible occurs.
The two cap'talists, on hearin' the whoops, nacherally comes to
the O. K. door to see what's up. One of 'em, who's got on a plug
hat, is speshul interested. As Cottonwood sails by, w'irlin' his
six-shooter on his finger, the plug hat stranger seems to go into
a trance of admiration, perceivin' which Cottonwood yanks his
pony up short, an' surveys him plenty disdainful.

" 'Whoever licensed you to wear sech a warbonnet as that?'
demands Cottonwood, dictatin' at the plug hat with his gun.
'Don't you-all know it's ag'in the rooles of our set?'

" 'Whatever be you talkin' about!' exclaims the plug hat party,
plumb took aback.

" 'Do you-all reckon,' goes on Cottonwood, disregyardin' the
question, 'that we're sech prairie dogs as to let a schemin' shorthorn go onderminin' us with his deboshed plug hat? If so, why
was Bunker Hill an' wharfore Yorktown? Unless I nips this plug
hat movement in the bud, you'll be playin' a w'ite shirt on us
next.'

"Before the astonished tenderfoot can say a word, Cottonwood whips off the plug hat an' claps it on the muzzle of his gun. This done, he begins shakin' the loads out of his weepon same as if it's a bunch of crackers. He shorely does make a colander of that headgear! Jest as he's fetched loose the last shot, Jack Moore snatches him from the saddle like he's a sack of flour.

" 'Whatever's the row now?' demands Cottonwood. 'Do the ordinances of this yere puerile outfit extend to the protection of plug hats? If they do, I quit you right now.'

" 'You'd better keep your feelin's hobbled,' says Jack, 'ontil you see Old Man Enright. An', as for quittin' Wolfville, the chances are that, when he gets done with you, you'll deecide to stay yere till the final trump.'

"Which I never did see two tenderfeet so yoonanimous for goin' back before! In no time after Cottonwood ventilates that plug hat, they're orderin' speshul buckboards from the corral, an' gettin' packed to pull their freight. They allows they've been imposed on by the barkeep at the Oriental over in Tucson, he havin' described Wolfville as bein' as quiet as a church.

" 'He sends us like lambs to the slaughter!' they says; 'an', once we're back, we'll onfurl to him our views concernin' the lies he tells.'

"Shore! Enright talks, an' Peets talks; but what's the use? They tries to make these yere visitors see things in their troo light, an' that it's only Cottonwood's way of bein' sociable. They even offers to hang Cottonwood, if the ceremony will promote a better onderstandin'. It's of no avail; after that gun play any gent who says 'Wolfville' to them cap'talists is barkin' at a knot. They simply won't have it! An' so, when the buckboard is ready, they goes tearin' off to the north, a handkerchief over the plug-hat party's skelp, the plug hat in his lap. He allows he'll take it East, to show what Arizona really is.

" 'I reckon, Tutt,' says Boggs a heap moody, 'I owes you a red stack. I'll consider the money well invested if it results in my seein' that miserable Cottonwood's moccasins ten feet in the air.'

"Enright calls the committee together in the New York Store, though he states that the session is informal.

" 'It's only intended to consider,' says he, 'in what manner we can best get this Cottonwood killed, with least disgrace to ourselves.'

" 'Whatever have I done?' demands Cottonwood, some querulous, as Jack Moore brings him before Enright an' the rest of us by the scruff of his neck. 'Whatever have I done now?'

" 'What have you-all done?' repeats Enright, between rage an' disgust. 'You aims a blow at our prospects. Which you shows yourse'f a menace. An' you with half your milk-teeth yet! It's astonishin! Cottonwood, if you was at years of discretion, thar wouldn't have been no pesterin' round with committee meetin's. I'd have had Dan, or Texas, or Jack yere, s'anter to the door with a Winchester, an' solve the trouble by shootin' you all up. Now answer me: What made you go swoopin' at that cap'talist?'

" 'Cap'talist!' says Cottonwood. 'However, do I savey he's a cap'talist? "Yere's a short horn," thinks I, "an' the camp plumb dead! I'll about jump in, liven things up a whole lot, an' give him a good impression." That's why I throws myse'f loose like I do.'

" 'An' do you allow,' returns Enright, savage an' sarkastic, 'that to burn up the causeway with your pony, make a pinwheel of your six-shooter, an' finish off by shootin' a gent's only hat full of holes, is doo to make a good impression? Is that your idee of invitin' the confidence of a stranger?'

"After waitin' a while, an' Cottonwood makin' no reply, Enright goes on.

" 'I can't get over the notion that you're more eediotic than crim'nal. An' yet that don't let us in or out, but leaves us sort o' straddle of a log. Which I confesses, not without shame, that I'm nonplussed. Yere you go stampedin' them cap'talists—said conduct bein' a bet which no se'f-respectin' commoonity can overlook! An' yet thar's no jail to put you in! Besides, in that school of joorisproodence wharin I was reared, it's allers been held that when you've got a party you ought to lock up, you've got one you ought to kill. Cottonwood, I can't see nothin' for it but hang. Troo, you ain't bumped off no one; but, as reads the Constitootion, we're jestified in sending you over the divide onder the gen'ral welfare clause of that instroment. That's my view; what do you say, Doc?'

" 'Which I'm lost in the same neck of woods with yourse'f,' says Peets. 'I asks myse'f what else is thar to do?'

"Enright beats on the table, an' looks about. 'Has any gent a su'gestion?' he asks. Thar bein' no response, he turns again to Cottonwood, who stands round-eyed an' amazed like a young ground owl. 'Have you anything to offer before an outraged public uses you wharwith to dec'rate the wind-mill? As I states, we regrets this finish, but you forced our hands yourse'f. As for me, personal, I've stood between you an' pop'lar clamor all I will. If you've anything to say, speak out; an' while he's talkin', Jack, you might as well go for a lariat.'

"The locoed Cottonwood begins to take an interest. 'See yere,' he says, an' his manner is a heap plausible an' wheedlin'. 'You-all gents don't want to hang me. An', between us, thar's reasons private to me personal why I don't want to be hanged none. At least you-all ought to give a gent a show-down. I'll tell you what: I'll nacherally cut the kyards to see whether I hang or go free? Or, if you objects to kyards, I'll throw the dice—first flash out of the box?'

"Enright, doorin' these proffers, is regyardin' Cottonwood doobious an' oncertain, like he can't make up his mind.

" 'Or say,' goes on Cottonwood; 'I'll take a chance on this? You throw three dice; an' I'll agree to tell you, before you roll 'em, what number you'll throw, addin' spots on top to spots on the bottom. If I fail I hang.'

"Enright at this looks at Cottonwood commiseratin'ly; then he speaks low to Peets. 'This boy is out of his head, Doc,' he says. 'The fright has onsettled his intellects.'

"'I'm not so shore,' says Peets, 'Which I'm afraid, I don't share your belief in him bein' upset mental. I figger he's got an ace buried. Still, since I'm mighty averse to stringin' up a yearlin', partic'lar when no life has been took, I shorely trusts he has. My su'gestion is to call his bluff.'

" 'Do I onderstand,' says Enright, ag'in addressin' the guileful‧ Cottonwood, 'that I'm to throw three dice; an' that you agrees to say before the throw, jest what the spots on top plus the spots next the table will count up?'

" 'Preezackly,' returns Cottonwood, beginnin' to cheer up. 'If I fall down, it's a case of bring on the rope an' lead the march to the windmill. Failin' of a shore thing like this, I shore ought to have no further care to live.'

" 'Pore boy!' sighs Enright. Then, turnin' to Boggs: "Dan, go over to the Red Light, an' fetch the dice.'

"Enright shakes the three dice, while Jack Moore, who's got back from the corral, takes his stand at Cottonwood's elbow, the lariat over his arm. Enright raises his hand, makin' ready to throw. At that, Cottonwood shets his foxy eyes, pretendin' to think.

" 'Which, top plus bottom,' he says, 'you'll throw twenty-one.'

"Enright sends the dice rattlin' along the table, while we-all crowds about. The dice show 'six-two-four'—twelve in all. We turns 'em over one by one, an' the bottoms shows 'one-five-three', bein' nine.

" 'Thar you be!' cries Cottonwood, some exultant; 'twelve on top an' nine on the bottom, the same bein' twenty-one, I win.'

" 'You win,' says Enright, an' he says it like a load is off his mind. Then he raises his hand, mighty impressive. 'One word Cottonwood, an' Wolfville is through with you, onless by some renooed breaks you reopens the game. By first drink time to-morry, you line out for Tucson. An' don't you come projectin' round this outfit no more, onless we gives you speshul leave. Which I'd run you out this evenin', only I'm afraid you'd track up on them fleein' short-horns, an' reecommence your outrages.'

"Cottonwood moves for the door without a word, for he's no sech fool as to go tamperin' with his luck by givin' vent to on-timely or ill-considered oratory. He's got the sense to let well enough alone, an' don't aim to go talkin' himse'f into new or deeper holes. When he's gone, Enright looks at Peets a heap puzzled, an' asks:

" 'However do you reckon he does it, Doc?'

"Peets waves his hand like the play baffles him entire, an' appeals to Cherokee Hall, who's been watchin' them final proceedin's with a half grin in the corners of his mouth, like he's amused.

" 'What is it, Cherokee, that boy does to us?' asks Peets. 'He's had us ag'inst some deadfall or other, but what is it?'

" 'Why,' returns Cherokee, pickin' up the dice, 'it's as obvious as old John Chisholm's Fence-Rail brand. That Cottonwood simply hands you the old snap of Top-an'-Bottom in a new guise. An' I must concede that you falls for it like a bevy of farmers.'

" 'Explain,' says Enright, who's sheepish to be took in by a child. 'You says "Top-an'-Bottom;" but you don't eloocidate. Yere I am with three dice in my hand, an' Cottonwood says "twenty-one." I throws; an' it is twenty-one. Now however does he know?'

" 'How does he know?' repeats Cherokee, in smilin' tol'ration of Enright's ignorance. 'He knows, because it can't come anything else. If you was to throw these yere dice a thousand times, it would every trip come twenty-one. See yere!' an' Cherokee takes one of the dice between thumb an' finger. 'When dice is made, they puts the six opposite the ace, the doose opposite the five, the four opposite the trey. No matter how they roll or what comes up, the top an' bottom of each counts seven. Savey? Which bein' troo, throwin' three dice that a-way, the tops an' bottoms make three sevens—twenty-one.'

"In Enright's face chagrin an' knowledge is makin' an even struggle of it. After a bit he says, 'You've recounted, Cherokee, certain dice pecooliarities which hitherto evades my notice, me bein' otherwise engaged. It all shows the wisdom of possessin' a professional kyard sharp, as a yoonit of the body politic. Still,' he goes on, some reproachful, 'when you sees him settin' this trap, why don't you give us warnin'?'

" 'Which I would,' returns Cherokee, 'if the stakes is of real valyoo. But thar you be, only playin' for the life of that Cottonwood, an' I sees no call.'

" 'To think, Doc,' says Enright, kind o' pensive, as we-all go wanderin' back to the Red Light—'to think of me bein' let in by a babe in arms! An' yet I foretells a brilliant c'reer for Cottonwood. That boy ought to be in Congress right now! Bar-keep'— makin' a sign to Black Jack—'the reestoratives is on me.' "

With "Death: and the Donna Anna," the following is perhaps Lewis' masterpiece: the base achievement on which his fame must be re-erected. To repeat, the West belongs to all of us, and we will all help to clarify its treasures and its contribution. With respect to Alfred Henry Lewis' life and achievements, our stake is peculiarly manifest: westerners have no more title to him than easterners. None of us need be diffident in the matter, need fear that our comments or point of view might offend one or another smug parochialist.

LONG AGO ON THE RIO GRANDE

"Which books that a-way," observed the Old Cattleman, "that is, story-books, is onfrequent in Wolfville." He was curiously examining Stevenson's "Treasure Island," that he had taken from my hand. "The nearest approach to a Wolfville cirk'latin' library I recalls is a copy of 'Robinson Crusoe,' an' that don't last long, as one time when Texas Thompson leaves it layin' on a cha'r outside while he enters the Red Light for the usual purpose, a burro who's loafin' loose about the street, smells it, tastes it, approoves of it, an' tharupon devours it a heap. After that I don't notice no volumes in the outfit, onless it's some drug books that Doc Peets has hived over where he camps. It's jest as well, for seein' a gent perusin' a book that a-way, operates frequent to make Dan Boggs gloomy; him bein' oneddicated like I imparts to you-all yeretofore.

"Whatever do we do for amoosements? We visits the Dance Hall; not to dance, sech frivol'ties bein' for younger an' less dignified sports. We goes over thar more to give our countenance an' endorsements to Hamilton who runs the hurdy-gurdy, an' who's a mighty proper citizen. We says 'How!' to Hamilton, libates, an' mebby watches 'em 'balance all,' or 'swing your partners,' a minute or two an' then proceeds. Then thar's Huggins's Bird Cage Op'ry House, an' now an' then we-all floats over thar an' takes in the dramy. But mostly we camps about the Red Light; the same bein' a common stampin'-ground. It's thar we

find each other; an' when thar's nothin' doin', we upholds the
hours tellin' tales an' gossipin' about cattle an' killin's, an' other
topics common to a cow country. Now an' then, thar's a visitin'
gent in town who can onfold a story. In sech event he's made a
lot of, an' becomes promptly the star of the evenin'.

"Thar's a Major Sayres we meets up with once in Wolfville,—
he's thar on cattle matters with old man Enright—an' I recalls
how he grows absorbin' touchin' some of his adventures in that
War.

"Thar's a passel of us, consistin' of Boggs, Tutt, Cherokee, an'
Texas Thompson, an' me, who's projectin' 'round the Red Light
when Enright introodooces this Major Sayres. Him an' Enright's
been chargin' about over by the Cow Springs an' has jest rode in.
This Major is easy an' friendly, an' it ain't longer than the third
drink before he shows symptoms of bein' willin' to talk.

" 'Which I ain't been in the saddle so long,' says the Major,
while him an' Enright is considerin' how far they goes since sun-
up, 'since Mister Lee surrenders.'

" 'You takes your part, Major,' says Enright, who's ropin' for a
reminiscence that a-way, 'in the battles of the late war, I believes.'

" 'I should shorely say so,' says the Major. 'I'm twenty-two
years old, comes next grass, when Texas asserts herse'f as part of
the confed'racy, an' I picks up a hand an' plays it in common
with the other patriotic yooths of my region. Yes, I enters the
artillery, but bein' as we don't have no cannon none at the jump
I gets detailed as a aide ontil something resemblin' a battery
comes pokin' along. I goes through that carnage from soup to
nuts, an' while I'm shot up some as days go by, it's allers been a
source of felic'tation to me, personal, that I never slays no man
myse'f. Shore, I orders my battery to fire, later when I gets a
battery; an' ondoubted the bombardments I inagu'rates adds to
an' swells the ghost census right along. But of my own hand it's
ever been a matter of congratoolations to me that I don't down
nobody an' never takes a skelp.

" 'As I turns the leaves of days that's gone I don't now remember but one individyooal openin' for blood that ever presents

itse'f. An' after considerin' the case in all its b'arin's, I refooses the opportunity an' the chance goes glidin' by. As a result thar's probably one more Yank than otherwise; an' now that peace is yere an' we-all is earnestly settlin' to be brothers, No'th and South, I regyards that extra Yank as a advantage. Shore, he's a commoonal asset.'

" 'Tell us how you fails to c'llect this Yankee, Major,' says Faro Nell: 'which I'm plumb interested every time that some one don't get killed.'

" 'I reecounts that exploit with pleasure,' says the Major, bowin' p'lite as Noo Orleans first circles an' touchin' his hat to Nell.' 'It's one day when we're in a fight. The line of battle is mebby stretched out half a mile. As I su'gests, I'm spraddlin' 'round permiscus with no stated arena of effort, carryin' despatches an' turnin' in at anything that offers, as handy as I can. I'm sent final with a dispatch from the left to the extreme right of our lines.

" 'When we goes into this skrimmage we jumps the Lincoln people somewhat onexpected. They has their blankets an' knapsacks on, an' as they frames themse'fs up for the struggle they casts off this yere baggage, an' thar it lays, a windrow of knapsacks, blankets an' haversacks, mighty near a half mile in length across the plain. As we-all rebs has been pushin' the Yankees back a lot, this windrow is now to our r'ar, an' I goes canterin' along it on my mission to the far right.

" 'Without a word of warnin' a Yank leaps up from where he's been burrowin' down among this plunder an' snaps a Enfield rifle in my face. I pulls my hoss back so he's almost settin' on his hocks: an' between us, gents, that onexpected sortie comes mighty near surprisin' me plumb out of the saddle. But the Enfield don't go off none; an' with that the Yank throws her down an' starts to run. He shorely does *vamos* with the velocity of jackrabbits!

" 'As soon as me an' my hoss recovers our composure we gives chase. Bein' the pore Yank is afoot, I runs onto him in the first two hundred yards. As I comes up, I've got my six-shooter in my hand. I puts the muzzle on him, sort o' p'intin' between the shoulders for gen'ral results; but when it comes to onhookin' my weepon I jest can't turn the trick. It's too much like murder. Meanwhile, the flyin' Yank is stampedin' along like he ain't got a thing on his mind an' never turnin' his head.

" 'I calls on him to surrender. He makes a roode remark over his shoulder at this military manoover an' pelts ahead all on-abated. Then I evolves a scheme to whack him on the head with my gun. I pushes my hoss up ontil his nose is right by that No'thern party's y'ear. Steadyin' myse'f, I makes a wallop at him an' misses. I invests so much soul in the blow that missin' that a-way, I comes within' a ace of clubs of goin' off my hoss an' onto my head. An' still that exasperatin' Yank goes rackin' along, an' if anything some faster than before. At that I begins to lose my temper ag'in.

" 'I reorganizes,—for at the time I nearly makes the dive outen the stirrups, I pulls the hoss to a stop,—an' once more takes up the pursoot of my locoed prey. He's a pris'ner fair enough, only he's too obstinate to admit it. As I closes on him ag'in, I starts for the second time to drill him, but I can't make the landin'. I'm too young; my heart ain't hard enough; I rides along by him for a bit an' for the second time su'gests that he surrender. The Yank ignores me; he keeps on runnin'.

" 'Which sech conduct baffles me! It's absolootely ag'in military law. By every roole of the game that Yank's my captive; but de-fyin' restraint he goes caperin' on like he's free.

" 'As I gallops along about four foot to his r'ar I confess I be-gins to feel a heap he'pless about him. I'm too tender to shoot, an' he won't stop, an' thar we be.

" 'While I'm keepin' him company on this retreat, I reflects that even if I downs him, the war would go on jest the same; it wouldn't stop the rebellion none, nor gain the South her in-dependence. The more I considers, too, the war looks bigger an' the life of this flyin' Yank looks smaller. Likewise, it occurs to me that he's headed no'th. If he keeps up his gait an' don't turn or twist he'll have quitted Southern territory by the end of the week.

" 'After makin' a complete round-up of the sityooation I begins to lose interest in this Yank; an' at last I leaves him, racin' along alone. By way of stim'lant, as I pauses I cracks off a couple of loads outen my six-shooter into the air. They has a excellent effect; from the jump the Yank makes at the sound I can see the shots puts ten miles more run into him shore. He keeps up his gallop ontil he's out of sight, an' I never after feasts my eyes on him.

" 'Which I regyards your conduct, Major, as mighty hoo-mane,' says Dan Boggs, raisin' his glass p'litely. 'I approves of it, partic'lar.'

"The Major meets Dan's attentions in the sperit they're proposed. After a moment Enright speaks of them cannons.

"But you-all got a battery final, Major?' says Enright.

" 'Six brass guns,' says the Major, an' his gray eyes beams an' he speaks of 'em like they was six beautiful women. 'Six brass guns, they be,' he says. 'We captured 'em from the enemy an' I'm put in command. Gents, I've witnessed some successes personal, but I never sees the day when I'm as satisfied an' as contentedly proud as when I finds myse'f in command of them six brass guns. I was like a lover to every one of 'em.

" 'I'm that headlong to get action—we're in middle Loosiana at the time—that I hauls a couple of 'em over by the Mississippi an' goes prowlin' 'round ontil I pulls on trouble with a little Yankee gun boat. It lasts two hours, an' I shore sinks that naval outfit an' piles the old Mississippi on top of 'em. I'm so puffed up with this yere exploit that a pigeon looks all sunk in an' consumptif beside me.

" 'Thar's one feacher of this dooel with the little gun boat which displeases me, however. Old Butler's got Noo Orleans at the time, an' among other things he's editin' the papers. I reads in one of 'em a month later about me sinkin' that scow. It says I'm a barb'rous villain, the story does, an' shoots up the boat after it surrenders, an' old Butler allows he'll hang me a whole lot the moment ever he gets them remarkable eyes onto me. I don't care none at the time much, only I resents this yere charge, I shore never fires a shot at that gunboat after it gives up; I ain't so opulent of amm'nition as all that. As time goes on, however, thar's a day when I'm goin' to take the determination of old Butler more to heart.

" 'Followin' the gun-boat eepisode I'm more locoed than ever to get my battery into a fight. An' at last I has my hopes entirely fulfilled. It's about four o'clock one evenin' when we caroms on about three brigades of Yanks. Thar's mebby twelve thousand of us rebs an' all of fourteen thousand of the Lincoln people. My battery is all the big guns we-all has, while said Yanks is strong with six full batteries.

" 'The battle opens up; we're on a old sugar plantation, an' after manooverin' about a while we settles down to work. It's that day I has my dreams of carnage realised in full. I turns loose my six guns with verve an' fervour, an' it ain't time for a second drink before I attracts the warmest attention from every one of the Yankee batteries. She's shore a scandal the way them gents in bloo does shoot me up! Jest to give you-all a idee: the Yankees slams away at me for twenty minutes; they dismounts two of my guns; they kills or creases forty of my sixty-six men; an' when they gets through you-all could plant cotton where my battery stands, it's that ploughed up.

" 'It's in the midst of the *baile*, an' I'm standin' near my number-one gun. Thar's a man comes up with a cartridge. A piece of a shell t'ars him open, an' he falls across the gun, limp as a towel, an' then onto the ground. I orders a party named Williams to the place. Something comes flyin' down outen the heavens above an' smites Williams on top of the head; an' he's gone. I orders up another. He assoomes the responsibilities of this p'sition jest in time to get a rifle bullet through the jaw. He lives though; I sees him after the war.

" 'As thar's no more men for the place, I steps for'ard myse'f.

I'm not thar a minute when I sinks down to the ground. I don't feel nothin' an' can't make it out.

" 'While I'm revolvin' this yere phenomenon of me wiltin' that a-way an' tryin' to form some opinions about it, thar's a explosion like forty battles all in one. For a moment, I reckons that some-how we-all has opened up a volcano inadvertent, an' that from now on Loosiana can boast a Hecla of her own. But it ain't no volcano. It's my ammunition waggons which with two thousand rounds is standin' about one hundred yards to my r'ar. The Yanks done blows up the whole outfit with one of their shells.

" 'It's strictly the thing, however, which lets my battery out. The thick smoke of the two thousand cartridges drifts down an' blankets what's left of us like a fog. The Yanks quits us; they allows most likely they've lifted me an' my six brass guns plumb off the earth. Thar's some roodiments of trooth in the theery for that matter.

" 'These last interestin' details sort o' all happens at once. I've jest dropped at the time when my ammunition waggons enters into the sperit of the o'casion like I describes. As I lays thar one of my men comes gropin' along down to me in the smoke.

" ' "Be you hurt, Major?" he says.

" ' "I don't know," I replies: "my idee is that you better in-vestigate an' see."

" 'He t'ars open my coat; thar's no blood on my shirt. He lifts one arm an' then the other; they're sound as gold pieces. Then I lifts up my left laig; I've got on high hoss-man boots.

" ' "Pull off this mocassin." I says.

" 'He pulls her off an' thar's nothin' the matter thar. I breaks out into a profoose sweat; gents, I'm scared speechless. I begins to fear I ain't plugged at all; that I've fainted away on a field of battle an' doo to become the scandal of two armies. I never feels so weak an' sick!

" 'I've got one chance left an' trembles as I plays it; I lifts up my right boot. I win; about a quart of blood runs out. Talk of reprievin' folks who's sentenced to death! Gents, their emotions is only imitations of what I feels when I finds that the Yanks done got me an' nary doubt. It's all right—a rifle bullet through my ankle!

" 'That night I'm moved away, with twenty other wounded folks, in a little cabin off to one side, an' thar's a couple of doctors sizin' up my laig.

" ' "Joe," says one, that a-way, "we've got to cut it off."

" 'But I votes "no" emphatic; I'm too young to talk about goin' shy a laig. With that they ties it up as well as ever they can, warnin' me meanwhile that I've got about one chance in a score to beat the game. Then they imparts a piece of news that's a mighty sight worse than my laig.

" ' "Joe," says this doctor, when he's got me bandaged, "our army's got to rustle out of yere a whole lot. She's on the retreat right now. Them Yanks outheld us an' out-played us an' we've got to go stampedin'. The worst is, thar's no way to take you along, an' we'll have to leave you behind."

" ' "Then the Yanks will corral me?" I asks.

" ' "Shore," he replies, "but thar's nothin' else for it."

" 'It's then it comes on me about that gunboat an' the promises old Butler makes himse'f about hangin' me when caught. Which these yere reflections infooses new life into me. I makes the doctor who's talkin' go rummagin' about ontil he rounds up a old nigger daddy, a mule an' a two-wheel sugar kyart. It's rainin' by now so's you-all could stand an' wash your face an' hands in it. As that medical sharp loads me in, he gives me a bottle of this morphine, an' between jolts an' groans I feeds on said drug until mornin'.'

" 'That old black daddy is dead game. He drives me all night an' all day an' all night ag'n, an' I'm in Shreveport; my ankle's about the size of a bale of cotton. Thar's one ray through it all, however; I misses meetin' old man Butler an' I looks on that as a triumph which shore borders on relief.'

" 'An' I reckons now,' says Dan Boggs, 'you severs your relations with the war?'

" 'No,' goes on the Major; 'I keeps up my voylence to the

close. When I grows robust enough to ride ag'in I'm in Texas. Thar's a expedition fittin' out to invade an' subdoo Noo Mexico, an' I j'ines dogs with it as chief of the big guns. Thar's thirty-eight hundred bold and buoyant sperits rides outen Austin on these military experiments we plans, an' as evincin' the luck we has, I need only to p'int out that nine months later we returns with a scant eight hundred. Three thousand of 'em killed, wounded an' missin' shows that efforts to list the trip onder the head of "picnics" would be irony.

" 'Comin', as we-all does, from one thousand miles away, thar ain't one of us who saveys, practical, as much about the sand-blown desert regions we invades as we does of what goes on in the moon. That Gen'ral Canby, who later gets downed by the Modocs, is on the Rio Grande at Fort Craig. While we're pirootin' about in a blind sort o' fashion we ropes up one of Canby's couriers who's p'intin' no'th for Fort Union with despatches. This Gen'ral Canby makes the follow in' facetious alloosion: After mentionin' our oninvited presence in the territory, he says:

" ' "But let 'em alone. We'll dig the potatoes when they're ripe."

" 'Gents, we was the toobers!' An' yere the Major pauses for a drink. 'We was the potatoes which Canby's exultin' over! We don't onderstand it at the time, but it gets cl'arer as the days drifts by.

" 'I'm never in a more desolate stretch of what would be timber only thar ain't no trees. Thar's nothin' for the mules an' hosses; half the time thar ain't even water. An' then it's alkali. An' our days teems an' staggers with disgustin' experiences. Once we're shy water two days. It's the third day about fourth drink time in the evenin'. The sun has two hours yet to go. My battery is toilin' along, sand to the hubs of gun-carriages an' caissons, when I sees the mules p'int their y'ears for'ard with looks of happy surprise. Then the intelligent anamiles begins a song of praise; an' next while we-all is marvellin' thereat an' before ever a gent can stretch hand to bridle to stop 'em, the mules begins to fly. They yanks my field pieces over the desert as busy an' full of patriotic ardour as a drunkard on 'lection day. The whole battery runs away. Gents, the mules smells water. It's two miles away,—a big pond she is,—an' that locoed battery never stops, but rushes plumb in over its y'ears; an' I lose sixteen mules an' two guns before ever I'm safe ag'in on terry firmy.

" 'It's shore remarkable,' exclaims the Major, settin' down his glass, 'how time softens the view an' changes bitter to sweet that a-way. As I brings before me in review said details thar's nothin' more harassin' from soda to hock than that campaign on the Rio Grande. Thar's not one ray of sunshine to paint a streak of gold in the picture from frame to frame; all is dark an' gloom an' death. An' yet, lookin' back'ard through the years, the mem'ry of it is pleasant an' refreshin', a heap more so than enterprises of greater ease with success instead of failure for the finish.

" 'Thar's one partic'lar incident of this explorin' expeditions into Noo Mexico which never recurs to my mind without leavin' my eyes some dim. I don't claim to be no expert on pathos an' I'm far from regyardin' myse'f as a sharp on tears, but thar's folks who sort o' makes sadness a speshulty, women folks lots of 'em, who allows that what I'm about to recount possesses pecooliar elements of sorrow.

" 'Thar's a young captain—he ain't more'n a boy—who's brought a troop of lancers along with us. This boy Captain hails from some'ers up 'round Waco, an' thar ain't a handsomer or braver in all Pres'dent Davis's army. This Captain—whose name is Edson,—an' me, bein' we-all is both young, works ourse'fs into a clost friendship for each other; I feels about him like he's my brother. Nacherally, over a camp fire an' mebby a stray bottle an' a piece of roast antelope, him an' me confides about ourse'fs. This Captain Edson back in Waco has got a old widow mother who's some rich for Texas, an' also thar's a sweetheart he aims to marry when the war's over an' done. I reckons him an' me talks of that mother an' sweetheart of his a hundred times.

" 'It falls out that where we fords, the Pecos we runs up on a Mexican Plaza—the "Plaza Chico" they-all calls it—an' we camps thar by the river a week, givin' our cattle a chance to roll an' recooperate up on the grass an' water.

" 'Then we goes p'intin' out for the settin' sun ag'in, allowin' to strike the Rio Grande some'ers below Alburquerque. Captain Edson, while we're pesterin' 'round at the Plaza Chico, attaches to his retinoo a Mexican boy; an' as our boogles begins to sing an' we lines out for that west'ard push, this yere boy rides along with Edson an' the lancers.

" 'Our old war chief who has charge of our wanderin's is strictly stern an' hard. An' I reckons now he's the last gent to go makin' soft allowances for any warmth of yooth, or puttin' up with any 'primrose paths of gentle dalliance,' of any an' all who ever buckles on a set of side arms. It thus befalls that when he discovers on the mornin' of the second day that this Mexican boy is a Mexican girl, he goes ragin' into the ambient air like a eagle.

" 'The Old Man claps Edson onder arrest an' commands the girl to saddle up an' go streakin' for the Plaza Chico. As it's only a slow day's march an' as these Mexicans knows the country like a coyote, it's a cinch the girl meets no harm an' runs no resks. But it serves to plant the thorns of wrath in the heart of Captain Edson.

" 'The Old Man makes him loose an' gives him back his lancers before ever we rides half a day, but it don't work no mollifications with the young Captain. He offers no remarks, bein' too good a soldier; but he never speaks to the Old Man no more, except it's business.

" ' "Joe," he says to me, as we rides along, or mebby after we're in camp at night, "I'll never go back to Texas. I've been disgraced at the head of my troop an' I'll take no sech record home."

" ' "You oughter not talk that a-way, Ed," I'd say, tryin' to get his sensibilities smoothed down. "If you don't care none for yourse'f or for your footure, you-all should remember thar's something comin' to the loved ones at home. Moreover, It's weak sayin' you-all ain't goin' back to Texas. How be you goin' to he'p it, onless you piles up shore-enough disgrace by desertin' them lancers of yours?"

" ' "Which if we has the luck," says this Captain Edson, "to cross up with any Yanks who's capable of aimin' low an' shootin' half way troo, I'll find a way to dodge that goin' back without desertin'."

" 'No, I don't make no argyments with him; it's hopeless talkin' to a gent who's melancholly an' who's pride's been jarred; thar's nothing but time can fix things up for him. An' I allers allows that this boy Captain would have emerged from the clouds eventooal, only it happens he don't get the time. His chance comes too soon; an' he shore plays it desperate.

" 'Our first offishul act after reachin' the Rio Grande is to lay for a passel of Yank cavalry—thar's two thousand of 'em I reckons. We rides up on these yere lively persons as we sounds a halt for the evenin'. It looks like our boogles is a summons, for they comes buttin' into view through a dry arroya an' out onto the wide green bottoms of the Rio Grande at the first call. They're about a mile away, an' at sight of us they begins in a fashion of idle indifference to throw out a line of battle. They fights on foot, them bloo folks do; dismountin', with every fourth man to hold the hosses. They displays a heap of insolence for nothin' but cavalry an' no big guns; but as they fights like infantry an' is armed with Spencer seven-shooters besides, the play ain't so owdacious neither.

" 'Thar's mebby a hour of sun an' I'm feelin' mighty surly as I gets my battery into line. I'm disgusted to think we've got to fight for our night's camp, an' swearin' to myse'f in a low tone, so's not to set profane examples to my men, at the idee that these Yanks is that preecip'tate they can't wait till mornin' for their war-jig. But I can't he'p myse'f. That proverb about it takin' two to make a fight is all a bluff. It only takes one to make a fight. As far as we-all rebs is concerned that evenin' we ain't honin' for trouble, leastwise, not ontil mornin'; but them inordinate Yanks will have it, an' thar you be. The fight can't be postponed.

" 'Thar's no tumblin' hurry about how any of us goes to work. Both sides has got old at the game an' war ain't the novelty she is once. The Yanks is takin' their p'sition, an' we're locatin' our lines an' all as ca'mly an' with no more excitement than if it's dress p'rade. The Yanks is from Colorado. My sergeant speaks of 'em to me the next day an' gives his opinion touchin' their merits.

" ' "Where did you say them Yankees comes from, Major?" says my serjeant.

" ' "Colorado," I replies.

" ' "Which thar's about thirty minutes last evenin'," says my serjeant, "when I shorely thinks they're recrooted in hell," an' my serjeant shakes his head.

" 'While I'm linin' up my battery mighty discontented an' disgruntled, an orderly pulls my sleeve.

" ' "Look thar, Major!" he says.

" 'I turns, an' thar over on our right, all alone, goes Captain Edson an' his lancers. Without waitin', an' without commands, Captain Edson has his boogler sound a charge; an' thar goes the lancers stampedin' along like they're a army corps an' cap'ble of sweepin' the two thousand cool an' c'llected Yankees off the Rio Grande.

" 'For a moment all we does is stand an' look; the surprise of it leaves no idee of action. The lancers swings across the grassy levels. Thar's not a shot fired; Edson's people ain't got nothin' but them reedic'lous spears, an' the Yanks, who seems to know it, stands like the rest of us without firin' an' watches 'em come. It's like a picture, with the thin bright air an' the settin' sun shinin' sideways over the gray line of mountains fifty miles to the west.

" 'I never sees folks more placid than the Yanks an' at the same time so plumb alert. Mountain lions is lethargic to 'em. When Captain Edson an' his lancers charges into 'em the Yanks opens right an' left, each sharp of 'em gettin' outen the way of that partic'lar lancer who's tryin' to spear him; but all in a steady, onruffled fashion that's as threatenin' as it is excellent. The lancers, with Captain Edson, goes through, full charge, twenty rods to the r'ar of the Yankee line. An', gents, never a man comes back.

" 'As Edson an' his troop goes through, the Yanks turns an' opens on 'em. The voices of the Spencers sounds like the long-roll of a drum. Hoss an' man goes down, dead an' wounded; never a gent of 'em all rides back through that awful Yankee line. Pore Edson shore has his wish; he's cut the trail of folks who's cap'ble of aimin' low an' shootin' half way troo.

" 'These sperited moves I've been relatin' don't take no time in the dooin'. The hairbrain play of Captain Edson forces our hands. The Old Man orders a charge, an' we pushes the Yanks back onto their hosses an' rescoos what's left of Edson an' his lancers. After skirmishin' a little the Yanks draws away an' leaves us alone on the field. They earns the encomiums of my serjeant, though, before ever they decide to *vamos*.

" 'Edson's been shot hard and frequent; thar's no chance for him. He looks up at me, when we're bringin' him off, an' says:

" ' "Joe," an' he smiles an' squeezes my hand, while his tones is plenty feeble, "Joe, you notes don't you that while I ain't goin' back to Texas, I don't have to desert."

" 'That night we beds down our boy Captain in a sol'tary Mexican 'doby. He's layin' on a pile of blankets clost by the door while the moon shines down an' makes things light as noonday. He's been talkin' to me an' givin' me messages for his mother an' the rest of his outfit at Waco, an' I promises to carry 'em safe an' deliver 'em when I rides in ag'in on good old Texas. Then he wants his mare brought up where he can pet her muzzle an' say *Adios* to her.

" ' "For, Joe," he says, "I'm doo to go at once now, an' my days is down to minutes."

" ' "The medicine man, Ed," I says, "tells me that you-all has hours to live."

" ' "But, Joe," he replies, "I knows. I'm a mighty good prophet you recalls about my not goin' back, an' you can gamble I'm not makin' any mistakes now. It's down to minutes, I tells you, an' I wants to see my mare."

" 'Which the mare is brought up an' stands thar with her velvet nose in his face; her name's "Ruth," after Edson's sweetheart. The mare is as splendid as a picture; pure blood, an' her speed an' bottom is the wonder of the army. Usual a hoss is locoed by the smell of blood, but it don't stampede this Ruth; an' she stays thar with him as still an' tender as a woman, an' with all the sorrow in her heart of folks. As Edson rubs her nose with his weak hand an' pets her, he asks me to take this Ruth back to his sweetheart with all his love.

" ' "Which now I'm goin'," he whispers, "no one's to mention that eepisode of the Pecos an' the little Mexican girl of Plaza Chico!"

" 'Edson is still a moment; an' then after sayin' "Good-by," he lets on that he desires me to leave him alone with the mare.

" ' "I'll give Ruth yere a kiss an' a extra message for my sweetheart," he says, "an' then I'll sleep some."

" 'I camps down outside the 'doby an' looks up at the moon an' begins to let my own thoughts go grazin' off towards Texas. It's perhaps a minute when thar's the quick *crack!* of a sixshooter, an' the mare Ruth r'ars up an' back'ard ontil she's almost down. But she recovers herse'f an' stands sweatin' an' shiverin' an' her eyes burnin' like she sees a ghost. Shore, it's over; pore Edson won't wait; he's got to his guns, an' thar's a bullet through his head.' "

A Sort of Appendix

The Sunset Trail *(1905) suffered from Lewis' unabashed admiration for its subject, the author's friend ex-Marshal Bat Masterson. Lewis treated him with elaborate courtesy—see his "Some Cowboy Facts" again, for comments on Plains courtesy— and accepted his stories without question. I doubt very much that they merited such a stance. As I have remarked, the famous or notorious westerners understood that they were legends in the East, and had no hesitation about cashing in on the awe they inspired. Buffalo Bill is an excellent example of this tendency, and there are many others. In any event, Lewis' unqualified hero-worship, sharpened by distance from the events involved, when mixed with his penchant for the anecdotal and the picturesque, resulted in a kind of gullible prose which was neither fact nor fancy. Still, woven into the doubtful and the shoddy are references to real people who and real events which are part of the lore of the West. They provide contrasts. They contribute to our understanding of the fanciful and the real. Here, then, is a section from* The Sunset Trail.

THE RESCUE OF CIMARRON BILL

Opinion has been ever divided as to the true reason of Ogallala's objection to Cimarron Bill. Some there were who said it was born of Ogallala's jealousy of Dodge, the latter metropolis being as all men know the home of Cimarron. Others held it to be off-spring of the childish petulance of Ogallala, which resented the unseemly luck of Cimarron who had played at cards with its citizens. The latter would appear the better solution; for when the committee, which consisted of Mr. Jenkins of the Sheaf of Wheat Saloon, Mr. Sopris and Mr. Smart, notified Cimarron to depart, the ostracism was expressly based upon the good fortune which throughout four nights of draw-poker had waited upon the obnoxious one.

The committee, in a spirit of fairness that did it credit, explained how Ogallala did not intend by its action to accuse Cimarron of having practiced any fraud. Had such been the case, Ogallala would have hanged him instead of bidding him depart in peace. What was meant came to be no more than this: Ogallala was new and small, and per consequence poor, and could not afford the luxury of Cimarron's presence. Under the circumstance the com-mittee urged him to have avail of the first train that passed through. Leaving with him a time table and the suggestion that he study it, the committee withdrew.

Cimarron Bill was possessed of many of the more earnest characteristics of a bald hornet. Also, he held that the position assumed towards him by Ogallala was in violation of his rights under a scheme of government which guaranteed him life, liberty and the pursuit of happiness. The last franchise in particular he construed as covering in his favour the privilege of remaining what space he pleased in Ogallala, and diverting himself with cards at the expense of those members of the body politic willing to play with him. Thinking on these lines, he resolved to defy the sentiment of Ogallala, and stay where he was.

In preparation for what might happen, Cimarron Bill repaired to the Midland Hotel and got his six-shooter, which weapon, in compliment to Ogallala, he had theretofore avoided wearing. Being girt for his defence, he wended to the Arcade, a place of refreshment next neighbour to Mr. Jenkins' Sheaf of Wheat, and seating himself at a table called calmly for a drink. Word of these manœuvres was conveyed to Mr. Jenkins, who as chairman of the notification committee felt compelled to vindicate the dignity of Ogallala.

It was an hour later and, being in the hot middle of an August afternoon, the Sheaf of Wheat was deserted. Likewise was the Arcade, save for the presence of Cimarron Bill. Mr. Jenkins made sure of this by glancing through the window of the Arcade when returning from a brief invented trip to the post-office.

Believing that the time to move had come, Mr. Jenkins arranged a shotgun on the shelf below the level of the Sheaf of Wheat bar. There was a charge of buckshot in each barrel, and Mr. Jenkins entertained hopes of what might be accomplished therewith. When fully organized, Mr. Jenkins took a six-shooter and blazed away at the floor. He relied on the curiosity of Cimarron, certain in this fashion to be aroused, to bring him within range.

Mr. Jenkins was so far correct as to the inquisitive nature of Cimarron Bill that the smoke was still a-curl about the low ceiling of the Sheaf of Wheat when the latter came rushing through the door. But the door of Cimarron's advent was the rear and not the front door, as had been confidently anticipated by Mr.

Jenkins. He had dropped the six-shooter and caught up the Greener with a purpose of potting Cimarron the moment he appeared. This reversal of doors, however, was so disconcerted that in the hurry of wheeling, and because of the nearness of Cimarron, he missed that lively gentleman altogether.

Cimarron Bill replied to Mr. Jenkins with his Colt's-45, and the bullet glancing on the fore-end of the Greener cut away the second, third and little fingers of Mr. Jenkins' left hand. The blow to his nervous system sent Mr. Jenkins to the floor, where, being a prince for prudence and no mean strategist, he remained a-sprawl, feigning death. This pretense imposed upon Cimarron who, after helping himself to a drink at the expense, as he supposed, of Mr. Jenkins' estate, shot a hole through the bar mirror in registration of his contempt, and sauntered into the street.

Mr. Jenkins, following the going of Cimarron Bill, scrambled to his feet, thrust a fresh cartridge into the empty barrel of the Greener, and hastened to the door. Having advantage of the back of Cimarron, that personage being distant forty yards, he poured a charge from the Greener into him. As Cimarron went down, Mr. Jenkins—who was no one to slight his work—unslewed the second barrel. It went wild, and did no scathe beyond sending one buckshot through the Ogallala *Harbinger,* which Mr. Sopris, chair tilted against the front of the Cowboy's Rest, was reading, while the balance of the load shattered the front window of that justly popular resort. Mr. Jenkins, believing that the honor of Ogallala had been retrieved, sought the local doctor, while several unengaged members of the public gathered about the prostrate Cimarron.

The luck which had attended upon Cimarron Bill during his stay in Ogallala did not abandon him in his off-and-on duel with Mr. Jenkins. Sundry of those cartridges which were as the provender of the Greener had been filled with bird not buckshot, being designed for the destruction of prairie hens. Mr. Jenkins, in the hurry of reloading that right barrel, had selected a prairie-hen cartridge. So far from resembling one of those diminutive fowls, Cimarron was a gentleman of vitality and powers of recuperation. The birdshot peppered but did not kill. Even as they gazed, those who surrounded Cimarron observed signs of returning life.

This revival of the stricken one bred sorrow in the Ogallala heart; not because of an innate inhumanity, but, as events had adjusted themselves, it would have been better had Mr. Jenkins extinguished Cimarron. There is that unwritten jurisprudence of the gun; and the politer, not to say more honourable, technicalities were peculiarly on the side of Cimarron. If the story were sent abroad it would serve for the discredit of Ogallala; and a western town is as nervously concerned for its good fame as any woman. Hence the popular sadness over Cimarron's restoration.

Acting for the best under circumstances so discouraging, the public, first caring for Cimarron's pistol in order to preserve a future's quiet, formally placed him under arrest. Then, since Ogallala had no jail and because he lay wounded to helplessness, he was conveyed to the Midland, and Mr. Smart detailed to hold him prisoner. In these steps it is believed that Ogallala planned nothing beyond a version of the affair that should bear upon its own repute as lightly as it might. Beyond saving its skirts from criticism, it would restore Cimarron to a pristine health, and finish by devising ways and means, honourable of course to Ogallala, for letting him go free.

When the doctor had tied up the three finger-stumps of Mr. Jenkins, he repaired to the Midland and picked the shot—number eight, they were—out of Cimarron. Following these improvements, the latter called for a drink; then, addressing himself to Mr. Smart, he exhausted invective upon Ogallala and her manner towards sojourners within her limits.

Cimarron Bill was still in bed and still reviling Ogallala when Mr. Masterson was given a recount of his troubles. Aside from their several years of friendship, it chanced in times gone by that during a dance-hall rumpus at Tascosa, Cimarron Bill had stood over Mr. Masterson, on the floor with a bullet-shattered knee, and with six-shooters spitting fire held the crowded foe at bay. This, according to the religion of Mr. Masterson, made a claim upon his gratitude which would last while Cimarron lived. Wherefore, and because a Western gratitude is never passive, Mr. Masterson no sooner heard of Cimarron's plight than he started to his relief.

Since he must go by roundabout trails, it was precisely one week from the day of Cimarron's battle with Mr. Jenkins before Mr. Masterson drew into Ogallala, and wrote "William Brown, Hays City," in the account book which the Midland employed in lieu of a more formal register. Also, Mr. Masterson developed an unusual fastidiousness, and asked to be shown the rooms before one was assigned him. The request being complied with, Mr. Masterson in his ramble located Cimarron's room by locating Mr. Smart, who stood or rather sat on guard at the door—for Mr. Smart had brought out a chair to comfort his watch and ward—and chose the room next to it.

"Thar's a prisoner in thar," doubtfully observed the proprietor of the Midland, who was acting as guide to Mr. Masterson's investigations, "an' as he mostly cusses all night, he may disturb you."

"Disturb me?" repeated the bogus Mr. Brown. "Never! I know of nothing more soothing to the slumbers of an honest man than the howls of the wicked under punishment."

Being installed, Mr. Masterson's earliest care was to provide himself with a demijohn of Midland whiskey; for he had noted an encarmined nose as a facial property of Mr. Smart, and that florid feature inspired a plan. There would be a train from the West, at three o'clock A. M.; it was now two o'clock P. M. This would give Mr. Masterson thirteen hours wherein to ripen his device; and thirteen is a fortunate number!

When Mr. Masterson passed Mr. Smart in the hall, bearing—as the Greeks bore gifts—that engaging demijohn, he spake casually yet pleasantly with Mr. Smart; and next, after a fashion perfect in the West, he invited Mr. Smart to sample those wares which the demijohn contained. Mr. Smart tasted, and said it was the Midland's best. Upon this promising discovery Mr. Masterson proposed a second libation, which courtesy Mr. Smart embraced.

Mr. Masterson apologised to Mr. Smart for a thoughtlessness that had asked him to drink with a total stranger. He made himself known to Mr. Smart as "Mr. Brown of Hays." Mr. Masterson remarked that he would go abroad in Ogallala about the transaction of what mythical business had brought him to its shores. Meanwhile, the demijohn was just inside his door. Would Mr. Smart do him the honour to cheer his vigils with such references to the demijohn as it might please him to make?

Mr. Masterson was about to depart when a volley of bad words was heard to issue from Cimarron's room. The voice was strong and full, and fraught of a fine resolution; this delighted Mr. Masterson as showing Cimarron to be in no sort near the door of death. A second volley climbed the transom to reverberate along the hall, and Mr. Masterson, jerking the thumb of inquiry, asked:

"Any gent with him?"

"No," responded Mr. Smart, leering amiably, albeit indefinitely, "no; he's plumb alone. He's jes' swearin' at a mark."

When Mr. Masterson returned he found Mr. Smart blurred and incoherent. It was no part of Mr. Masterson's policy to reduce Mr. Smart to a condition which should alarm the caution of Ogallala, and cause it to relieve his guard. Mr. Smart was the man for the place; to preserve him therein, Mr. Masterson withdrew the demijohn from circulation.

Mr. Smart, even through the happy mists which enveloped him, spoke well of this step. After supper, the demijohn could be recalled. The friendship which Mr. Smart and Mr. Masterson had conceived for one another might then be expanded, and its foundation deepened and secured. Thus sufficiently if not distinctly spake Mr. Smart; and Mr. Masterson coincided with him at every angle of his argument.

It was nine o'clock, and supper had been over two hours when Mr. Masterson again sought Mr. Smart at that gentleman's post in the hall. Mr. Masterson had much to talk about. The more he had seen of Ogallala the better he liked it. As for Mr. Smart, he was among Ogallala's best features. It had become Mr. Masterson's purpose to go into business in Ogallala. Possessing boundless capital, he would engage in every scheme of commerce from a general outfitting store to a corral. Mr. Smart should be with him in these enterprises. While Mr. Masterson dilated, Mr. Smart drank, and the pleasant character of the evening was conceded by both.

At one A. M. Mr. Masterson supported Mr. Smart to his cot in Cimarron's room. The invalid roused himself to say more bad words of both Mr. Smart and Mr. Masterson; for the room being unlighted, he assailed Mr. Masterson ignorantly and in the dark. Mr. Smart no sooner felt the cot beneath him than he fell into deep sleep, and his snorings shook the casements like a strong wind.

At half after two Mr. Masterson stepped confidently into Cimarron's room. He found Mr. Smart as soundly asleep as a corpse. Mr. Masterson shook Cimarron gently by the shoulder:

"Steady!" he whispered.

"Is that you, Bat?" Cimarron asked, coming at once to an understanding of things.

"How hard are you hit?" asked Mr. Masterson. "Can you walk?"

"I'm too stiff and sore for that."

"Then it's a case of carry."

It was within five minutes of the train. Mr. Masterson wrapped the wounded Cimarron in the bed-clothes, thus disguised he resembled a long roll of gray army blankets.

Being a powerful man, Mr. Masterson tossed Cimarron over his shoulder, and started down the stair. The injured one ground his teeth with the anguish of it, but was as mute as a fox. There was still a drunken voice or two in the barroom of the Midland, but Mr. Masterson—who had looked over the route in the afternoon—eliminated whatever risk existed of meeting anyone by making for a side door.

Once in the dark street, by circuitous paths, Mr. Masterson sought the station. He did not go to the depot proper, but found a place a little distance up the track, where the smoking-car would stop. Also, he took the side opposite to that on which passengers got on and off the train. There he waited in the deep shadow of a line of freight cars, supporting the drooping Cimarron against the nearest car. The two were in time; Mr. Masterson could see the headlight, and hear the scream of the engine.

The express swept in and stopped; by the best of best fortunes the forward platform of the smoking-car paused squarely in front of Mr. Masterson and Cimarron. Cautiously Mr. Masterson picked up his charge and placed him upon the topmost step. Then he swung himself aboard and made ready to drag Cimarron inside. The latter met the situation in a manner excessively limp and compliant; for all his iron nerve, he had fainted.

As Mr. Masterson bent over Cimarron, some unauthorized person came from out the darkness.

"Whom have you got there?"

As the one in search of knowledge hove in reach, Mr. Masterson smote him upon the head with his heavy eight-inch pistol. The inquiring one went over backward, and Mr. Masterson was pleased to see that he fell free of the wheels. Yes, it was right; the unknown had sinned the sin of an untimely curiosity.

The engine whistled, the train moved, and Mr. Masterson packed the unconscious Cimarron into the car and placed him in the nearest seat. There were half a dozen passengers scattered about; all were soundly slumbering. Mr. Masterson drew a breath of relief, and wiped his face; for the night was an August night and the work had been hot. Then he rearranged Cimarron's blankets, and threw a cupful of water in his face by way of restorative. That, and the breeze through the lifted window, caused Cimarron to open his eyes.

"Give me some whiskey."

Mr. Masterson looked conscience-stricken.

"I forgot the whiskey!"

"Forgot the whiskey!" repeated Cimarron, in feeble scorn. "What kind of a rescue party do you call this? I'd sooner have stayed where I was! Besides, I had it laid out how I'd finish shootin' up that Jenkins party the moment I could totter over to the Sheaf of Wheat."

Mr. Masterson, to whom the petulance of the sick was as nothing, vouchsafed no return, and Cimarron sank back exhausted.

When the conductor appeared, the wary Mr. Masterson met that functionary in the car door.

"Got any children?" asked Mr. Masterson.

"Five," said the conductor, whom it is superfluous to say was a married man; "five; an' another in the shops."

"The reason I ask," observed Mr. Masterson, "is that my brother over there has measles, and I wouldn't want you to go packing it back to your babies. I have to wrap him up to keep him from catching cold. The doctor said that if he ever caught cold once we'd have some fun."

While Mr. Masterson was exploring Ogallala and perfecting his scheme of rescue, he had purchased tickets to Grand Island. He bought tickets to Grand Island because he intended to get off at North Platte; the ticket-buying was a ruse and meant to break the trail. The conductor, as he received Mr. Masterson's tickets, thanked him for his forethought in defending his children from the afflicted brother.

"I'm a father myself," said Mr. Masterson, who in amplification of any strategy was ever ready to round off one mendacity with another.

The dawn was showing when the train drew in at North Platte. Shouldering the helpless Cimarron, Mr. Masterson stepped onto the deserted station platform. Cimarron gave a querulous groan.

"Where be you p'intin' out for now?" he demanded. "I'm gettin' a heap tired of this rescue. It's too long, an' besides it's too toomultuous."

"Tired or no," responded Mr. Masterson, steadily, "you're going to be rescued just the same."

The Cochino Colorow was a gentleman whose true name was Mr. Cooper. He had been rebaptised as the "Cochino Colorow," which means the "Red Hog," by the Mexicans and the Apaches when he was a scout for General Crook, and about the time the latter gained from the same sources his own title of the "Gray Fox."

Mr. Cooper was not heralded as the Cochino Colorow because of any aggressive gluttonies; but he was round and with a deal of jowl, and suffered from a nose that, colour and contour, looked like the ace of hearts. Besides, Mr. Cooper had red hair. These considerations induced the Mexicans and Apaches to arise as one man and call him the Cochino Colorow; and the name stuck.

Mr. Masterson and the Cochino Colorow had been fellow scouts under the wise Ben Clark when the latter guided the Black Kettle wanderings of General Custer. Since then the Cochino Colorow had adopted more peaceful pursuits as proprietor of the Bank Exchange in North Platte, and on the morning when Mr. Masterson, with Cimarron over his shoulder like a sack of oats, came seeking him, he was a familiar as well as a foremost figure of that commonwealth.

The Bank Exchange was almost empty of customers when Mr. Masterson and his burden arrived; a few all-night souls were still sleepily about a faro table, and the Cochino Colorow himself was behind the box.

"Hello, Bat!" exclaimed the Cochino Colorow, manifestly surprised, and turning the box on its side to show a recess in the deal. "Where in the name of Santa Ana do you come from? What's that you're totin'?"

"I'm totin' a friend," replied Mr. Masterson.

The Cochino Colorow hastily assigned a talented person who was keeping the case, to deal the interrupted game, while he in person waited upon the wants of the fugitives. Mr. Masterson told the story of their adventures to the Cochino Colorow.

"And for all my walking in the water about those tickets," concluded Mr. Masterson, "I'm afraid the Ogallala outfit will cross up with us before ever I can freight Cimarron into Dodge. The moment that drunkard Smart comes to, or the rest of 'em find they're shy Cimarron, they'll just about take to lashing and backlashing the situation with the telegraph, and I figure they'll cut our trail."

"Which if they should," confidently returned the Cochino

Colorow, "we'll stand 'em off all right. Between us, I'm the whole check-rack in North Platte."

Mr. Masterson's fears were justified. As early as the afternoon of the same day, Mr. Sopris and a companion, whom Mr. Masterson, because of the handkerchief which bound his brows, suspected to be the inquisitive one, walked into the Bank Exchange. Mr. Masterson and the Cochino Colorow had remarked their approach from a window while they were yet two blocks away.

"Is either of 'em that Jenkins crim'nal?" asked the Cochino Colorow.

"No," said Mr. Masterson.

"I'm shore sorry," replied the Cochino Colorow, "If one of 'em now was that Jenkins crim'nal, we'd nacherally prop pore Cimarron up by this yere window, an' let him have a crack at him with my Winchester."

The Cochino Colorow suggested that Mr. Masterson retire to the room where lay the invalid Cimarron. He said that he could best treat with the visitors alone.

Cimarron was tossing to and fro on a couch in a cubby-hole of an apartment immediately to the rear of the Bank Exchange bar. Since the intervening partition was of pine boards, an inch for thickness, what passed between the Cochino Colorow and the invaders fell plainly upon the listening ears of Mr. Masterson and Cimarron.

The visitors laid bare their mission. They set forth the escape of Cimarron; and while they would not pretend that Ogallala hungered to destroy that individual, they did urge a loss to the Ogallala honour if he were permitted to walk off in a manner of open, careless insolence.

"It ain't what this Cimarron does," explained Mr. Sopris; "it ain't that he's done more'n shoot away three of Jenk's fingers, an' as they was on the left hand, they may well be spared. What Ogallala objects to is the manner of this person's escape. It not only puts Mr. Smart in the hole, speshul, but it reflects in Ogallala for hoss sense."

"Well, gents," returned the Cochino Colorow with cool non-chalance, "you can't expect me to bother myse'f to death about what comes off in Ogallala. Which, speakin' general, I'm that numbed by my own misfortunes, I don't care much what happens, so it don't happen to me."

"It wasn't," retorted Mr. Sopris, "that we allowed you'd feel a heap concerned, but we got a p'inter that you're harborin' these yere felons personal."

"Is that so?" observed the Cochino Colorow, assuming airs of chill dignity. "Gents, since you impugns my integrity, my only word is, 'Make your next move.' "

"Our next move," observed Mr. Sopris, "will be to go squanderin' about into the uttermost corners of this yere deadfall, an' search out our game."

"Shore!" exclaimed the Cochino Colorow, picking up a rifle that stood in the corner. "An' bein' plumb timid that a-way, of course I'll neither bat an eye nor wag a year ag'in the outrage."

The Cochino Colorow cocked the Winchester. Mr. Sopris shook his head, as might one whose good nature had been abused.

"That's plenty!" said Mr. Sopris. "Since sech is your attitoode of voylence, we jest won't search this joint."

"No, I don't reckon none you will," retorted the Cochino Colorow, fingering the Winchester. "You two delegates from Ogallala had better hit the trail for home. An' don't you never come pirootin' into North Platte searchin' for things no more."

Mr. Masterson and Cimarron overheard this conversation, and the dialogue so affected the latter that Mr. Masterson had his work cut out to keep him in his blankets. As the colloquy ended and the retreating footfalls told the departure of the committee from Ogallala, Cimarron, sore, sick and exhausted, turned his face to the wall with a sigh of shame.

"Bat," he said, pleadingly, "would you mind leavin' the room a moment while I blush?" Then he continued while his tears flowed: "We're a fine pair of centipedes to lie bunched up in yere while the Red Hog plays our hands!"

"They were only four-flushing," said Mr. Masterson, sooth-
ingly, by way of consolation.

In the corral to the rear of the Bank Exchange stood a ram-
shackle phaeton, which was one of the sights that North Platte
showed to tourists. This conveyance belonged to the mother-in-
law of the Cochino Colorow. The lady in question, who was of
a precise, inveterate temper, was in the East visiting relatives, and
the Cochino Colorow, after sundry drinks to convey his courage
to the needed height, endowed Mr. Masterson and Cimarron with
the phaeton to assist them in a cross-country break for Dodge.
After this generous act the Cochino Colorow was troubled in
spirit.

"I'll fight Injuns for fun," explained the Cochino Colorow,
defensively to Mr. Masterson, "but whether you deems me weak
or not, I simply shudders when I think of my said mother-in-law
an' what she'll say about that buggy. But what could we-all do?
Cimarron has got to *vamos*. Them Ogallala sharps will most likely
be showin' up to-morry with a warrant an' a comp'ny of milishy,
an' that vehicle is the one avenoo of escape. While her language
will be mighty intemperate, still, in the cause of friendship, a
gent must even face his mother-in-law."

"What do you reckon she'll do?" asked Mr. Masterson, who
was not a little disturbed by the evident peril of the good Cochino
Colorow. "Mebby Cimarron had better give himself up."

"No," replied the desperate one. "It shall never be said that
anything, not even a well-grounded fear of that esteemable lady
whom I honours onder the endearin' name of mother-in-law,
could keep me from rushin' with her phaeton to the rescue of a
friend beset."

The Cochino Colorow roped and brought up a mud-hued, ewe-
necked, hammer-headed beast of burden, and said its name was
Julius Cæsar. This animal, which had a genius for bolting one
moment and backing up the next, he hooked to the phaeton.
Cimarron, whose helplessness was not of the hands, could hold
the reins and guide Julius Cæsar. Mr. Masterson would ride a pinto

pony furnished by the generous partisanship of the Cochino Colorow. It would take a week to make Dodge, and a week's provisions, solid and liquid, were loaded into the phaeton.

The faithful Cochino Colorow rode with them on a favourite sorrel as far as Antelope Springs. Arriving at that water, he bade the travellers farewell.

"Good luck to you," cried the Cochino Colorow, waving a fraternal hand. "Give my regyards to Wright an' Kell an' Short."

"I hope you won't have trouble with that outfit from Ogallala," returned Mr. Masterson.

The Cochino Colorow snapped his fingers.

"Since my mind's took to runnin' on my mother-in-law," he said, "I've done quit worryin' about sech jimcrow propositions."

And thus they parted.

"You cert'nly had a strenuous time, Bat," observed Mr. Short, sympathetically.

"Strenuous!" repeated Mr. Masterson. "I should say as much! Cimarron was as ugly as a sore-head dog, and wanted everything he could think of from a sandwich to a six-shooter. I was never so worn to a frazzle. It was certainly," concluded Mr. Masterson, replenishing his glass, "the most arduous rescue in which I ever took a hand; and we'd have never pulled it off if it hadn't been for the Cochino Colorow. Here's hoping he can square himself with that relative he robbed. She's as sour as pignuts, and I don't feel altogether easy about the Cochino Colorow. However, if the lady puts up too rough a deal, I told him he'd find a ready-made asylum here."